THE
GEOGRAPHY OF CANADA

The
GEOGRAPHY of CANADA

by

J. Lewis Robinson, Ph. D.
Associate Professor of Geography, University of B. C.

Assisted by

M. Josephine Robinson, M. A.
Formerly of New Brunswick Elementary Schools

With Maps by the Author

GREENWOOD PRESS, PUBLISHERS
NEW YORK

Originally published in 1950
by Longmans, Green and Company

First Greenwood Reprinting 1969

Library of Congress Catalogue Card Number 69-14059

SBN 8371-1877-8

INTRODUCTION TO THE AUTHOR

The author of The Geography of Canada, J. Lewis Robinson, is Associate Professor in charge of geography courses in the Department of Geology and Geography at the University of British Columbia. His graduate B.A. came from the University of Western Ontario. He has an M.A. in geography from Syracuse University and a Ph.D. from Clark University. In 1950 he was President of the Association of Pacific Coast Geographers.

He is well-known for his frequent contributions to the Canadian Geographical Journal, many of which have dealt with the Canadian Northland, where he has spent many months over a period of several years doing research work for the Federal Government. In addition, he has travelled widely from coast to coast in southern Canada carrying out geographical field work.

In British Columbia he has been consultant for the Provincial Government on problems of land utilization in that province, and is on the committee revising the provincial Social Studies curriculum. Professor Robinson is both a theoretical and practical geographer.

ACKNOWLEDGEMENT

The authors wish to acknowledge, with thanks, the editorial assistance and comments of Mr. Daniel Mewhort, B.A., Principal of Oriole Park School, Toronto, and Mr. George Wood, M.A., formerly of B.C. Secondary Schools System.

PREFACE

It was said that "the Twentieth Century will be Canada's". Half of that century has now gone, and some of the optimism of 40 years ago has not proven to be justified. The promise of the first decade has suffered from two World Wars which changed the picture within Canada and curtailed freedom in international relations. At the turn of the half-century it seems wise to take stock of what we have within this large area of Canada. We now know more about the physical environment of Canada that we did 50 years ago. How this physical setting and known resources are to be used is the problem of the next half-century and a new generation.

The future of Canada is still bright, perhaps one of the brightest in this evershrinking world. But the optimism about the next half-century should be based upon known facts rather than hopeful, glowing phrases. The first step before considering and planning that future is inventory.

Canada is more than a large area on the world map; it is a region with certain definite physical characteristics. It has topography, drainage, climate, vegetation and soils which can be changed very little, and to which Canadians must adjust to make a living and multiply. The distribution pattern of these natural factors is the study of physical geography. In the physical setting, or environment, are resources—the raw materials for industry; their distribution and movement are in the study of economic geography. Since physical features and resource distribution vary greatly over Canada, its geography cannot be generalized but should be studied regionally. Such regional geography should show the relationships which are established when man adjusts himself to certain physical and economic conditions. It is the author's hope that you will understand Canada better if you see how these regions differ in their setting and problems, and if you see how each fits into the total picture of Canadian economy.

The teacher of Canadian geography has an important task and an interesting one. We have a variety of problems within this large area of Canada which should stimulate thought and class discussion for months. The author has suggested exercises and research at the end of each chapter which will permit pupils to think about specific geography problems. The questions are meant to be guides. The teacher's discretion should decide which are suitable for her class or area, and which need to be changed to apply to local conditions. Since this book can not cover all of Canada in full detail, the success of many of the assignments and suggested reports, which direct the pupil to further information, will depend upon the size and quality of the school library.

Attention should be drawn to the pictures and maps. The former have been selected to give a typical representation of what a person would see in each region. The maps assist with place-name location, but are not meant to replace an atlas. In particular, they locate places within certain important distribution patterns which influence their character.

Finally, any new subject should introduce new terminology into the student's vocabulary. It should be the teacher's duty to explain these terms as they are met, as part of the general process of learning.

This is our country; we should know it well. Its future development lies in the hands of the generation which is now learning about it. The Geography of Canada is a sound base from which to consider our place in the second half of this century.

J. Lewis Robinson.

Vancouver, B.C.,
October, 1950.

TABLE OF CONTENTS

LIST OF MAPS

LIST OF GRAPHS

Where the hills are rocky and harbours are good, men turn to fishing to make a living.
A fishing village on Cape Breton Island.

CHAPTER 1

WHAT CANADIANS DO

If you climb to the roof of the highest building in your town or community, you will see that the streets and buildings are arranged in a definite pattern. The finest homes are usually grouped in one section, and the poorer houses in another. Along the railroad or near the water the factories are together. The stores and office buildings are in a central area and in several smaller centres towards the outskirts of the community. (See map on page 120.)

If you look closely at the various sections of a city you see that people are moving about. Women are out shopping, and men are busy at work in offices, stores or factories. Everyone is doing something

for a living. A city is more than a collection of houses, stores, and factories. It contains people. Each person has a special job, and in working together, all unite to make the town or city an active, interesting community.

Maybe you are not in a town or city. Perhaps you are looking over the countryside from a high building or a hill. You will see big farms and little farms, fields of pasture or grain, and dark patches of woodland. Again you will see people moving about. Farmers are working in the fields. Men are driving trucks which carry away the milk. The countryside shows a regular pattern of houses and

1

fields, but it is different from that in a town or city. In the country people are also doing special tasks.

Suppose that you were to climb into an aeroplane and fly far, far over your part of Canada. You would see many towns and cities. Some would be small and some

Canada—Provinces and Capitals.

would be large. Some towns might have a street-pattern and buildings similar to your town. Others would be different. You would see many kinds of farms. Some farms would have only fields of golden grain. Some would have small vegetable gardens or cattle grazing on broad grasslands. Some large farms would be on flat land, and small ones might be on rocky, hilly land. Do you wonder why these things are so? Why are some towns or farms bigger than others? Why do some farmers grow vegetables and some only grain? Why are the towns and cities located where they are? All these questions and many more will puzzle you.

Let us again use our imagination, and climb into a rocket-ship which will shoot us high into the atmosphere. We can then look down on all of Canada from New-foundland to Vancouver Island, and from the Great Lakes to the Arctic Islands. Let us suppose that we can hòld our space-ship in one place and study Canada with our super long-range glasses. We can get

this same feeling by standing in front of a map of Canada, and pretending that we are high in the air. We see plains, hills, valleys and rugged mountains. We see cities, towns and villages. There are green fields, vast forests and barren country. Rivers, roads and railways join the many

Courtesy Quebec Publicity Bureau.

Men working in a logging camp near Rimouski, Quebec. The logs have been cut in the winter and carried on sleds to the nearest river. Other men will make pulp out of the logs at a mill farther down stream.

places and areas together. In these places all across Canada people are working. When we are far above them we realize that there is some connection between the various tasks.

Let us look down closely at a mine. The miners are working underground to break up rock containing valuable minerals. At the surface, men operate machinery which crushes or heats the rock, helping to separate it from the metal. Other men operate boats or trains to carry the precious metal to factories in towns and cities. There, men and women make tools, machinery and utensils for other factories and our homes.

The miners and workers are so busy that they have no time to grow their food. Therefore, farmers grow vegetables near-by to sell to the mine and factory workers. In turn, the farmer buys some of the factory products. In the same way, lum-bermen are busy cutting trees, and other men are making the logs into lumber, matches or newsprint. They also have to buy their food from other people.

Suppose that we look at a prairie farm. The large fields are covered with grain. After harvest-time the grain is taken to large elevators where it is stored until needed. Later, at the mills, this grain is ground into flour. Other people work in bakeries where the flour is made into food. Other men deliver the food to our stores and homes.

Each person across Canada is doing a special job, but his work depends on that of others. There could be no manufacturing unless there were minerals to mine and men to do the mining. There could be no food canned unless there were fertile soils and farmers to raise the crops. The products which most workers use come directly or indirectly from the land or sea. Roads, railroads and rivers permit the moving of these products from one group of workers to another.

In order to understand why people are doing special jobs in some sections we are going to study the geography of Canada. Geography is a study of the land, its resources and its peoples. It emphasizes the relationships between these factors. Geography describes how each affects the other. It brings together many facts to explain *"why people do what they do where they do it"*. Geography is concerned with *what*

Courtesy Nova Scotia Bureau of Information.

From an aeroplane we can see the farmlands of Canada. Orchards near Grand Pré, Nova Scotia, are separated by green fields of pasture. Dark patches of woodland are also located near most farms.

people do—the ordinary day-to-day activities of all of us. It describes *where* people do their work—in towns, cities or rural areas. And lastly, it explains *why* people have certain activities and not others.

Since people's activities are in some direct or indirect way connected with their surroundings, and its resources, we must know many facts about Canada. We must know where the mountains, hills and plains are located because we know that farming is carried on in plains, lumbering in hills, and mining in mountains. We must know about the climate of different parts of Canada to realize what sections are too dry or too wet for certain crops, and which sections are too hot or too cold. We must know where the rivers and lakes are located to understand how they can be used as routes for transportation or sources of fish. If we can see in our minds what each part of the country looks like, we can understand what activities are possible there. Then we can study how the people fit themselves into their surroundings. If we use geography in this way, we are learning to become good citizens. Our country is large. The more we learn about the different parts of it the better will be our understanding of the problems which Canadians face.

The following table lists the chief activities in each province. You will see that the industries differ in importance from place to place. Since they depend upon natural resources for their raw materials, we can guess that resources must also vary from place to place. For example, a province with many persons engaged in lumbering and few people in agriculture would have vast forests and very little fertile farm land. As you study the geography of Canada, turn back to this table frequently to see if you can explain "*why* people do *what* they do *where* they do it".

What People Do

(in percentage, 1941)

Occupation	Maritimes	Quebec	Ontario	Prairies	B.C.	Canada
Agriculture	32	27	23	56	16	32
Fishing, Logging	12	4	2	2	10	4
Mining	5	1	2	2	4	2
Manufacturing	11	19	23	8	17	17
Construction	6	7	6	3	7	6
Transportation	9	8	8	6	10	9
Trade, Finance	6	9	10	8	10	9
Service	6	10	10	8	12	9
Clerical	3	6	7	3	5	5
Labourers	8	8	8	4	10	7
Total numbers:	299,000	928,000	1,140,000	737,000	259,000	3,363,000

Things To Do

1. Draw a sketch map of your town or city and locate on it in colour:

   (i) The main business section or sections.

   (ii) The chief factory or industrial areas.

   (iii) The sections of most expensive homes.

   (iv) The sections of poorer class homes.

2. Make a list of the ways a map of a nearby town would differ from the map of your town. Is the chief business district larger or smaller? Are there as many factories.? List the industries located in the nearest town that are not in your town. Explain each difference that you list.

3. (a) Name the chief industries of your city or the nearest town.

   (b) Where do the raw materials come from?

   (c) What kind of transportation is used to bring them to the city?

4. (a) Name the chief occupations of people in your city (or nearest town).

   (b) How is each occupation dependent upon some natural resource?

   (c) Describe the occupations of a few people whom you know, as examples in answer to this question.

Facts For Reference

Political Divisions and Capitals

Capital of Canada	Ottawa
Newfoundland	St. John's
Prince Edward Island	Charlottetown
Nova Scotia	Halifax
New Brunswick	Fredericton
Quebec	Quebec
Ontario	Toronto
Manitoba	Winnipeg
Saskatchewan	Regina
Alberta	Edmonton
British Columbia	Victoria
Yukon Territory	Dawson
Northwest Territories (Districts—Mackenzie, Keewatin, and Franklin).	Administered from Ottawa, Department of Resources and Development.

Areas of Provinces and Territories of Canada (square miles)

Northwest Territories	1,258,217
Quebec	523,860
Ontario	363,282
British Columbia	359,279
Alberta	248,800
Saskatchewan	237,975
Manitoba	219,723
Yukon Territory	205,346
Newfoundland and Labrador	162,000
New Brunswick	27,473
Nova Scotia	20,743
Prince Edward Island	2,184
Canada (total)	3,628,882

The Fraser River with Vancouver and its harbour in the background.

CHAPTER 2

WHERE CANADIANS LIVE

Although Canada is one of the large countries of the world in total area, it is one of the small countries in population. According to the 1941 census there were 11,506,655 people in Canada. By 1950 however, there were more than 13,000,000 persons within our ten provinces and two territories. If we look at the map of population distribution on page 9 we note that some areas have greater numbers of people than others. Only small sections of each province are densely populated. We should know where Canadians live. Later we shall study the resources in each area to explain why people are there.

The table of provincial populations at the end of this chapter shows that more than half the people of Canada live in Quebec and Ontario. Most of the population actually lives in the southern sections, in the St. Lawrence Lowlands. Thus, more than half the people of Canada live in an area which is only one-sixtieth of the whole country. The rest of Canada is little settled because there are vast areas which are too mountainous, too rocky, too dry, or too cold. Since people tend to live in regions with the most favourable physical features, they have concentrated in Southern Ontario and Quebec which have level land, good soil, and a fine climate. You will find other reasons for the greater numbers of people in these areas in your study of history. These sections have been settled much longer than the western part of Canada. They, therefore, had a head start in the development of resources which support a large population. An understanding of the geography of Canada when reading history helps to explain many of the problems of the early settlement of our country.

If we look again at the map of population distribution, we can see where the other half of the Canadian population lives. In the Maritimes and Newfoundland most of the people are found along the coasts. In Nova Scotia there are a few cities, such as Halifax and Sydney, but most of the inhabitants live in small towns or villages on the good harbours scattered along the coast. When we remember that fishing was one of the important activities listed in Nova Scotia, we understand why most of the people live near the sea. The only large group of people living in the interior of the hilly peninsula which is Nova Scotia is found in the Annapolis

Valley. This is one of Nova Scotia's chief sections of level agricultural land, and it produces good apple crops.

Population is evenly distributed over tiny Prince Edward Island. Since both fishing and agriculture are important on the island, the population is found along

Sunrise Valley, Cape Breton Island, has many farmhouses scattered over the flat valley bottom, but no one lives in the steep hills.

the coast, and also scattered over the gently rolling interior. The only city is the capital, Charlottetown. There are more people living on farms on the Island than there are in towns.

In New Brunswick the population is found along the coast and interior valleys much as in Nova Scotia. The greatest number of people live in the broad and fertile St. John River Valley. Lumbering and agriculture are their chief occupations. Logs from New Brunswick's forests are floated down the St. John River to the lumber mills and pulp-and-paper mills which employ many persons. Agriculture is well developed on the smooth slopes above the river banks. The coastal people are employed in the fishing industry. They are either fishermen or workers in the factories which make fish products or can the fish. Other people work in pulp mills at the mouths of rivers on the east coast.

The people of Newfoundland live in tiny fishing villages around the coast, or are scattered over the rolling hills of the Ava-

7

lon Peninsula on the eastern side of the island. St. John's is by far the largest city on the island. The chief settlements in the interior of the island are along the railroad.

About half the people of Canada live on the southern lowlands of Quebec and On-

Courtesy Ontario Department of Travel.

Many small towns are found in the densely-populated lowland of Southern Ontario. The town of Picton is surrounded by many prosperous farms. Locate Picton in your atlas or on a road map.

tario. The French-speaking people of Quebec live chiefly on the fertile agricultural lands of the St. Lawrence Valley. With the exception of the large city populations in Montreal, Quebec and Three Rivers, most of the people are farmers. They work hard and carefully on their long narrow farms which extend back from the river. Quebec also has a large population south of the St. Lawrence River, particularly in the section known as the Eastern Townships. To the north, pioneer farmers are working happily around Lake St. John and in the northwest near the Ontario boundary.

Most of the people in Ontario are found along the north sides of Lakes Ontario and Erie. They live in the fertile peninsula jutting southwestward towards the United States. These rich farming lands have supported a large population busily employed in many manufacturing indus-

tries and businesses. The development of the region has been helped by a good system of roads and railroads over the broad, rolling lowland. Southern Ontario, from Toronto to Windsor, is the richest and most thickly populated large section of Canada.

There are fewer people in Northern Ontario. The towns are small and the people work either in the mining or lumbering industries, except in the grain-shipping cities of Port Arthur and Fort William on Lake Superior. South of James Bay, the agricultural region known as the Clay Belt, which extends eastward from Ontario into Quebec, has more settlement than the surrounding country. The increase in population in the Clay Belt has come only recently. People from southern Ontario and Quebec have moved northward to raise food for the workers in the mining and lumbering industries.

Most of the people of the three Prairie Provinces are evenly distributed over the good agricultural lands in the south. The northern parts of Manitoba and Saskatchewan are in the rocky Canadian Shield which has very little agricultural land and therefore can support few people. About half of the people of the prairies live on farms raising bushels and bushels of golden grain. The prairies have a higher percentage of farm dwellers than any other part of Canada, except Prince Edward Island. This tells us how rich and important are the agriculture and soils of this "bread-basket of Canada".

More than half the people of British Columbia live in a small area in the southwestern corner around Vancouver. The interior of the province is rugged and mountainous, with very little level land on which to raise food. The largest towns and cities have grown up along the coast, especially near the fertile soils of the delta mouth of the Fraser River. People have concentrated in this chief port region to load ships, transfer freight and carry on

8

business. They also manufacture the products of British Columbia's mines and forests when they are brought to the coast.

After reviewing the chief areas where the people of Canada live, we can look down at the map to see the general distribution of Canadians. Nearly all live in the southern parts of Canada; few are more than 200 miles from the United States border. We might think of the population of Canada as a long narrow belt across the southern part of the Dominion. It has a bulge east of the centre represented by the large number of people in southern Ontario and Quebec. Only within recent years has this belt of population finally stretched from coast to coast. It is gradually drawing the various geographic regions of Canada closer together.

As Canadians we want to know more about the others who live along this belt. We want to know what their cities, towns and farms are like, what the people do for a living, and, in particular, what resources each section has which make it possible for people to live there. We like to learn about people in other regions, to compare their lives with ours. In order to do that, however, we must know the geography of the region and the history of the people who occupy it. Geography and history are therefore somewhat alike in that they both deal with people. Geography describes the land and its resources and how they influence the activities of people. History records the events which happen to those same people. Often these historical events occur because of the particular geography of the region. The first step towards understanding the problems and development of other parts of Canada is to know the physical geography of our country and to see how it influences our lives and activities.

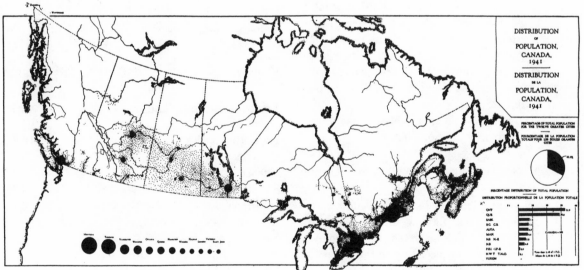

Map Courtesy the Canada Year Book.

One dot represents 1,000 people. The population of each of the 12 larger cities is shown by a disc. Reading from left to right the discs represent Montreal, Toronto, Vancouver, Winnipeg, Ottawa, Quebec, Hamilton, Windsor, Halifax, London, Victoria, Saint John.

Things To Do

1. (a) Refer to the population chapter of the Canada Year Book to discover the population of your community.

   (b) How does it compare in size with other towns or cities in your region? The Canada Year Book is published by the Bureau of Statistics, Department of Trade and Commerce, Ottawa.

2. (a) List the national origins of people in your community.

   (b) From which countries have the most recent settlers come?

   (c) What percentage of the people in your town were born in Canada? This information might be obtained from the Clerk's Office in the City or Town Hall.

3. What is the population density (average number of persons in a square mile) of your county or census division, as listed in the Canada Year Book? How does this compare with nearby counties?

4. (a) Make a map of population density of your county or census division. Locate the chief towns and cities with small black squares. Make the squares proportionate in size to the population of the urban centres. Place small dots wherever you know there are groups of houses, such as along roads, railroads, or rivers.

   (b) Explain why there are blank spaces on the map where no one lives.

   (c) List the reasons for the great numbers of people in certain small areas.

5. (a) Make a map of population density of your province, using the county or census district figures in the Canada Year Book. Colour or shade the counties or divisions according to their densities. The county with the highest density should have the darkest colour. Your teacher will explain how to group the counties under the same colour. For between 5 and 10 persons per square mile would be one colour, and all counties with densities between 10 and 20 person per square mile would be another colour.

   (b) After your map is finished explain why there are few persons per square mile in certain sections.

Facts For Reference

Population of Canada by Provinces, 1941 and 1948.

	1941	1948
Ontario - - - - -	3,787,655	4,300,000
Quebec - - - - -	3,331,882	3,800,000
Saskatchewan - - - -	895,992	855,000
British Columbia - - -	817,861	1,090,000
Alberta - - - - -	796,169	850,000
Manitoba - - - -	729,744	760,000
Nova Scotia - - - -	577,962	640,000
New Brunswick - - -	457,401	505,000
Newfoundland (1945) -	316,000	325,000
Prince Edward Island -	95,047	94,000
Northwest Territories -	12,028	17,000
Yukon Territory - - -	4,914	7,000
Canada (total) - - -	11,506,655	13,238,000

Population Density by Provinces, 1941 (people per square mile)

Prince Edward Island - - - - - -	43.5
Nova Scotia - - - - - - - - -	27.8
New Brunswick - - - - - - --	16.6
Ontario - - - - - - - - - -	10.4
Quebec - - - - - - - - - -	6.3
Saskatchewan - - - - - - - -	3.8
Manitoba - - - - - - - - - -	3.3
Alberta - - - - - - - - - -	3.2
British Columbia - - - - - - -	2.3
Newfoundland (ex. Labrador) - - -	.13
Yukon Territory - - - - - - - -	.02
Northwest Territories - - - - - -	.01
Canada (average) - - - - - -	3.3

The rocky hills of the Canadian Shield rise steeply above the north shore of Lake Superior at the mouth of the Nipigon River. The trans-Canada highway in the foreground winds through a section where the forests have been cut down.

CHAPTER 3

TOPOGRAPHY AND LAND FORMS

Canada has seven regions which differ from one another in topography or land forms. Each region, however, has physical features which are much the same within its boundaries. These physical features so greatly influence the activities which are carried on, that we shall read about the geography of Canada under the headings of these physical regions. (Map on p. 15).

1. Appalachian-Acadian Highlands

The far eastern part of Canada is a hilly region. It is the northward extension of the old, rounded Appalachian Mountains which start far south in Alabama in the United States. This mountain range continues northward through eastern United States and into the Maritime Provinces. It appears again to the north-eastward in the hilly, plateau country of Newfoundland.

The Canadian section of the Appalachian Mountain chain is located in the

11

Eastern Townships of Quebec, south of the St. Lawrence River and east of Lake Champlain. There the mountains are called the Notre Dame Mountains. This range is a series of three parallel lines of low mountains of about 3,000 feet altitude. Deep valleys lie between them. The mountains continue northeastward from Lake Champlain and reach the St. Lawrence River at Levis, opposite Quebec. They decrease in height to the eastward, but rise again in the higher Shickshock Mountains of the Gaspé Peninsula. (Do you know how high 3,000 feet is? Can you compare a mountain of that height with anything in your neighborhood?)

The Appalachian Mountains of the United States for a long time were a barrier to inland settlement from the American colonies along the coast. Similarly, their northern continuation in Canada has been a barrier between the Maritime Provinces and the rest of Canada. The building of transportation lines over the mountains was difficult. Only two railroad lines and two roads connect the Maritimes with the interior of Eastern Canada. Fortunately for central Canada, the broad St. Lawrence River is a convenient water route north of this physical barrier of rock. But the fact that the St. Lawrence *does* go around the mountains has meant that the Maritimes are further cut off, for they are often missed by incoming boats. This mountain barrier of the Appalachians has played, and still plays, an important part in the history and development of both the United States and Canada.

The hills of the Maritime Provinces are not as high as the mountains in the Eastern Townships and Gaspé. The forested hills of the Acadian Highlands rise in north and central New Brunswick. Another highland extends down the centre of Nova Scotia, giving it a rocky backbone. These highlands are little used for raising food because the soil is poor and frosts are more frequent than in the valleys. They

are, therefore, left in native forest to supply timber and pulpwood to the forestry industries of New Brunswick and Nova Scotia.

Newfoundland is a plateau with some hilly areas and some lowland sections. The highest part of the island is the Long Range which extends along the western section. The plateau is steep along the south coast of the island but slopes down to low rocky hills along the northeast coast. The Avalon Peninsula of the eastern part of Newfoundland is low and hilly. It is composed of a different kind of rock than the rest of the island.

Although a hilly region, the Maritimes and Newfoundland have local lowlands and valleys which are very important. Agriculture can be carried on in these level sections and people can live there and raise their own food. The lowlands have more people than the highlands and mountains.

The most extensive lowland is found along the east coast of New Brunswick. It continues across Northumberland Strait to include the tiny province of Prince Edward

Courtesy New Brunswick Information Bureau.

The beautiful St. John River flows through a plateau in northwestern New Brunswick. People live in the valley and cultivate farms on the slopes, but the upper plateau remains in forest.

Island. The same rolling lowland forms the good dairying region around Moncton and continues eastward across Chignecto Isthmus into Nova Scotia. The St. John River Valley of New Brunswick and the Annapolis Valley of western Nova Scotia are the most important of the several valleys of the Maritimes. They both have rich agricultural land raising special crops. The topography of the Maritimes illustrates that there are relationships between areas of lowland and centres of population density. As we learn more about the physical features of Canada, we shall see that there are other relationships.

2. The St. Lawrence and Ontario Lowlands

Maps show how the wide St. Lawrence River narrows gradually west of the Gulf of St. Lawrence, and leads into the heart of the North American continent. In its eastern section hills rise quite steeply along both shores of the river in dark, forested slopes. West of Quebec City, however, the river is narrower. The hills disappear in the distance, leaving a flat lowland above each bank. The lowland becomes broader to the west, reaching as far south as the Notre Dame Mountains, and northward to the steep slopes of the Canadian Shield. At the head of ocean transportation, and in the centre of this fertile lowland, lies Canada's largest city, Montreal. Aided by many advantages of physical geography, this city holds about one-tenth of the Canadian population. The fertile St. Lawrence Lowland around the city is one of the reasons for the prosperity of this large group of people. The industrious French farmer on the Lowland can raise more food than is needed for himself and he sells his surplus to the city people who are occupied in manufacturing and business.

Long, long ago in geological time the St. Lawrence Lowland was once an arm of the sea, as the Gulf of St. Lawrence is now. Ocean waters extended inland beyond Montreal to near the city of Belleville in eastern Ontario and northward beyond Ottawa. Sands and clays were deposited on the flat bottom of this sea by the rivers which emptied into it. As the land slowly began to rise about 30,000 years ago, the sea drained to the east, and disappeared.

It left behind the level area of good soils in the region we now know as the St. Lawrence Lowland of southern Quebec and eastern Ontario.

West of the St. Lawrence Lowland the rocky hills of a southern extension of the Canadian Shield rise above the pasture

Courtesy Quebec Publicity Bureau.

At Quebec City the St. Lawrence Lowland is narrow. The dark hills of the Canadian Shield rise nearby to the north. Most of the lowland here has been cleared of trees, and now has excellent dairy farms.

lands of eastern Ontario. This southward extension continues into the United States where it is known as the Adirondack Mountains. In Canada it is an unproductive rocky section which separates the fertile lowland of the St. Lawrence River from the productive Ontario Lowland to the west.

The Ontario Lowland is more rolling than the lowland of southern Quebec. Its low hills and broad valleys extend southwestward into the peninsula between Lake Huron on the west and Lakes Ontario and Erie on the south. A similar lowland south of the Great Lakes in the United States has developed into one of the main agricultural and industrial areas of that country. Likewise, the fertile Ontario Lowland has been well settled in Canada.

The early pioneers of the 19th century found that the soils of the Ontario Lowland made excellent farm land. As Ontario was settled these soils produced food for large numbers of people. Gradually the people gathered together into towns and cities. Manufacturing, based on the products of the surrounding farms and forests, increased in importance. We now find that this lowland region is not only a very prosperous agricultural region, but that it also supports several large cities and many towns. Almost one-third of the population of Canada lives in this important region of Southern Ontario.

3. The Canadian Shield

Stretching far to the north of the St. Lawrence and Ontario Lowlands is a huge, rough region of the oldest rocks known in Canada. Geologists call these rocks Precambrian and tell us that they have been there for millions of years as a firm, solid shield generally unshaken by other movements of the earth's crust. They say that thousands of feet of rock have been worn away from its surface over this period. The rocks we now see on the surface were once far underground. Rich minerals which are usually buried beneath the earth's surface are now exposed at the top and often reward the searching of prospectors.

Geologists also tell us that the lack of soil over much of the area is due to the huge ice-cap which once covered most of Canada about 30,000 years ago. This ice-cap was formed at a time in the earth's history when the climate was much colder than it is now. The snows accumulated each year in Northern Canada without melting. The snow gradually became so hard-packed that it was turned to ice. The weight of the ice in the centre pushed the ice at the edges outward in all directions. We can visualize this movement by thinking of cold molasses or honey being slowly poured upon a table. The molasses piles up in the centre, but the movement is outward at the edges. This huge ice-cap gradually covered all of Eastern Canada and pushed southward into the United States as far as the Ohio River. Most of the soil which once covered the Shield was carried along with the ice. As the ice gradually melted after thousands of years, the

rocks and soil carried by it were dumped near the edges. Much of it was deposited south of the Great Lakes in the United States.

The Canadian Shield makes up about one-half of the mainland area of Canada. It forms a vast horseshoe around Hudson and James Bays, extending from Labrador to beyond Great Bear Lake in the northwest. The Adirondack Mountains of New York State are a southward extension through eastern Ontario. Another arm is located in northern Minnesota, west of Lake Superior.

Within such a large region we might expect to find a great variety of physical features, but explorers and flyers tell us that the region looks much the same from place to place. The Shield averages about 2,000 feet in altitude over much of its area. It rises steeply on the south and slopes towards Hudson Bay. Its surface is carved up by countless lakes and rivers. The rugged character of the land makes transportation and movement across it difficult. The rivers have so many rapids that only canoes can navigate them. The large number of lakes, however, has helped air transport. When aeroplanes are supplied with float pontoons in summer and skis in the winter they can land nearly anywhere. Aeroplanes are now one of the important means of travelling in this region.

If we travel over the southern part of the Canadian Shield, for example, along one of the transcontinental railways, we pass through mile after mile of northern forest. We realize that the Shield holds a huge reserve of softwoods, such as spruce and pine. Some day these trees may be made into pulpwood. Our railroad trip shows that the region is too rough and rocky to be used for agriculture. We can see why lumbering and mining are the chief occupations of the people living on the Shield.

The Canadian Shield has played an important part in Canadian history. When we think of how difficult it is to travel in the heavily wooded southern parts of the Shield, we understand why early settlement in Eastern Canada stayed in the southern lowland regions. In the middle of the 19th century many families who first came to Canada from Europe found the

Physical Regions of Canada.

path to the west blocked by the rugged Shield. They moved westward over the Ontario Lowland which pointed into the fine farmland of the United States. Many settled south and west of the Great Lakes, depriving Canada of good settlers. It was not until the railway builders laid a line of steel rails across the Shield in the late 19th century that settlers were able to pour into the fertile lands to the west.

Even today the Canadian Shield is only sparsely settled. It forms a physical barrier between the densely settled lowlands of Quebec and Ontario and the rich farming lands of the Prairie Provinces. People are gradually moving into the Shield, however, especially along the railroad lines. These pioneers are developing the forest and mineral wealth of the area. Our knowledge of its geography should make us realize that the Shield cannot be as fully settled as the nearby lowlands.

4. The Hudson Bay Lowland
Southwest of Hudson Bay and west of James Bay there is a lowland region which

is different from the Canadian Shield around it. In this lowland the rocks are flat-lying, unlike the rocks of the Shield. They are similar to the rocks found in the St. Lawrence and Ontario Lowlands. The topography is also different from that of the Shield. The Hudson Bay Lowland is a flat, swampy and marshy region sloping very gently from the hilly edge of the Shield towards Hudson and James Bays. A few large rivers spill over the north edge of the Shield and flow slowly across the plain. They empty into the shallow waters of Hudson Bay, Canada's huge interior "sea". The region is well wooded away from the coast, but between the rivers, muskegs and muddy ground are the typical cover.

A few thousand years ago—a very short time in the world's history to geologists—this lowland was once covered by the salt water of Hudson and James Bays. Since then the land has slowly risen until the lowland is now above water. Streams drain only part of the flat, swampy area. Since the gentle slope of the land continues below the water of the bays, there is shallow water for many miles offshore. Along many sections of the coast the shoreline moves more than a mile each day, back and forth with the tide.

Unlike the lowlands south of the Canadian Shield, the Hudson Bay Lowland is sparsely settled. Since the land is so poorly drained, soils are not good. When this fact is combined with the danger of early frosts, because of the nearness of the cold waters of Hudson Bay, we can see why it has not been attractive to settlers. In addition, the Lowland is hard to reach. To the north, there is shallow water offshore, and seas that are frozen for eight months. Southward, rough rivers separate it from the thinly-settled Shield.

5. The Great Plains
Stretching to the west of the Canadian Shield is a broad, flat or gently rolling

region known as the Great Plains. It is the northern part of a similar level area in the United States. From south to north the plains extend through the middle of North America from the Gulf of Mexico to the Arctic Ocean. In Canada, the Great Plains cover much of our Prairie Provinces. They are about 800 miles wide along the 49th parallel boundary and gradually narrow to the north. The lowland of the Mackenzie River Valley in the Northwest Territories is the northern continuation of the Great Plains region. There the lowland varies in width from 50 to 100 miles.

On the eastern border there is little difference in height between the Great Plains and the Canadian Shield. When travelling from east to west one notices that the rocky hills of the Shield gradually become lower and farther apart, and the level areas between the hills become larger. Soon there are no rocky hills; flat land stretches for miles in all directions. The trees also become smaller and farther apart, and before long we are in the area of grassland and grain fields. This is the Prairie region of Canada.

The flattest part of the Great Plains is in southern Manitoba, around the largest

Courtesy Manitoba Travel and Publicity Bureau.

The level land of the prairies near Brandon, Manitoba, was once covered by a large glacial lake. The rich soils now produce thousands of bushels of wheat.

Prairie city, Winnipeg. This area was once the flat bottom of a big lake. The lake was formed by melting ice along the front of the huge ice-cap which covered most of Canada. After the lake drained away, the good soils in the former lake bottom grad-

ually developed into one of the finest large areas of agricultural land in Canada.

Because of its flatness, machinery can be used over large areas of the Manitoba Lowland. Topography therefore influences occupations since it allows a few men to farm many acres. In the hilly regions of Eastern Canada machinery cannot be used as easily, and farmers do more hand labour and thus have smaller farms. Population is more scattered across the level prairies than in hilly areas, because each family can look after a larger number of acres and therefore locates farther from each other.

Although the Great Plains seem level everywhere they actually slope gradually upward to the west. Lake Winnipeg is more than 700 feet above sea level, and at the foothills in western Alberta the plains have an altitude of 4,000 to 5,000 feet. The chief noticeable rise is found along a sloping escarpment, or steep bluff, in western Manitoba, separating the Manitoba Lowland from the higher plains of southern Saskatchewan. This sloping strip would be a small feature in a hilly country, but it stands out above the level plains. In particular, there is a difference in land-use. The escarpment is a zone of low trees and shrubs, different from the neatly cultivated fields on both sides of it. Farmers have not cultivated this sloping section, because prairie agriculture is more suited to level areas.

Another hilly area in the southern prairies is found in the Cypress Hills and Wood Mountain areas in southwestern Saskatchewan. There the land is again used differently from that of other level sections of the Plains.

The western and highest parts of the Plains are more rolling than the eastern section. The rivers which flow eastward from the Rocky Mountains have cut deep channels into the Alberta plains and often flow 200 to 500 feet below the general surface. These rivers cause some difficulties

16

for north-south transportation lines which try to cross them. Otherwise, the Plains have no physical barriers to transportation. Roads and railroads follow straight lines for miles and miles. From the air the region looks like a giant checkerboard. The fields are all laid out in squares, and

Courtesy H. Pollard.

In the foothills of Alberta the wheat fields are located on rolling hills. Some of this region is too dry for wheat and is used for ranching.

at every mile the roads cut each other at right-angles.

There is a difference in appearance between the southern and northern parts of the Great Plains. The southern section is a dry area of grassland, having no trees except along some rivers. Trees become more numerous north of a line extending from about Brandon, in southwestern Manitoba, to Red Deer, south of Edmonton, Alberta. The northern part, continuing into the Mackenzie River Valley, is wooded country. The vegetation zones in the Canadian Shield are in the opposite order to those of the Plains since the northern part is treeless, and the southern part is forested.

6. The Cordillera

West of the Great Plains the Rocky Mountains rise about 6,000 feet directly above the rolling foothills to heights of 10,000 to 12,000 feet above sea level. The sharp, jagged peaks of these young mountains make some of the most thrilling scenery in North America. Combined with the other mountain ranges of the Cordillera, the Rockies are a solid wall of rock

separating the West Coast settlements from the rest of Canada.

The Cordillera is the name given to the series of mountain ranges and plateaus which extend north-south from Alaska to Mexico along the west side of North America. In Canada the most easterly range is the Rocky Mountains, which also extends southward into the United States. The row of peaks of the Rockies marks the Alberta-British Columbia boundary in its southern section. The mountains continue northward into British Columbia, ending at the Liard River. Another mountain system known as the Mackenzie Range continues to the north of the Liard River. The Yukon-Northwest Territories boundary is drawn along the western section of this range. The Mackenzie Range is similar to the Rockies in having bold, jagged, snow-capped peaks. Both of these ranges are serious barriers to transportation; the few natural passes through them are important for rail and road lines.

The western boundary of the Rocky

Courtesy J. L. Robinson.

The Rocky Mountains near Jasper are walls of bare rock rising west of Alberta. Rivers have cut through the mountains, and the railroad now follows the same path.

Mountains is a narrow deep valley known as the Rocky Mountain Trench. This long, north-south valley is occupied by several rivers, such as the Kootenay, Columbia and Fraser, flowing in different directions. The Trench can be traced farther north into Yukon Territory as a deep gash in this mountainous country.

West of the Rocky Mountain Trench, and south of what is known as the "Big Bend" of the Columbia River, lie more high mountains. They rise proudly into the sky to heights almost as high as the Rockies. This is the Columbia Mountain System, which is made up of several north-south ranges.

Since these mountains are so high and steep, few people live there permanently. The only agricultural settlers are found in the valleys, on the flat terraces above the river banks. Other people are occupied in mining and lumbering. The mountains of the Cordillera hold rich minerals just like the old rocks of the Canadian Shield. As the many rivers and streams wear away the rocks this mineral wealth is exposed at the surface. Many places now have producing mines.

West of the Selkirk and Monashee mountains the topography becomes a hilly plateau, cut by deep valleys. This is the Interior Plateau of British Columbia, which has altitudes of 2,000 to 4,000 feet. The Plateau lies between higher mountain peaks to the east and west. There is some general farming carried on in the north-central area, and cattle and sheep are grazed in the drier central parts of the plateau. Fruit farms are located in the narrow valleys in the southern section. The Plateau, being high and hilly, is not as productive as the Prairie and St. Lawrence Lowland regions, but it supports a larger population than the surrounding mountains. The residents grow more food than they need and send the surplus to the coast cities.

Northward of the Interior Plateau in northern British Columbia lies a confused mass of mountains. The Cassiar Range is one of the largest in this little-known section. For many years even the names of the many mountains were not definite, because the same mountains were often given more than one name when seen by explorers from different sides.

The Yukon Plateau lies north of these rugged mountains. The Mackenzie Range rises above it on the east and the very high

The bare rock cliffs of Mount Assiniboine rise like a pyramid above the other mountains of the Rockies. Glaciers are discharging ice over the edge of the cliffs on the right. Find Mount Assiniboine on a map of the Rockies. How high is it above sea-level?

St. Elias Range towers to the southwest. The Yukon Plateau is about 2,000 feet above sea level, and is cut deeply by broad U-shaped valleys. Most of the upper plateau is too cold for tree growth. People live in the valleys where it is warmer in summer.

The Coast Range mountains form the western rim above the plateaus of central British Columbia. They rise directly from the sea to heights of over 5,000 feet and their rows of peaks increase in elevation inland. Farther north the St. Elias Mountains occupy the southwest corner of Yukon Territory and extend into Alaska. Their sharp, snow-covered peaks are the highest in Canada. Mount Logan, measured at 19,850 feet, is the highest peak. There are at least sixteen other peaks in the area higher than the 12,972 feet of Mount Robson in the Rockies.

All along the west coast of Canada these mountains make beautiful scenery. This coast has gradually sunk down into the ocean over a period of many thousands of years. The valleys are now filled with water and make numerous excellent deep harbours. These inlets shelter the many fishing boats which go out into the Pacific for salmon, halibut and herring. Off the coast the peaks of submerged ranges appear again as islands. The physical geography of the mountains holds out little hope for agricultural development, but it has been kind in giving many harbours which encourage the people to obtain a living from the sea.

7. The Arctic Islands

North of the mainland of Canada there are numerous large islands extending over a thousand miles towards the North Pole. These islands are much larger than most Canadians realize. Baffin Island is one of the world's largest, being about the size of the Province of Manitoba. Ellesmere Island, our northernmost island, is almost twice the size of New Brunswick and Nova Scotia together. In addition there are 17 islands larger than 1,000 square miles, which is half the size of Prince Edward Island.

The Arctic Islands have distinctive physical features. A very high mountain range runs through the eastern part of Baffin, Devon and Ellesmere Islands. Many parts of this mountain chain still contain permanent ice-caps, like that on Greenland, only much smaller. The islands of the central group are not as high as the eastern ones. They are either hilly, or low plateaus of about 1,000 feet above sea level. Some of the western islands are low and have more vegetation in the summer than the barren eastern islands.

The chief inhabitants of the Arctic Islands are Eskimos, who live along the coasts of only the southern islands. Because much of the land is mountainous and lacking in vegetation, they have turned to the sea for a living. They obtain much of their food, clothing, and many utensils from the animals of the sea, such as seals, walrus and white whales. There are only a few hundred white men living in this region because resources are lacking and ice-floes make transportation difficult in the short summer. Although topography discourages settlement in this region, just as it does in some southern areas, the stronger discouraging factor is the cold climate.

Summary

The physical features of Canada may be divided into seven major regions. On the east there are the mountains, hills and small lowlands of the Appalachian-Acadian region. Around Hudson Bay the huge rocky Canadian Shield rises steeply on the south and slopes down towards the cold waters of the Bay. Between the southern edge of the Shield and the Great Lakes, and along the St. Lawrence River, there is a rolling lowland which contains one-half of the people of Canada. Another lowland which is flat, swampy, and little used is found along the western shores of Hudson and James Bays. The largest flat area is that to the west of the Canadian Shield, where the Great Plains narrow northward to the Arctic Ocean. The western part of Canada is a series of high, north-south mountain ranges, with lower plateaus between. North of the mainland of Canada are hundreds of islands, large and small, extending into the ice-packed Arctic Ocean to within about 500 miles of the North Pole.

19

Things To Do

1. Make a topographic (landforms) map of a region near your home, or a region that your teacher may assign. Choose an area about 10 miles square. First mark on the rivers, lakes, roads, and railroads. Colour the lowlands green, the hills light brown, and the highest places dark brown. Make dots for the chief cities, towns and villages. In which colour are they located? In which colour are the roads and railroads? Explain why the cities are located in a certain type of topography.

2. Write a topographic description of an area that you have seen many times. What words best describe the hills? Are they sharp, or rugged, or rounded? Are the rivers straight and fast, twisting and slow, clear or muddy? Do the lowlands have swamps or marshes? Are the lowlands all near rivers?

3. (a) In what kind of topography would you like to spend your summer vacation? What sports or activities could you carry on there?

   (b) How will the topographic features influence these activities?

   (c) Name the winter sports or activities that could be carried on at the same place.

   (d) Are lowlands or hills better for winter sports? Explain why you think so.

Facts for Reference

Highest peak in Southeastern Canada—Mount Jacques Cartier in
Tabletop Mountain, Gaspé - - - 4,160 feet
    Peaks in the Torngat Mountains of Labrador - - - 5,500 feet
    Peaks in the Penny Highlands of Baffin Island - - 9,000 feet

Highest Peaks in Rocky Mountains (in feet above sea level)—

Robson	12,972
Columbia	12,294
Brazeau	12,250
Clemenceau	12,001

Highest Peaks of Selkirk Mountains—

Sir Sanford	11,590
Farnham	11,342
Hasler	11,113

Highest Peaks of Coast Mountains—

Waddington	13,260
Tiedemann	12,000

Highest Peaks of St. Elias Mountains—

Logan	19,850
St. Elias	18,008
Lucania	17,150
King	17,130

Large Islands of Canada (in square miles)—

1.	Baffin	201,000
2.	Victoria	79,000
3.	Ellesmere	75,000
4.	Newfoundland	42,700
5.	Banks	26,000
6.	Devon	20,000
7.	Melville	16,000
8.	Southampton	16,000
9.	Vancouver	12,408
10.	Cape Breton	3,970
11.	Anticosti	3,970
12.	Prince Edward Island	2,184

Talston River, which empties into southeastern Great Slave Lake, is typical of the many rapid-blocked rivers which drain the rocky Canadian Shield. Notice how small the trees are in this part of the Northwest Territories.

CHAPTER 4

DRAINAGE---RIVERS AND LAKES

Rivers in History

The rivers and lakes of Canada played an important part in the exploration of our country. While the American colonists to the south were held back from the interior by the Appalachian mountains, Canada had the wide route of the St. Lawrence River and the Great Lakes leading into her interior. From the Strait of Belle Isle, between Newfoundland and Labrador, it is over 2300 miles to the head of Lake Superior. This is half-way across the continent.

More French settled along the St. Lawrence River than in the Maritimes because the boats which brought them across the ocean could easily navigate as far as Montreal Island. French explorers and fur traders were able to push into the interior of North America by using a short-cut route up the Ottawa River and crossing to Georgian Bay and the Great Lakes. They sent their furs back along this route to the French merchants in Montreal and Quebec. In the early history of Canada, rivers were the chief routes of

21

travel and communication.

There were other rivers that played a leading role in Canadian exploration and trade. These were the rivers flowing into Hudson Bay, especially from the west. After the historic Hudson's Bay Company had found that ships could safely sail through Hudson Strait, it established trading posts at the mouths of rivers emptying into the Bay. Indians were encouraged to bring their furs downstream to them. After a time the Company found it profitable to send fur traders up the streams to the west to the Indian hunting grounds. Since these rivers were long, Europeans were led into the plains and the exploration of the vast Northwest was begun.

The Nelson and Saskatchewan Rivers led 1,600 miles into the interior of Canada to the foothills of the Rocky Mountains. The Churchill River could be followed 1,000 miles to its source. A short portage from the Churchill led to the Athabaska River and another 1,600-mile journey down the Mackenzie River to the Arctic Ocean. For many years the water routes from Hudson Bay and the Great Lakes were channels for the flow of Canadian history.

As settlement spread over the St. Lawrence and Ontario lowlands, the Great Lakes route increased in importance. Today it ranks as one of the most valuable inland water routes of the world. Long lake boats plough through these huge lakes and connecting rivers for eight months of the year. They bring the produce of the Great Plains, chiefly wheat, to the large population of the lowlands. The Great Lakes are even more important to industries of the United States. Iron ore from northern Minnesota is carried downstream by lake freighters, and coal is carried on the return trip. Large cities have grown up all around the Great Lakes, both in the United States and in Canada, because they

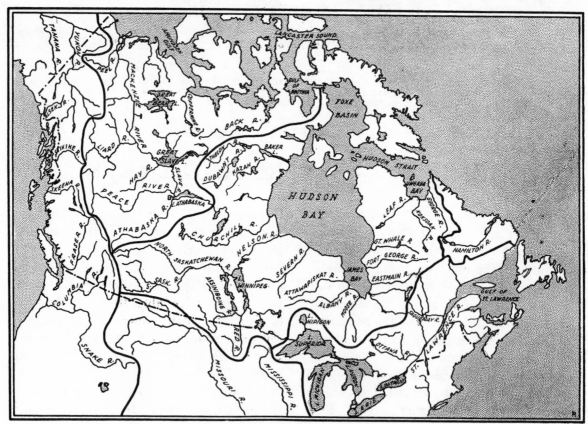

Rivers, Lakes and Drainage Systems.

22

have been able to use cheap water transportation to develop their industries.

Drainage Basins

The St. Lawrence and Great Lakes drainage basin carries most of the commercial water traffic in Canada, but it does not have the largest drainage area. More than one-third of the mainland area of Canada is drained into huge Hudson Bay. We have noted how the Canadian Shield rises steeply on the south and slopes towards Hudson Bay. The rivers in the southern part of the Shield, flowing into the St. Lawrence and its tributaries, are therefore short and rapid. The rivers flowing to the north are longer. In Ontario and Quebec these fast south-flowing rivers often have large waterfalls where the power can be captured to make electricity for industries and homes. Much of the prosperity of the lumbering and mining industries in the Shield is due to the presence of this cheap water power.

It is not as easy to use the rivers which flow into Hudson Bay. Most of them flow over the rough country of the Shield, and have numerous rapids along their courses. In addition, the rivers empty into cold Hudson Bay whose waters are ice-covered for eight months of the year. In one-third of Canada, therefore, the rivers flow in the wrong direction to be useful. They cannot be used in the lumbering industry as the southern rivers of the Shield are, since they would carry logs down to the little-inhabited shores of Hudson Bay.

Another one-third of the mainland is drained into the ice-filled Arctic Ocean. There are several small rivers draining towards the northern Arctic Coast, but the mighty Mackenzie River, along with its main tributaries, the Athabaska, Peace, Hay, Liard and Peel Rivers, has the largest drainage basin. The Mackenzie River system is 2,500 miles long. It begins in the headwaters of the Findlay River in the mountains of British Columbia and extends to its delta mouth at Beaufort Sea in the Arctic Ocean.

Many of the rivers of the Mackenzie system are navigable for flat-bottomed river boats. The products of the region, chiefly furs and minerals, are usually carried by this means. Since there are no railroads in the central and northern Mackenzie Valley and no roads except the Alaska Highway and the Grimshaw-Hay River road, the river is the chief means of cheap transportation.

Most of the rivers flowing into the Pacific Ocean are short, and many are rapid. Since the Cordillera region has both heavy rainfall and steep slopes, there are

Courtesy B.C. Travel Bureau.

The Fraser River flows in a steep-sided valley through the dry interior plateau of British Columbia. People live on the flat upper terraces on both sides of the stream rather than beside the river.

many rivers to carry away the water. Because the mountains are near the coast, the rivers are usually short. A few large rivers, such as the Fraser, Stikine and Skeena, cut through the Coast Mountains from the interior. Although they are not navigable themselves, roads have been built along their valleys to make it possible to cross through the mountain barrier.

The longest river of the Northwest

region is the Yukon River, but most of its course lies in Alaska. The Yukon River has its sources both on the northeast side of the Coast Range in British Columbia, and on the west side of the Mackenzie Mountains in the Yukon. It flows about 700 miles north through Yukon Territory, and then swings westward in a wide arc for another 1300 miles through central Alaska. River boats can navigate the Yukon River from its mouth in the Bering Sea to Whitehorse, Yukon. Many prospectors who hurried to the Yukon gold rush of 1897-98 came upstream by boat from Alaska, while others floated downstream after crossing the passes through the Coast Range. The presence of a navigable river has greatly helped the development of Yukon Territory all through its history. At the same time the mountain barriers in the headwaters have made the Yukon hard to reach from southern regions. Much of the romance and colour of the far-away Yukon are a result of its geography.

A few rivers in southern Alberta and Saskatchewan flow southward towards the Missouri and Mississippi rivers. Since the waters of these short rivers are used by the dry lands of both countries near the International Boundary, United States and Canada have made friendly agreements as to the control and use of the rivers.

Lakes

It has been estimated that six percent of Canada is covered with freshwater lakes. They are particularly abundant in the Canadian Shield and other poorly drained areas of Northwestern Canada. For example, there is an area southwest of Reindeer Lake in northern Manitoba where aerial photographs show over 7,500 lakes in a section of 5,300 square miles.

These numerous lakes serve three useful purposes for northern Canada. Most of them have many fish which are used for food by the Indians of our northern forests. Good fishing also attracts tourists and vacationists from the United States and southern regions of Canada. Finally, the lakes are useful for landing sites for planes with floats or skis, thus permitting rapid transportation in a country over which travelling by foot is difficult.

Canada has several large lakes as well as a great number of small ones. These large lakes are found around the southern and western boundaries of the Canadian Shield. In addition to the five Great Lakes (one of which, Lake Michigan, is entirely in the United States), there is a line of big lakes stretching northwestward through Lakes Winnipeg, Athabaska, Great Slave and Great Bear. Commercial fishing is carried on in all of Canada's large lakes except Great Bear Lake.

Summary

Canada has important navigable rivers, such as the St. John in New Brunswick, St. Lawrence in Quebec, Mackenzie in the Northwest Territories, and Yukon in Yukon Territory. Each has played a part in the development of Canada. Vast areas, however, have poor river transportation. The Canadian Shield has fine canoe routes, but the rivers are navigable for only short distances at a stretch. The Prairie rivers are too shallow, and change depth with the seasons. The most important river and lake system is that of the St. Lawrence-Great Lakes. It carries most of the commercial water transportation of Canada and much of that of the United States. The numerous lakes of the Canadian Shield, including the large ones along its western borders, are useful for fishing and aeroplane landing sites.

Things To Do

1. Read about a canoe trip down the Mis- sinaibi River in the Canadian Geographical Journal of August, 1946. Follow the route on a map of Northern Ontario. Look at the pictures of the scenery along the way. The Canadian Geographical Journal is published monthly by the Canadian Geographical So- ciety, Ottawa.

2. Plan a canoe trip in the northern part of your province. Start from a large town or city if possible, and plan to come back a dif- ferent route from that taken outwards.

   (a) How many rapids will you have to port- age?

   (b) On how many rivers and lakes will you travel?

   (c) Describe the scenery along your route.

   (d) Will you meet any other people or see any settlements?

   Sectional maps of your province on a scale of 8 miles to 1 inch may be obtained from the Maps and Surveys Division, Department of Mines and Technical Surveys, Ottawa, or from your provincial resources department.

3. Read about the early exploration of Canada in your history book. On an outline map of Canada trace such river routes of the brave explorers as your teacher assigns. Use a dif- ferent colour or broken lines for each ex- plorer. Make one map for the period 1600- 1700, and another map for the period 1700- 1800.

4. In one of your reference books read about transportation on the Great Lakes system. Make a map of the Great Lakes. Show the sources of the products (wheat, iron and coal) which are carried on the lake boats. Draw lines to show the routes which the boats follow in delivering these products. Locate and name the chief cities that are found on the shores of the Great Lakes.

Facts For Reference

Areas of Drainage Basins in Canada (in square miles)

Hudson Bay Basin	1,379,160
Arctic Basin	930,357
Atlantic Basin	420,463
Pacific Basin	400,730
Gulf of Mexico Basin	10,121

Longest River Systems in Canada (in miles)

Mackenzie (to head of Findlay)	2,514
St. Lawrence (to head of Great Lakes)	1,900
Yukon (including Alaska)	1,924
(in Canada only)	714
Nelson (to head of Bow)	1,600
Peace	1,054
Churchill	1,000
Columbia (including United States)	1,150
(in Canada only)	459
Fraser	850
Athabaska	765
North Saskatchewan	760

Largest Lakes in Canada (in square miles)

Superior (including United States part)	31,820
Huron (including United States part)	23,010
Great Bear	11,490
Great Slave	11,170
Erie (including United States part)	9,940
Winnipeg	9,398
Ontario (including United States part)	7,540
Athabaska	3,058
Reindeer	2,444
Winnipegosis	2,086

At Glacier National Park in the Selkirk Mountains, there is heavy snowfall on the western slopes. The moist snow clings to the thin evergreens which cover the mountain sides.

CHAPTER 5

WEATHER AND CLIMATE

Canada is a vast country. In such a large area we should expect to find many kinds of climate. It is about 2800 miles from the warm southern tip of Pelee Island in Lake Erie to the icy point of Cape Columbia on northern Ellesmere Island. It is more than 3000 miles from the rainy slopes of Vancouver Island on the west to the foggy coasts of Nova Scotia and Newfoundland on the east. Canada is so big that we cannot say that the climate is hot or cold, dry or wet, because some parts of it are hot while at the same time other parts are cold. Some places have had over 300 inches of rain in one year, while other places have had only five inches. To understand why there are such great differences in the climate of Canada we have to know where our weather comes from, and why it affects our country differently from place to place.

Canada lies in the path of the westerly winds. In our latitude the air which is always circulating around the world moves from west to east. Within the general movement, big whirlpools of air often form in which the winds blow from every direction. These big circulations of air are carried along by the Westerlies and also move from west to east.

As the whirlpools of air pass over us, winds change direction from day to day. When winds are from the south the weather is usually warmer, and when they blow from the north we shiver in winter and are cooled off in summer. In some parts of Canada rain comes with westerly winds, and in other parts winds from the east bring rain or snow. If we watch our local weather closely we see that the common kinds of weather often come with certain directions of wind.

Temperature

Canada is surrounded by oceans on three sides. The temperature of the water of two of these oceans greatly affects our climate. The cold waters of the Arctic Ocean to the north and northwest of Canada have the greatest influence. Air collects over the ice-covered waters of this ocean, and becomes very cold. It finally pushes southward, spreading over northern Canada, and bringing low temperatures.

Since the Mackenzie Valley is a lowland, cold air can move southward up the valley without barriers. It brings the cold winter weather which people on the prairies know so well. Because there is little difference in height between the Great Plains region and the Canadian Shield to the east, the

southward-moving cold Arctic air joins the Westerlies and moves eastward without hindrance. It soon covers northern Ontario and northern Quebec and sometimes extends into the St. Lawrence Valley. Canada in winter, therefore, may have cold temperatures over all the Great Plains

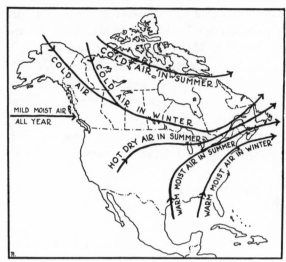

Usual Routes of Air Masses.

and Canadian Shield regions. In Eastern Canada people can tell when one of these cold waves is coming by watching for reports in the newspapers of temperatures of Prairie and northern Ontario cities.

In summer the westerly winds are farther north than in winter and the cold air from the Arctic moves almost directly eastward. It crosses over the low western Arctic Islands towards the opening of Hudson Strait. In summer, southern Canada is influenced by air from another direction. Warm air which gathers over the sun-heated waters of the Gulf of Mexico spreads northward up the Mississippi Valley Lowland in the United States. It is gradually turned eastward by the Westerlies and moves out to the Atlantic Ocean through the lowlands of the Great Lakes and St. Lawrence Valley. This southern air brings the hot, humid summer weather which people know in the Ontario and St. Lawrence Lowlands. During the same season, hot air from the deserts of southwestern United States also moves northward and often brings hot, dry weather to the southern parts of the Prairie Provinces.

The warm air from southwestern United States and the Gulf of Mexico is sometimes strong enough to push northward into Canada in the winter. This causes the winter thaws which often come after several days of cold Arctic air. The southern part of Canada is a "no-mans land" in the battle between these two sources of air in the winter. In northern Canada the Arctic air is the stronger, and in southern United States the warm air rules. In between, however, in southern Canada and northern United States, they fight back and forth in winter. We have cold clear weather when the Arctic air passes over, and there are warm spells when the air is from the tropics.

Most Canadians live in southern Canada, and are used to all kinds of weather in winter. Winters are seldom the same from year to year. Some winters are long and cold with few tropical air masses to bring relief; other winters may be mild with only an occasional cold period. We never know from one winter to the next which air mass is going to win the battle of making our weather. Some geographers say that this changing weather makes Canadians progressive. We are used to quick changes and never have a chance to get bored with the same kind of weather. We are forced to think because each day we have to plan for a different kind of weather. Our climate in the south is, therefore, one of the best to encourage human activity.

There is still another ocean which affects the climate of Canada. The warm waters of the northern Pacific Ocean lie to the west of Canada. The westerly winds blow across this huge ocean and come up against the mountains of the British Columbia coast. The warm air brings mild weather to the whole coastal region in winter. While northern Canada is cold

and southern Canada has both cold and mild spells, the west coast has warm winter weather.

The warm air from the Pacific Ocean also brings heavy rainfall to the coast and snowfall to the mountains. Meteorologists tell us that rainfall and snowfall are caused

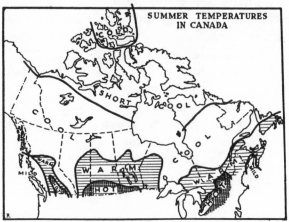

by the cooling of moist air. The Pacific air is warm and moist, because it has been travelling over the waters of the warm ocean, and picking up moisture. When this air is forced up to pass over the Coast Mountains it is cooled. We know that the upper air is colder than air at the ground because of the pictures we see of aviators in warm clothes when they fly high in the air. We can understand what happens to this rising warm air if we blow out our warm breath on a cold day. It forms a little cloud in front of us and we say that "we can see our breath". On a much larger scale, that is what happens to the warm Pacific air. It is cooled in rising into the higher altitudes, and clouds form. Either rain or snow may fall, depending on whether the temperature of the upper air is above or below the freezing point.

Inland in British Columbia, the western slopes of the mountain ranges have heavy rains caused by the air rising over them. The eastern slopes are dry, however, because the air becomes warm rather than cool as it comes down the slopes. The rain is heaviest on the Coast Mountains, and less and less falls to the eastward as part of the moisture in the air is gradually deposited on each mountain range. By the time the air crosses all the ranges of the Cordillera there is no moisture left for the grasslands of Alberta. It has been so high over the snow-capped mountains for such a long time that it is no longer warm. It

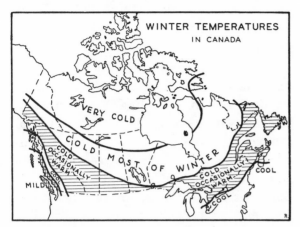

therefore has no mild influence upon the winter climate of the interior provinces except for the occasional Chinook wind in western Alberta. A Chinook is a warm wind which comes down the east slope of the Rockies in winter melting most of the snow in a few hours.

The coast of British Columbia is cool in the summer whereas the southern prairies are often very hot, and southern Ontario has many hot days. This coolness is due to the nearness of water. All of us have noticed while swimming in the summer that the water was cooler than the hot land. The land is able to heat much more quickly than water. The water catches up by autumn, however, and then is able to hold its heat longer during the winter. Therefore, in winter, its temperature is warmer than that of the nearby land.

On the west coast in summer the waters of the Pacific Ocean are cooler than the warm land. The air which blows over these waters towards British Columbia keeps temperatures cool in summer. At the same time the hot air from the southern United States is prevented from coming west by the prevailing Westerly winds and the high mountain barrier of the Cordillera. The coast of British Columbia, therefore, has cool summers.

We should now realize how difficult it is to speak of the climate of Canada in general terms. Canada is vast and is subject to many kinds of climatic influences, each working from different directions. The climates of the various regions therefore differ greatly. On the same summer day we might have cold temperatures on Baffin Island, cool temperatures on the British Columbia coast, warm in southern Ontario and hot on the Prairies. Similarly, on a winter's day it might be very cold at Churchill, cold at Edmonton, moderately cold in Montreal, and mild in Victoria.

Courtesy S. Kluchan.

During their long, cold winter, Eskimo children from Baffin Island wear warm clothing made from caribou skins. The girl in the middle is wearing a coat with the fur turned in; the boys wear a second coat with the fur turned outwards.

Precipitation

Canada has different precipitation regions as well as different temperature regions. We have already learned why the west coast is so wet, but we might wonder why the Great Plains are so dry. Canada east of the Rocky Mountains receives its moisture from the warm air from the Gulf of Mexico. Just as Pacific air carries moisture to the coast of British Columbia, so does air from the Gulf of Mexico carry moisture up the Mississippi Valley. The land slopes upward very gently, and moisture is deposited widely over the lowland in the United States. The remaining moisture in the air brings precipitation to the Great Lakes region and the St. Lawrence Valley. Because this air is turned to the east, only a little moisture is brought to the eastern Prairies.

The cold air coming from the Arctic Ocean in the north contains very little moisture. Some is dropped in the Mackenzie Valley, and there is not enough to reach the dry lands of southern Alberta and Saskatchewan. Mountains stop the moisture which might come from the Pacific Coast. The southern Prairies are dry, therefore, because they are farthest from water sources. Canada is not the only country like this, for several other large countries also have dry interiors.

The Atlantic coast receives the second greatest amount of precipitation in Canada. Whereas on the Pacific coast winds usually blow from the water to the land, on the Atlantic coast they blow to the east

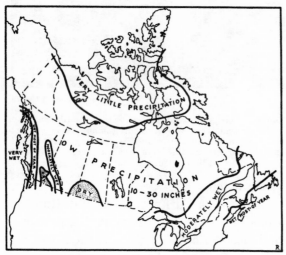

Annual Precipitation in Canada.

from the land to the ocean. The mild and moist marine influence felt on the west coast is therefore not as strong on the east. Some of the huge whirlpools of air which cross the continent, however, do cause

east winds in the Maritimes and New-foundland. These east winds increase the amount of rainfall from the Atlantic Ocean. They also bring milder winters to the south coast of Nova Scotia. In summer the cool ocean gives the coasts of the Maritimes and Newfoundland low temperatures, but this coolness is not felt far inland.

Summary

The climatic regions of Canada have definite characteristics. The Appalachian-Acadian region, including Newfoundland, has cold winters away from the coast, cool summers on the coast and warmer summers inland. The St. Lawrence-Ontario Lowlands have milder winters than the Shield or Great Plains, and the region has frequent hot periods in the summer. The Canadian Shield has very cold winters, a short warm summer on its southern edge, and cooler and shorter summers to the northward. The Great Plains region has very cold winters, especially in the Mackenzie Valley. Summers are hot in the south, gradually becoming cooler to the northward. The coastal side of the Cordillera has mild winters and cool summers. The Interior has colder winters, especially in the Yukon, and warmer summers, particularly in the south.

Precipitation, which is important for crops, decreases inland from the coasts. The greatest amount falls on the Pacific coast region, but because of the mountains it is not carried far inland. The second wettest region is the Atlantic coast, and the amount which falls gradually decreases inland. The driest parts of Canada are found in the western interior—in southeastern Alberta and southwestern Saskatchewan.

Things To Do

1. (a) Keep a record of the daily weather at your school for 10 days or 2 weeks. Make a chart which would looke like this:

Time	Day	Temp-erature	Wind	Cloud-iness	Precipi-tation	Remarks
10:00 A.M.	Oct. 15	62°	N.W. strong breeze	Scattered cumulus	none	Rained during night, with thunder.
3:00 P.M.	Oct. 16	70°	S. gentle wind	Low clouds, sky covered	light rain	Raining since noon.

Observations should be taken twice a day at about 10:00 a.m. and 3:00 p.m., or three times a day at 8:30 a.m., 12:00 noon, and 4:00 p.m. You can do it at home over the weekend.

(b) At the end of the two weeks write a report describing the weather of the preceding period. Mention the relationships which you can discover between the various columns. For example, what direction was the wind when it rained and what kinds of clouds were there at that time? Was there colder weather when the sky had no clouds?

(c) Watch the weather carefully for the rest of the month to see if these relationships happen most of the time. Predict tomorrow's weather by watching for signs which tell of approaching weather.

2. Plan a trip to your nearest meteorological station. While there, obtain the monthly averages for temperature and precipitation for your town.

(a) For how many years have records been kept at the station?

(b) Make two graphs, one showing the average temperatures month by month, and the other showing precipitation figures for each month.

(c) How do your monthly averages for July and January compare with the cities listed in the table at the end of this chapter?

(d) Can you explain why your figures are different?

3. Ask your meteorology station to report the monthly averages for each month throughout the school year.

(a) How do these compare with the long-term averages for the same months on your graph?

(b) Why was the average of this month of this year higher or lower than the average for many years?

Your graph should look like the following graph of Vancouver:

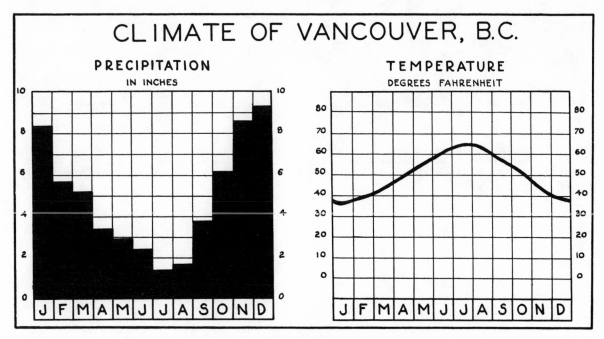

CLIMATE OF VANCOUVER, B.C.

PRECIPITATION IN INCHES

TEMPERATURE DEGREES FAHRENHEIT

Facts For Reference

City	July Temp. (°F.)	January Temp. (°F.)	Annual Precipitation (inches)
Vancouver	64	36	57
Prince Rupert	56	35	95
Trail	71	23	22
Prince George	60	13	20
Dawson	60	—21	13
Calgary	62	13	17
Edmonton	62	6	17
Fort Smith	60	—16	13
Aklavik	56	—19	10
Regina	65	— 1	15
Prince Albert	63	— 4	16
Cambridge Bay	47	—25	6
Winnipeg	67	— 3	21
The Pas	65	— 9	15
Churchill	54	—19	16
Chesterfield	49	—27	11
Port Arthur	63	7	24
Sudbury	66	10	29
Moose Factory	61	— 6	20
Windsor	72	24	31
Toronto	69	23	32
Montreal	70	14	41
Quebec	67	10	40
Mistassini	64	— 2	32
Cape Hopes Advance	42	— 8	13
Pond Inlet	42	—26	6
Gaspé	62	10	32
Edmundston	64	8	35
Saint John	61	19	42
Halifax	65	24	56
St. John's	59	23	54

(The above figures are averages of many years of records. They are arranged by regions.)

Courtesy Ontario Department of Lands and Forests.

Picture of the South Nation River in flood. Although the spring precipitation is not high in Eastern Ontario, the run-off may be rapid because trees have been cut down. The amount of precipitation cannot be controlled, but its influence after it strikes the land can be.

CHAPTER 6

VEGETATION AND SOILS

Vegetation

Trees grow where the climate is most suitable. In order to grow they need rainfall and warm summer days. If there is little rainfall, only grass can grow well, and trees are few. If summers are too short and cool, trees cannot live. The vegetation zones in Canada are therefore similar to the climatic zones. Some scientists can tell approximately what the climate of a place is like by knowing the kind of vegetation.

There are three major vegetation zones in Canada. They are: (1) the prairies, (2) the tundra, (3) the forests. On the edge of the dry region in the southern Prairie Provinces, there is not enough precipitation for trees. As a result, tall prairie grasses are the only kinds of natural vegetation which grow well. Toward the dry centre in southeastern Alberta and southwestern Saskatchewan, only short grasses, bunch grass, and sage-brush are able to survive. We call this grassland zone the prairies.

Northern Canada receives a small amount of rain and snow, and has cool summers in the northeastern regions. Because this climate is unfavourable to trees, northeastern Canada is another treeless zone. Geographers use the Russian word "tundra" for this land of mosses, lichens and grass. The tundra is larger than the prairies, and covers about one-third of Canada.

On the map on Page 35 the trees zones are shown without shading. The line marking the northern limit of trees begins along the coast of northern Alaska and Yukon, and crosses the Mackenzie River delta almost at the Arctic Ocean. It then bends to the south and east, past the eastern ends of Great Bear and Great Slave Lakes, reaching Hudson Bay near Churchill, Manitoba. The coast of Hudson Bay in northern Manitoba and Ontario is also treeless almost to James Bay. The eastern side of Hudson and James Bays is forested half-way to the north, where the tree-line appears again. The line extends to the northeast to Ungava Bay. Trees are found along the southern shore of this Bay but not along the rocky coast of northern Labrador.

Although lines on the map mark the northern and southern edges of the forested area, nature does not make her boundaries so definite on the earth. The lines indicate zones of change. In the southern prairies, south of the tree-line, trees are still found, especially along the banks of rivers, but there are more areas of grassland than of forest. The edge of the forested zone is called a "park-land". The trees are farther apart than in the bush country to the north, and open meadows are common within the forested sections.

The northern tree-line has the same characteristics. It changes gradually from forest region into mossy tundra. The trees become smaller and farther apart as one travels northward. Soon trees grow only in the valleys, like fingers pointing northward into the empty Arctic. At one time these vast treeless areas were known as "Barren Grounds". They are not really "Barren" because there is vegetation made up of mosses, lichens, and grasses. In the summer hundreds of beautifully coloured flowers blossom in the valleys.

The Arctic is more grassy in its western sections—in northeastern Mackenzie District, and in the Arctic Islands of Victoria, Banks and Melville. The northeastern regions have larger areas of bare rock. In addition, in the mountainous parts of Baffin and Ellesmere Islands, there are several small ice-caps. The name, "Barren Grounds", would be more descriptive of the flat region west of Hudson Bay in winter. A layer of drifting snow covers the land except for the bare rock ridges; all signs of vegetation are buried. As far as one can see on a clear day there is an endless expanse of bleak snow and long shadows.

Between the two regions where it is either too cold or too dry for trees, a vast area of Canada is densely forested. Canada's forests are exceeded in area only by the tropical forests of Brazil, and the coniferous forests of the Soviet Union. Canadian forests, most of which are softwoods of coniferous species, cover more than one million square miles. Coniferous trees are those which we know as "evergreen"— they usually bear cones and have needles instead of leaves. The broad-leaved trees which drop their leaves are called deciduous and are usually hardwoods. They are found in regions of mild climate.

In such a large forested area the same

In Ontario, the lake-dotted Canadian Shield is covered with a dense forest of spruce, balsam and pine. Many summer resorts with good swimming and boating are located in this forested lakeland.

kinds of trees are not found everywhere. Because of differences in amounts of rainfall, length of summer, kind of soil and underlying rock, and type of drainage, different species of trees grow better in certain regions. It would be difficult for us to know all of the 130 species of trees which

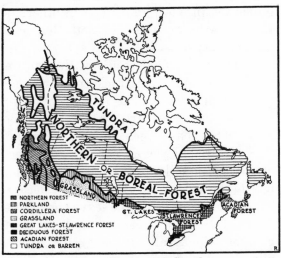

Forest Regions of Canada.

are found in Canada. Some trees, however, are more numerous in some areas than in others. Forest regions are therefore drawn up according to the predominate trees which are found in them.

Canada's Northern or Boreal forests stretch like a vast horseshoe around Hudson Bay from Newfoundland and Labrador on the east to the Yukon in the northwest. Because of rugged topography, poor soils, and short summers in the Canadian Shield, only the hardiest coniferous trees thrive. The white spruce is the most common tree in this region, but black spruce, balsam fir, tamarack, and jack-pine also grow in abundance.

In the mild part of Southern Ontario, soils are fertile and summers are long and warm. This climate encourages the growth of deciduous trees which do not thrive under more severe conditions. Most of the northeastern United States has the same type of hardwood vegetation and the zone extends northward into Canada along the north side of Lake Erie. The chief broad-leaved trees are the colourful maples and birches, but there are also many hickory, oak, and walnut trees.

A forest belt which contains both coniferous and deciduous trees is located between the region of needle-bearing trees to the north and broad-leaved trees to the south. This belt extends from northwest of the Great Lakes eastward into the St. Lawrence Valley. It is a mixed forest which has white pine, hemlock, and red pine most numerous in its northern parts. Sugar and red maple, yellow birch, and beech are common trees in the southern sections. A similar kind of mixed forest continues eastward into the Maritimes, where, in addition, there are many red spruce trees.

To the west of the grasslands and northern forests the high mountains of the Cordillera have the same effect upon trees as does the cold of the Arctic regions. If we climb up into the mountains it becomes colder, and the peaks may even be snow-capped for much of the year. Trees find it hard to grow on the steep slopes and in the cool air of high elevations. They do grow, however, in the lower valleys and slopes where rain is more plentiful. In the northern part of the Cordillera trees are small and few at elevations of 3,000 to 4,000 feet. At higher elevations short grasses and mosses are the only vegetation.

The west coast of British Columbia has the tallest and largest trees of Canada. Owing to the heavy rainfall and warm climate, forests grow everywhere on the lower slopes and in the valleys. The chief kinds of trees are western red cedar and western hemlock, but there are also a great many Douglas fir in the southern sections and Sitka spruce in the north. A similar kind of forest grows inland on the rainy western slopes of the Selkirk Mountains, and in the headwater valleys of the Columbia, Thompson, and Fraser Rivers. Douglas fir is found throughout the Selkirk region, and, in addition, western white pine and larch are common in the northern sections.

The central plateau of British Columbia lies between the two heavily forested regions. Rainfall is scanty, since the winds pass over the valleys, and summer days are often hot. The vegetation in the valleys

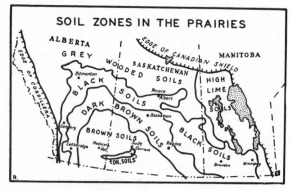

is grassland, much like that of the dry southern Prairies. On the higher slopes, yellow pine and Douglas fir are the common trees, along with many aspens and lodgepole pines.

Natural vegetation is Nature's way of indicating where things will grow best. It will be hard to raise crops in the Arctic region if it is too cold for trees to grow there. Crops will not do well in the dry regions if there is not enough rainfall for grasses. Areas which have delicate decidu-

ous trees must have more favourable climates than those with hardy coniferous trees.

Soils

The soils of Canada also may be divided into broad zones of similar types, as are the forests. Just as certain trees are more numerous in one region than in others, so there are many kinds of soils but some dominant types.

Soils are the final result of the working together of underlying rock, covering vegetation, and climate. The "dirt" which you have in your back yard was once pieces of rock. They have been so broken up into tiny pieces that you do not recognize them as rock. But soil, not "dirt", is more than powdered rock. Added to it are the decayed roots from grass, and the leaves or needles which fall from trees. The leaves and grasses which fall to the ground gradually decay and work into the soil. They then become food to help more plants to grow.

Nature's balance between vegetation growth and soil development is speeded up or delayed by the climate of each region. If the climate is warm, vegetation grows faster and in greater quantities. If the climate is cold for all, or part, of the year,

Courtesy Manitoba Travel and Publicity Bureau.

The black soils of the prairie provinces are excellent for growing wheat. Because rainfall is usually sufficient in this area of Manitoba, some trees grow with grain and grasses.

there is less vegetation to die and decay and therefore soils are not so fertile. On the other hand, if there is too much rainfall, plant food may be dissolved out of the top layers of the soil, leaving it poorer. There will be, therefore, many kinds of soils in Canada. Each varies according to the vegetation growth, and the type of climate.

In the prairies there are four chief kinds of soils. In the driest parts the soil is a light brown colour. It supports only a little vegetation except in the irrigated sections. Much of this area is pasture land since the soil is not fertile enough, nor rainfall sufficient, for general farming.

Soils which are a dark brown colour surround the dry zone on the west, north, and east. They receive a little more rainfall in summer, and the vegetation consists of short grasses. This region has an excellent soil and climate for wheat and large acreages are grown.

Surrounding the dark brown soils on three sides is another zone of almost black soils. Rainfall is more plentiful and vegetation consists of tall grasses with some trees and bushes in patches. The soils are the best in Canada because they receive neither too little nor too much rainfall. They have ample vegetation to decay into plant food. The rich prairie farms that raise wheat, oats and barley are found throughout this black-soil zone.

North of the black soils the forested region appears. It has a different kind of soil because leaves and needles fall to the ground, and are worked into the soil, in addition to decaying grasses. The slightly more rainfall is enough to carry away some of the plant food, leaving a thin grey layer near the surface. When cleared, these grey soils make good agricultural land, but are not as fertile as the grassland soils to the south.

When we read about the agricultural regions of Canada in the next chapter, we should remember what we learned about the soils of the prairie region. An agricultural crop is actually a kind of vegetation which man encourages to grow in a region instead of the natural vegetation of trees and wild grasses. These man-made crops will do well or poorly according to the fertility of the soil beneath them.

Besides the prairies, another large area of level land is found in the St. Lawrence and Ontario Lowlands. The soils there, which are grey-brown in colour, have formed under a cover of broad-leaved trees. The region has greater rainfall than the Prairie Provinces. The soils are not as fertile as the best prairie soils, but still they are rich enough to make good agricultural land. Although the whole region has similar soils, those to the west of the Niagara escarpment are more fertile, whereas many soils east of Montreal are sandy.

Courtesy Ontario Department of Planning and Development.

The fertile soils of the St. Lawrence Lowlands erode easily on slope land. This picture shows the damage a small stream can do to good cropland. Such "sheet erosion" can be controlled by proper farming practices.

In the Acadian-Appalachian region there are many local differences in soils, because of the many kinds of topography. The heavier rainfall of the east coast makes poorer soils than those found westward in Canada. In the river valleys, however, new soil is added each year by spring floods. Valley soils are therefore better than those of the surrounding hilly areas. Much of the hilly upland of Newfoundland lacks good soils. The peculiar reddish soils of Prince Edward Island and parts of Nova Scotia and New Brunswick are due to a red sandstone in the underlying rock.

Most of the soils in the Canadian Shield have been removed from the uplands by the huge ice-cap which moved down over this area thousands of years ago. Some of Canada's soil is now found where the glaciers deposited it, in the Ohio and Missouri valleys of the United States. Poor soils have slowly formed in some of the valleys of the Shield, but most of the hills and ridges are still bare. Since summers are short in the Shield, it takes longer for soils to develop. The largest area of agricultural soil in the Shield is the Clay Belt of northeastern Ontario and northwestern

Quebec. This area was once a large lake at the front of the slowly melting ice-cap. Since there is very little good soil in the Shield, the Clay Belt will play an important part in settling northern Ontario and Quebec.

There are only a few sections of good soils in the Cordillera region. Soils need level or gently rolling land to develop satisfactorily, and such areas are very small in this region. The heavy rains of the west coast make poor soils because plant food is dissolved out of the soil almost as quickly as it is formed. There are better soils, however, at the delta mouth of the Fraser River where new soils were carried down from the mountainous interior and spread out over the flood plain of the river. These floods are now controlled by dykes along the river banks. The soils of the central plateau region are suitable for agriculture, since rainfall is less than it is on the coast, but the growing season is shorter.

Summary

If we climb into our rocket ship once more and shoot into the air, we see below the following picture of vegetation. The

Courtesy Alberta Government (H. Pollard photo.).

On the light brown soils of the southern prairies the grassland vegetation supports thousands of sheep and cattle. This ranch is located in the rolling hills near Cardston, Alberta.

Arctic islands to the north and the mainland east and west of Hudson Bay are barren of trees, but have grasses and low shrubs in the valleys. The rest of Canada is thickly forested, except for the mountain tops, and the grasslands of the southern Prairie Provinces. The forested region varies from place to place, but generally the dark green of the "evergreens" is found to the north, and the beautiful autumn colours of the broad-leaved trees are found in the south.

We are not able to see the differences in soils from the air, but our map shows that the two largest areas of good soils are found in the south-central parts of the Prairie Provinces and in the lowlands of the St. Lawrence River and Great Lakes. Good soils are found elsewhere, but in smaller areas which are separated from each other by land which is poorly drained, or rocky, hilly or mountainous.

The basic facts of the physical geography of Canada have been presented. We have read about topography, drainage, climate, vegetation and soils. We shall now begin to apply our knowledge to explain why and where certain occupations are being carried on all over Canada. We shall see that physical geography usually influences the type of occupation.

Things To Do

1. (a) Name the kinds of trees which grow in your neighbourhood.
   (b) Which species are most numerous?
   (c) Name some other parts of Canada that have the same kinds of trees.

2. How much of your township is forested? Make a map of your township and colour in the forested areas.

3. Read the Forestry Lessons booklet issued by the Dominion Forest Service, Department of Resources and Development, Ottawa, to learn more about Canadian forests.

4. (a) List the kinds of soils found near your school. Look at a fresh cut along the side of the road, or along a stream bank, or in the excavation for a new building.
   (b) Do the soils have many stones? From where do the stones come?
   (c) Are the grains of soil fine or coarse?
   (d) Is this type of soil good for raising crops?

5. Talk to your local government agricultural agent. Perhaps he will give you a map of the soils in your county or district.
   (a) Describe some of the crops that are grown on the different soils.
   (b) What kinds of soils do not have crops in your county?

Courtesy B.C. Travel Bureau.

In the Okanagan Valley of British Columbia well kept orchards produce much of Canada's fruit. Very little rain falls in the valley, but the orchards are irrigated with water which is dammed in the distant hills.

CHAPTER 7

AGRICULTURE

Primary industries are those depending directly upon natural resources. They are the activities by which a country turns the wealth which Nature gave it into useful things. About four out of every ten Canadians are in occupations which use our natural resources directly. The occupa-tions based on primary industries are farming—dependent on soils; mining—on rocks, and their mineral resources; lumbering—on forest cover; fishing—on fish in coastal waters, inland lakes and rivers; and trapping—on wild life and game in the forests. In each case we must know something of the natural resource before we can understand the occupation dependent upon it. In order to know why Canadians do what they do, we shall study the resources which keep many of them occupied.

Early History

In the early days of Canadian history settlers raised food for their own use. As more land was cleared some farmers raised more crops than they needed and traded the surplus in towns for manufactured articles such as furniture or farm implements. People who gathered into the towns and small cities to manufacture articles no longer had time to raise food. To feed them the farmer cleared away more forest, planted more crops, and sold his extra food to the growing towns. As our nation grew, this simple exchange of goods and services expanded our industries and our manufacturing. We should remember that behind the hustle and bustle of the busy towns are the many small farms all over Canada supplying food to our workers.

In the 19th century, Eastern Canada was the centre of the farming industry. Settlers cultivated the limited valley regions of the Maritimes, and cleared narrow farms back from the St. Lawrence River to the edge of the hills on the north and south. New settlers moved westward into the fertile country north of Lakes Erie and Ontario. Shortly after the middle of the century most of the good land in the Ontario Lowland had been occupied. Settlement could not expand to the north because of the rocky Canadian Shield, so it followed the natural route through the peninsula of southwestern Ontario into the United States. It was not until Canada's transcontinental railroads were built across the rugged Shield that a route was opened to the fertile grasslands of the West.

The prairie regions of the United States were occupied before those of Canada because they did not have the same barriers to settlement. As the 20th century opened the Canadian prairies were being settled rapidly by immigrants from the British Isles and Continental Europe. Since the prairies of the United States were occupied by this time, many American settlers continued northward to help settle the agricultural regions of the Canadian prairies. This northward movement helped to balance the loss of Canadians who went into the United States in the latter part of the 19th century. It caused a further intermixing of the Canadian and American people.

By 1920, expansion of the Canadian farming frontier was almost completed. Most of the good lands of the southern parts of the prairies were occupied, and the Peace River country to the north was being settled rapidly. By 1930 most of the readily available agricultural land in Canada was occupied. Canadians were growing more food than they could eat, and were having trouble trying to sell their surplus to the rest of the world.

Present-day Agriculture

Farming is Canada's largest primary industry. There are more people engaged in farming than in any other industry which depends upon a natural resource. About 3½ million Canadians live on farms. These farmers raise much of the food for the people who live in towns and cities.

Canada is a large country for such a small population. People who do not know the geography of Canada are apt to look at the map and wonder why so much of it is unoccupied. Our study of the physical geography of Canada shows that climate and topography do not permit settlement in some places.

It is estimated by scientists that less than one-fifth of Canada could be used for farming. This amounts to less than 750,000 square miles of possible agricutural land. We now occupy less than half of this area. Only one-tenth of Canada's total land area is, therefore, being used for crops. This is a small area on the map, but Canada's physical geography is not favourable to great agricultural expansion. Canada has agricultural land available and unoccupied, however, both in northern pioneer areas and within the present farming areas. We could probably expand our farm acreage to two, and possibly three times its present area, but many parts of Canada can never hope to be settled.

Agriculture is the most valuable of the Canadian primary industries. In fact, manufacturing which is a secondary industry is the only one which produces goods of a greater total value than agriculture. Agriculture also assists manufacturing because four out of every ten Canadian manufacturing plants work on farm products. Agricultural products are important in Canada's export trade, because we produce more of some foods than we can eat ourselves. Before the world-wide depression of 1930, over half of the value of Canada's exports were made up of agricultural products. In recent years Canada has been increasing her exports of manufactured goods, but agricultural products still make up one-third of our total exports.

Type and Size of Farms

Canada has farms of many types all across the country. There are some that raise chiefly wheat, and others that grow several grains. Some farms are chiefly in pasture and keep large numbers of livestock. Others raise special crops like tobacco or seed corn. Often the type of farm crop is determined by the physical geography of the region. The chief physical factors determining crop growth are climate, soils, and topography.

In order to understand the agricultural possibilities of a region we should know the following facts about its climate: the number of continuous days without a killing frost during the growing season, the

usual amounts of rainfall, and the season when rain is most plentiful. Each of these conditions will vary from place to place, and from year to year. A good combination of all of them will encourage the growth of certain crops. Oats and potatoes, for example, grow well in places with cool summers and a short growing season, whereas corn needs many hot summer days. Alfalfa grows well in dry regions, but clover needs more rainfall. After several attempts a farmer usually finds out that the climate of his region is more suited to some crops than to others. He will then tend to grow more and more of the crop which is most successful.

The kind of soil also helps to determine what crop is best suited to an area. Even within climatic regions where all crops do well, yields will vary from field to field depending upon the fertility of the soil. A local difference in fertility is often due to the type of rock below the ground, or the kind of drainage, or the length of time that the land has been cultivated. For example, wheat grows best on soils made up of fine particles, whereas vegetables need a coarser, sandy soil. Potatoes grow in acid soils which are unsuited to alfalfa.

The type of farming found in a region is often a result of the general topography. If there are large areas of level land, machinery can be used to help with the work. If the land is hilly, machines have less room to work and turn and are not so useful. The sides of hills should be left in grassland for pasture because rains will wash away the loose soil on plowed hillsides. In some places hillsides are used for orchards or vineyards because there is less danger from frost on slopes.

The large farms of the level prairies are different from those of the rolling plains of southwestern Ontario. Owing to differences in climate, soil, and topography, the prairies are a grain-growing region where a few men, using big machines, operate large farms. In the St. Lawrence and Ontario Lowlands much of the farm land is cultivated hay and pasture, and crops such as oats, corn, and early vegetables are common. The agricultural valleys of the Maritimes are also different. Farmers there find it more economical to have their land in hay or pasture, rather than in grains. In addition, they raise special crops such as seed potatoes and apples.

Differences in crops are sometimes due to cultural reasons. These may be determined by the history of the local region, or perhaps the racial background of the farmers living there. For example, many of the men in the flower-bulb industry of British Columbia once lived in the Netherlands where numerous tulips and other bulbs are raised. Similarly, many of the farmers raising flax on the prairies came from Poland where flax has been grown for many, many years.

The agriculture of present-day Canada

tural factors determine the local crop.

The following table illustrates the distribution of farms in Canada by provinces. It also gives us some idea of the average size of farms in each province, and the number of acres which each farmer has cleared and improved.

Province	(1941) No. of Occupied Farms	Average No. of Total Acres	Average No. of Improved Acres
British Columbia	26,000	150	35
Alberta	100,000	435	200
Saskatchewan	139,000	430	265
Manitoba	58,000	290	170
Ontario	178,000	125	75
Quebec	155,000	125	65
New Brunswick	32,000	125	40
Nova Scotia	33,000	115	25
Prince Edward Island	12,000	95	60
Newfoundland (1945)	2,800	50	22

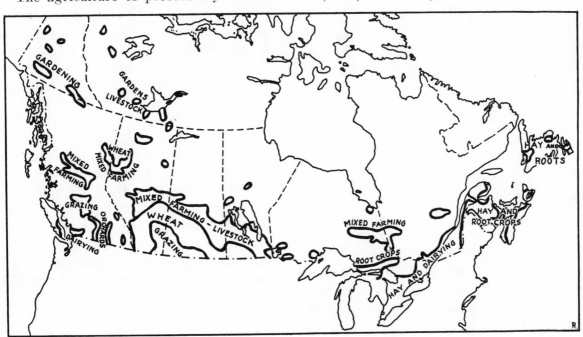

Agricultural regions of Canada.

is the result of the intermixing of geographic, economic and cultural factors. In general, the conditions of climate, soil, and topography determine the broad boundaries within which agriculture is possible. Within these boundaries economic and cul-

This table tells us that Ontario and Quebec have the most farms, but that the farms on the prairies are much larger than those in other parts of Canada. Of the three Prairie Provinces, Saskatchewan has the most farms, whereas the huge ranches and farms of Alberta are the largest in Canada. Manitoba has less than half as many farms as the other Prairie provinces since the Great Plains region is much narrower there. New Brunswick and Nova Scotia have the same number of farms, and actually have more occupied farms than the much larger, but mountainous, province of British Columbia. We would expect Prince Edward Island to have the fewest farms. Despite its small size, however, the Island has many farms because so much of the land is cultivated. The number of farms in Newfoundland is not many. They raise chiefly hay, oats and root vegetables.

The prosperous farming provinces are noted in the column showing the average number of improved acres on each farm. In some provinces many acres on each farm are not cultivated but lie unused or in bush land. Saskatchewan farmers are using most of their farms. In the other Prairie provinces, the Ontario and St. Lawrence Lowlands, and Prince Edward Island more than half the acreage of each average farm has been improved. On the other hand, farmers in the provinces with less level land and more hills and mountains—British Columbia, New Brunswick, and Nova Scotia—have been able to improve only small parts of their farms.

Crops

The chief crops grown in Canada are wheat, oats, barley, and cultivated hay. These four crops occupy more acres than any other farm products. The following table shows the distribution of each crop by province, and indicates how the various parts of Canada compare in production. While studying the table we should also look at the maps showing the agricultural regions in each province. Although the table lists the average acreage for the province as a whole, the crops are grown only in parts of each province. The agricultural sections are those having suitable

level land, and enough warm and rainy days in the summer.

Average Number of Acres per Farm of Chief Crops in Canada (1941)

Province	Wheat	Oats	Barley	Cultivated Hay
British Columbia	3	3	.7	10
Alberta	65	28	15	6
Saskatchewan	88	29	12	3
Manitoba	42	22	26	7
Ontario	3	11	2	21
Quebec	.2	11	1	25
New Brunswick	.1	6	.5	17
Nova Scotia	.1	2	.3	12
Prince Edward Island	.8	10	1	18

The prairie farms have the greatest number of acres of each of the chief grains. Since Saskatchewan has the most farms, and the largest average number of acres in wheat, it produces more wheat than any other province. In August the rolling plains are covered with a golden mantle of ripened grain, waving gently in the hot breeze. Alberta is the next leading producer. Although Manitoba produces less wheat than the other Prairie provinces, it raises much more than any of the remaining provinces. The farmers of Ontario and Quebec grew much wheat in the last century, but the broad flat lands and rich black soils of the prairies are now better suited to the raising of grains.

Prairie farms also have the largest acreages in oats. Oats are raised in crop rotation in the wheat belt and a short distance to the north of it. Because wheat soon uses up the minerals in the soil if grown on the same land every year, crop rotation and fallowing are practised to conserve the soil for other years. Many bushels of oats are grown in dairy cattle regions of Ontario and Quebec, especially on the flat land south of the St. Lawrence River in Quebec.

The chief centre of barley production in Canada is in southern Manitoba. Barley is used chiefly for livestock feed and is grown on most of the grain farms of the prairies. In Manitoba, it is used to fatten cattle which are later slaughtered in Winnipeg and shipped to markets in Eastern Canada.

The farmers of Quebec and Ontario raise most of the cultivated hay. The hay

Dairy farming is one of the chief agricultural activities on the St. Lawrence Lowland of Quebec. This scene shows how carefully the Quebec farmer looks after his farm and land.

is grown to feed cattle, since the St. Lawrence Lowlands are one of the most important dairying regions in Canada. The common hay crops are usually mixed clover and timothy. One of the striking facts that a prairie boy would remember about the farms of Eastern Canada is the lack of grain. Most of the cleared land is in pasture. The acreage of cultivated hay is small in the prairies because it is a grassland region where feed grows naturally.

In addition to the four chief crops, there are numerous others which are raised in each of the agricultural regions of Canada. Some of the crops are: rye, corn, flax and buckwheat; all kinds of vegetables, especially potatoes; special crops such as sugar beets and tobacco; and fruits such as apples, peaches, plums, pears, cherries, apricots, and grapes.

Livestock

Cattle are raised on nearly every farm in Canada, but are more numerous in some farming regions than in others. Cattle are kept either for dairying or for meat, but in some regions they are raised for both purposes. The dairying areas are usually near the large cities because fresh milk is not shipped very far. Because a large number of cities and towns are located in the St. Lawrence and Ontario Lowlands, this is the chief dairying region of Canada. Owing to the many cattle there, this region also produces most of the cheese and much of the butter of Canada. Other notable dairying regions are found in the St. John River Valley of New Brunswick, near the large prairie cities, and in the lower Fraser Valley of British Columbia.

Beef cattle are usually raised farther from the cities because beef can be shipped more easily than milk. The Prairie Provinces supply much of Canada's meat. It comes chiefly from the mixed farming re-

Beef cattle are raised on large ranches in the Alberta Foothills. Much of the grassland is too dry for agriculture but produces good quality meat.

gion north of the wheat belt, but also from the ranches in the dry region of southern Alberta and Saskatchewan. The ranges are dotted with small herds of sturdy beef cattle. From time to time they are moved to fresh grasslands by cowboys. In Ontario many beef cattle are raised east of Lake Huron. In British Columbia the ranches of the Interior Plateau supply meat to the large city population in the southwestern part of the province.

Most Canadian farms raise a few pigs. Pork production increased during World War II, and Canadian hams and bacon were sent to the British Isles. In Canada most of the swine are raised in the general farming regions of the St. Lawrence and Ontario Lowlands and the Prairie Provinces. A muddy pig sty behind the horse barn is one of the common sights in rural Canada. Pigs are often raised in dairy regions where they can be fed skim milk. When they are given better care and food they produce better grades of pork.

Courtesy Ontario Department of Planning and Development.

The blocking of this stream created a small pond which can be used for watering livestock. It also keeps up the local ground water table. Such farming practices conserve water and help to prevent floods downstream.

Poultry is kept on most farms and the eggs are used or sold locally. Poultry raising is common near towns and cities where there are more people who want eggs. The region of most intensive poultry

farming in Canada is the lower Fraser Valley of British Columbia. Its mild winter climate is an important advantage. Eggs from these farms are sold in the cities of southwestern British Columbia and are also shipped to Great Britain.

Courtesy National Parks Bureau.

In Nova Scotia the valleys suitable for agriculture are narrow. These lower slopes on Cape Breton Island raise hay and clover, and the upper slopes remain in forest.

Summary

Types of farming and farm crops differ from place to place in Canada. In the Maritimes, farms are in the river valleys, on the lowland around the head of the Bay of Fundy, and on Prince Edward Island. Much of the land is in hay and pasture, but special crops such as seed potatoes and apples are grown. Most of the farms of Newfoundland are on the Avalon Peninsula on the east, but new farms are being cleared near the central west coast. The agricultural regions of the St. Lawrence and Ontario Lowlands raise a great deal of cultivated hay, but have many other crops, such as oats, tobacco and corn. There are also fine orchards and vineyards along the north shores of Lakes Erie and Ontario.

In the prairies, the dry region of southern Alberta and Saskatchewan is a grazing land with big ranches. Many parts of it are now being irrigated and are raising fine crops of alfalfa and sugar beets. North and east of the dry region is the wheat belt. It is typified in Saskatchewan by large flat farms on which much modern machinery is used. Farther north, in the forested zone, mixed farming is carried on and other grains as well as livestock are raised along with wheat.

In British Columbia farms are few. The largest area in use is at the mouth of the Fraser River. Many crops are raised there during the long summer in order to feed the large population in southwestern British Columbia. Agriculture is not as well developed in the Interior Plateau but there are possibilities for more farms near Prince George. The Okanagan and Kootenay valleys in the south are small but productive areas specializing in fruit.

Things To Do

1. (a) What crops are grown in the rural areas near your home?

   (b) Make a list of those crops which are sold in the nearest town, and another list of the products which are transported away.

   (c) Are the products of the farms in your neighbourhood eaten directly or manufactured into some other form?

   (d) Name some other areas of Canada which raise the same crops as farms near your home.

2. (a) Read Chapter 7 again and list the chief agricultural products raised in Canada.

   (b) What are the chief uses of each of these products?

   (c) Which of the products are exported in large amounts?

3. Write an essay on the history of agriculture in your township or county. In your essay answer the following questions:
   Have the crops changed since the early days? If so, explain why. Did the first settlers have their farms in the same places as the modern farmers? Where did the first settlers sell their crops? Are there more farmers in your area now than there were fifty years ago?

Facts For Reference

Chief Cash Crops sold from the Average Canadian Farm (1946)

Totals only 81%. Others are too small and numerous to mention.

Wheat	20%
Dairy Products	16%
Cattle and calves	15%
Hogs	11%
Eggs and poultry	9%
Oats	3%
Fruits	3%
Barley	2%
Vegetables	2%

Turner Valley in southwestern Alberta once produced most of Canada's petroleum. Oil wells, refineries and storage tanks grew up in the area. Production from these wells has now passed its peak.

CHAPTER 8

MINING AND MINERAL RESOURCES

The mining industry of Canada is third in the production of wealth, ranking next in value to manufacturing and agriculture. The number of miners in Canada is much smaller than the number of workers employed in manufacturing and on farms, but their production is very important. Much of Canadian manufacturing depends upon the minerals which miners bring up to the surface. Without the raw materials from the mines many of the tools and utensils which we use in our homes and on our farms could not be made.

Canada's mineral resources fall into four groups: metallic (67%), fuels (18%), non-metallic (8%) and structural materials (7%). These minerals generally come from distinctive kinds of rock, and therefore geologists who know the rocks can often tell us where certain minerals may be found. Among the chief metallic minerals are gold, silver, copper, lead, zinc, and nickel. About two-thirds of Canada's mineral production comes from this group. They are found in the ancient rocks of the Canadian Shield, in the Acadian region, and in the younger rocks of the Cordillera.

The fuels—coal, petroleum, and natural

48

gas—are commonly found in flat-lying sedimentary rocks. They represent the remains of pre-historic marshes and sediments of shallow seas of many thousands of years ago. This ancient, decayed vegetation and animal matter was covered over by thick deposits of rock; then centuries of pressure gradually changed its form. Canada's chief source of fuels is in the flat-lying rocks of the Great Plains region.

Non-metallic minerals are usually not as valuable as the two preceding types. They include such minerals as asbestos, gypsum, and salt. The latter two are also obtained from flat-lying rocks. Canada has sufficient quantities of each of these minerals. Structural minerals are obtained in large quantities and are generally used locally. The chief ones are cement, lime, building stone, sand and gravel.

Four chief minerals make up about two-thirds of the value of Canadian mineral production. In order of importance they are gold, coal, nickel and copper. Despite the many other mineral resources which Canada has, the mining industry is greatly dependent upon these four. Among other valuable minerals produced in Canada are: asbestos, zinc, lead, natural gas, petroleum and platinum. (See table below).

Canada's mining industry is still quite

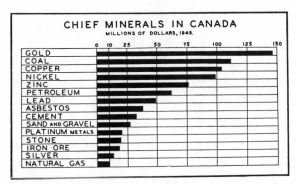

CHIEF MINERALS IN CANADA
MILLIONS OF DOLLARS, 1949.

young in years. Several small mines operated in the Maritimes and along the St. Lawrence Valley in the last century. The greatest development, however, has taken place in northern Ontario and Quebec in the present century. The building

of Canada's transcontinental railroads made the Canadian Shield more accessible. The construction of the Temiskaming and Northern Ontario Railroad in 1902-07 opened up further riches.

Canada's mineral wealth comes chiefly from the agriculturally poor Canadian Shield. About two-fifths of the value of Canadian mineral production comes from Ontario's part of the Shield. Another one-fifth is produced in Quebec. The tall tower over a mining shaft is one of the common sights rising above the many small towns of northern Ontario and Quebec. When the production of these two provinces is added to the smaller output from Manitoba and Saskatchewan, about seven out of every ten dollars obtained from mining comes from the Shield. Mineral production from Saskatchewan and Manitoba is less than that of Ontario and Quebec, probably because the Shield has only recently been prospected. As more exploration is carried on it is expected that these provinces, too, will find wealth similar to that which the prospectors of the older provinces have uncovered.

British Columbia and Alberta each produce from 10 to 20 per cent of Canada's annual mineral wealth, and are increasing in importance. The folded rocks of the Cordillera are known to contain minerals, but the scarcity of roads and railroads has slowed development there. Alberta's wealth comes chiefly from two important fuels—coal and petroleum. The hundreds of wells dotting the landscape at Turner Valley and Leduc illustrate the importance of this latter resource.

Nova Scotia is the only other province that has any noticeable mineral production. It comes from coal on Cape Breton Island, and gold in the Atlantic Upland.

New Brunswick's mineral production is less than one per cent of the total Canadian value. Similarly, the Yukon and Northwest Territories are small producers, although the latter is growing rapidly. Newfoundland's chief mineral resource is the large deposit of iron ore in Conception Bay near St. John's. The island also produces lead and zinc from its central part, and fluorspar from the south coast.

Gold

Before World War II, almost 40 percent of the value of Canadian mineral production came from gold. It was mined across Canada from Nova Scotia to the far Northwest. Gold has been produced in Canada for over a century, and our history books tell us the important role it played in the opening up of many new areas.

The modern history of British Columbia begins with tales of great wealth obtained in the Cariboo district of the Fraser Valley in 1858. Many stories have been written about the famous Yukon gold rush of 1897-98. The great rush of thousands of miners to that far-away area caused the Canadian Government to create a new Territory, called the Yukon, but known then as "The Land of the Klondike". When we read the thrilling stories of how prospectors crossed the snow-covered mountain passes and floated down the broad Yukon River, we learn something of the physical geography of the Yukon.

In those days, prospecting for gold was done by "panning". The prospector scooped up gravel from the river bed in a flat pan and swished the gravel and water around until the heavier gold fell to the bottom. Gold from river gravels now amounts to only about two percent of Canadian gold. Most gold is obtained from quartz veins in rocks. Miners work underground following the veins and digging out the quartz. The rock is brought to the surface to be crushed and later the fine gold particles are removed by chemicals, or by the use of mercury.

Canada's wealth in gold has raised her to second place in total world production. Only the Union of South Africa produces

more gold. More than half the Canadian gold comes from Northern Ontario. Timmins and Kirkland Lake are the chief mining towns but there are numerous other gold mines across Northern Ontario as far as the Manitoba boundary. Around each of these mines, small towns have

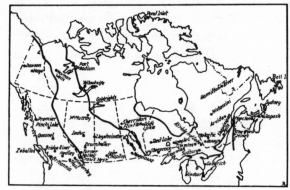

Mining centres in Canada.

grown up. Their size depends upon the value of the gold below the surface.

Quebec produces about one-quarter of the total gold of Canada. Most of it comes from the Noranda-Rouyn district which is just across the provincial boundary from the rich section of the Kirkland Lake mines in Ontario.

Other gold-producing regions are: the Interior Plateau of British Columbia, several places in northeastern Manitoba, and the Flin Flon region on the Saskatchewan-Manitoba boundary. Dawson district in the Yukon is still producing gold 50 years after the famous Rush of '98, and new discoveries have been made in the Yellowknife district of the Northwest Territories.

Copper

Copper is sometimes the second most valuable mineral mined in Canada. The production of Canada's important copper mines ranks in fourth place among the world's producers, exceeded by the United States, Chile, and the Belgian Congo.

The first important copper mine was discovered at Sudbury in 1884 when the

Canadian Pacific transcontinental railroad was being built. This was the first of many rich discoveries which showed that the Canadian Shield was not as worthless as people had believed it to be. New copper mines were found in British Columbia after the railroad reached that mountain province. Until 1929 British Columbia remained the leading copper-producing province of Canada. Since that time richer mines have been opened in Ontario, Quebec and Saskatchewan.

Ontario produces half the value of Canadian copper. Most of it comes from the Sudbury region, where the same rocks yield both copper and nickel. The progressive city of Sudbury has grown up in the centre of several good mines in the area. It is an example of how a resource can bring work and homes to many people. Quebec is another producer of copper which is mined in the Noranda-Rouyn district where gold is also found.

Saskatchewan and Manitoba rank next in value of copper production. Their chief mines are found along the provincial boun-

Courtesy Editorial Services Ltd.

The smelter at Copper Cliff treats the copper and nickel ore from nearby Sudbury. The fumes from the smelter have destroyed vegetation in the area.

dary at Flin Flon, north of The Pas. These towns are surrounded by the northern forests, but have rail connections to the south. The Britannia mine, on the west coast of British Columbia north of Vancouver, is the chief copper mine in that province.

Nickel

Nickel is one of the four most valuable minerals in Canada. Canada is fortunate because four-fifths of the world's supply of nickel is mined in our country. All of it is produced in one area, the Sudbury region of Northern Ontario. This rich area was first mined because of its copper ores, but it soon became possible to extract the nickel also. Hundreds of miners came to the area to dig out the ore. They were followed by storekeepers and others as the town grew.

During World War I, nickel became valuable because of its importance in making a hard steel which was used for armaments. In World War II Sudbury nickel was again very important in helping to build strong guns and equipment.

Coal

Coal is the fourth of the "Big Four" mineral resources of Canada. Unfortunately coal is found on the eastern and western sides of the Dominion, and the main industrial areas are located in the central regions. Southern Ontario and Quebec are closer to the large coal fields of Ohio and Pennsylvania in the United States than they are to the Canadian coal fields. Canadian coal mines produce from 15 million to 18 million tons each year, but we use about three times that amount. The difference is made up by importing coal from the United States to the central regions of Canada.

There are three main kinds of coal. They vary in hardness, and in the amount of heat and ash. The hardest type is called anthracite, and Canada has very little of this. It is nearly all imported from the United States, and is used to heat homes in central Canada. The second grade is bituminous or "soft coal". It is used chiefly by railways and in factories and industries which need large amounts of heat. It is also burned in homes in areas where anthracite is not available. The third type, lignite coal, is of low grade, and is used when other types are not found nearby.

Nova Scotia used to be the leading producer of coal in Canada, but it has been surpassed by Alberta. The latter mines about four out of every ten tons produced in Canada. Most of the small coal-mining towns are located on the eastern slope of the Rockies or nearby in the Foothills. The Cape Breton Island coal of Nova Scotia is a good bituminous grade, much of which is used in the blast furnaces making steel at Sydney. Some of it is exported to the nearby New England states. Alberta coals are bituminous and lignite. Only small amounts are shipped east to the industrial cities. The rest is used in local industries and for heating homes in the Prairie Provinces and British Columbia. Alberta could mine much more coal if it were not so expensive to transport it to the East.

Coal is also mined in British Columbia, Saskatchewan, and in a small section in New Brunswick. British Columbia's bituminous coal is found near the Crowsnest Pass, where it is used for the railroad, and on eastern Vancouver Island, from where it is shipped to the nearby cities. Saskatchewan coal, mined at Estevan, is a low-grade lignite coal which is important for local use. It may some day be turned into plastics and other synthetic products.

Ontario and Quebec, where most of the population lives, mine no coal. This region is fortunate, however, in having water-power for its industries. The St. Lawrence-Ontario Lowlands depend upon imported coal from the United States. Each year about 20 to 30 million tons of anthracite coal are imported for the thousands of homes in this region, and from 10 to 20 million tons of bituminous coal for the many industries and railroads. Many of the lake boats coming into the harbours at Toronto, Hamilton and Windsor are loaded with coal from the United States.

Other Minerals

Canada produces several other minerals of importance. We mine about four-fifths of the world's supply of asbestos, and it all comes from near Thetford in the Eastern Townships of Quebec. Canada ranks fourth in world production of lead, and is the second leading producer of zinc. Most of the lead and zinc comes from mines in the Kimberly area in the Selkirk Mountains of British Columbia. Canada mines more platinum—as a by-product from Sudbury nickel—than any other country. Most of Canada's petroleum is produced in southwest and central Alberta, but it is only about one-quarter of what we use. Petroleum is imported from the United States into all parts of Canada. Natural gas is also obtained in southern Alberta, where it is used for industries and for heating homes. Small and decreasing amounts of natural gas are produced in southwestern Ontario.

Iron

Although Canada has a great wealth of many minerals, there is one lacking which is very important in the making of an industrial country. That mineral is iron. Canada has been fortunate, however, in being able to obtain her ore from the rich Mesabi Range in Minnesota, U.S.A. and from Bell Island in Conception Bay in Newfoundland. Since the good ores in the former region may soon be exhausted, Canada may have to turn to iron deposits which have been known for a long time, but which have not been rich enough or near enough to transportation to develop.

Canada had one iron mine producing ore from 1900 to 1918. It was the Helen Mine in the Michipicotin area north of Sault Ste. Marie, Ontario. The mine did not profit and was closed until 1939, when the Ontario Government gave it assistance to begin work once more. In 1937 iron ore was discovered at the bottom of Steep Rock Lake, west of Lake Superior, but it was not until 1946 that the ore could be brought out in any quantity. In order to mine the iron, engineers had to dam and drain part of the lake. This illustrates how valuable iron ore is in our modern world.

There are other areas in Canada where iron deposits are known to exist. One of the largest is along the Labrador-Quebec boundary at the headwaters of Hamilton River. The ore from this region will soon be mined and may some day replace the Mesabi area in importance. The Belcher Islands of Hudson Bay also have iron deposits which may yet be used. Low-grade iron is found on the British Columbia coast on Texada Island. Although these areas are not mining regions at present, iron ore is so important in making all of the machines and equipment which the world uses that Canadians should know where possible sources are located.

Summary

The Canadian mining industry has developed rapidly, mostly within the present century. This expansion has been one of the important reasons why Canada has changed from an agricultural country to a manufacturing country. Canada now produces more minerals than it can use, and is known in the world as a leading exporter of several important minerals. It is estimated that 60 per cent of our production from mines and smelters is exported. When we realize how vast the Canadian Shield is, and how little of it has been prospected thoroughly, Canadians can be hopeful of further mining expansion.

The present Canadian mining industry is greatly controlled by the geology of Canada. Precambrian rocks of the Canadian Shield supply about 70 per cent of the total production and almost 90 per cent of the metallic minerals. Regions of sedimentary rock in the Great Plains, St. Lawrence Lowlands, and parts of the Maritimes, furnish the fuels and non-metallic minerals. The Cordillera has metallics, non-metallics and coal. The value of Canadian mining production comes chiefly from gold, copper, nickel and coal. Other minerals mined in quantity are asbestos, zinc, lead, natural gas, petroleum, platinum, gypsum and salt.

Things To Do

1. Make a graph showing the value of leading Canadian minerals as listed in the table at the end of the chapter. Make the bar representing the most valuable mineral the longest and make the others proportionate in decreasing size. (See page 49). Use the Canada Year Book to make another graph showing the value of production for each mineral for the latest year available. Compare your two graphs. Have there been any changes? Can you explain why?

2. (a) Where is the closest mine to your home?
   (b) List the minerals which it produces.
   (c) Where is the ore smelted or refined?
   (d) Describe the use made of the minerals in business or industry.

3. Modern industry is largely based on the manufacture and use of iron and steel. This industry needs large amounts of coal, iron and limestone.
   (a) Where are these products located in Canada?
   (b) Describe how these raw materials are transported to the three steel mills in Canada.

4. In your reference books in the library read about the Gold Rush to the Yukon in 1897-98.
   (a) Describe what the stories say about the geography of the Yukon.
   (b) Were the prospectors' difficulties chiefly due to lack of transportation, topographic barriers, climate, or all three of these factors?
   (c) Draw a map showing the routes taken by prospectors on their way to the Klondike gold fields.

Facts For Reference

Value of Chief Minerals in Canada (1947)		Production by Provinces (1947)	
Gold	$106 million		
Copper	91 "	Ontario	39%
Coal	76 "	British Columbia	18%
Nickel	70 "	Quebec	18%
Zinc	46 "	Alberta	10%
Lead	44 "	Nova Scotia	5%
Asbestos	32 "	Saskatchewan	5%
Cement	21 "	Manitoba	3%
Sand & Gravel	18 "	New Brunswick	1%
Petroleum	15 "	Yukon and N.W.T.	1%
Natural Gas	14 "		
Platinum and Palladium	10 "		

Courtesy Ontario Travel and Publicity Bureau.

Piles of lumber are stored outside the mill at Blind River, Northern Ontario. The logs
are kept in large circular booms, and then fed up a ramp (left centre) into the cutting
mill. The finished lumber is carried away by railroad.

CHAPTER 9

FORESTRY

In Chapter 6 we read about the large area of Canada that was covered with forests of several types. Now we want to see how this vegetation cover provides work for many Canadians. Forests are more than a natural covering for the rock and ground, they are the raw materials (resources) from which things can be made. They were the homes of the game and fur-bearers which helped to feed and clothe the first settlers of Canada. For-

ests prevent rain from washing away the good top soil. They are places where we can go for relaxation and quiet to enjoy the beauties of nature. Our lives would be much different if it were not for the advantages of our vast forests.

Forests were important in the early development of Canada. In the exploratory days, fur-bearing animals that were sheltered by the forests were the lure which led to travel into the vast regions of

Canada. Later, ship-building and the lumber trade in square-timbers brought prosperity to the Maritimes. When the best trees of the Maritimes were used, the lumbering frontier shifted westward. Lumbermen penetrated into the Canadian Shield, and strong men wearing calked boots rode the logs down the Ottawa River. When most of the white pine of the Shield was gone at the beginning of this century, lumbering shifted to the huge trees of the West Coast. In Eastern Canada, the pulp and paper industry moved into the forests after the lumbermen. Because it builds large, expensive mills the pulp and paper industry is interested in saving the forests and making the industry permanent. Much of the history of Canada is influenced by our forests.

About one-third of Canada is forested. Another one-third is Arctic and treeless, and the remaining one-third is made up of treeless mountainous regions and prairie grasslands. Canada is not so fully forested as we often imagine. We may have a better idea of the extent of Canada's forest wealth if we exclude the Northwest Territories (one-third of Canada), which is forested only in the Mackenzie Valley. It is estimated that forests cover more than one-half the land area of the provinces. Since Canada is a huge country this is a large area of forests. We are the third leading producer of forest products in the world, and export more lumber and newsprint than any other country.

Forest Reserves

Foresters have looked at much of Canada's forests carefully on the ground or by aerial photographs. They estimate that only 60 per cent of our forests have good timber for pulp, lumber or furniture. Only half of this amount is accessible for cutting at the present time. Canada therefore has an area of usable forest about the size of all Ontario plus the Maritimes. Canada's lumber and pulp companies are cutting

more than three billion board feet of timber each year. In addition another one billion board feet is lost each year as a result of forest fires and destruction by insects. At this rate of cutting our forests would last for another 50 years even if no more trees grew. The forests are growing all the

Courtesy Ontario Department of Lands and Forests.

Pulpwood has been cut in strips through the spruce forests of Northern Ontario. Small trees are left behind to grow larger and to seed the cut-over strips.

time, however, and new trees come up after others are cut down in a planned forestry program which aims at conservation. The foresters believe that growth is at the rate of about four billion board feet each year, which is about equal to what we are cutting or losing.

These figures deal with the Canadian forests in total. In local areas, such as the west coast of British Columbia, and in parts of Nova Scotia, the easily accessible forests are being cut much faster than they are growing. Canada will have a great wealth in wood for many years to come, but each year the forests will be a little harder to reach.

How are Canada's forests used? About one-third of the average annual cut becomes saw-logs, used chiefly for lumber. Another one-third is used for pulpwood. Part of the remainder is burned as fuelwood, and the rest is made into furniture.

One of the chief furniture centres is in the former hardwood forests northwest of Toronto, and around Kitchener, Ontario.

In most of the rural areas throughout Canada wood is the main fuel to combat the cold Canadian winters. In Eastern Canada almost every farmer has his own local woodlot from which he cuts his winter's supply. He usually sells a little for additional income. A typical farm will have a long row of three- or four-foot logs piled along a fence near the house. A woodshed is built at the back door so that the split wood is not far away on a cold winter morning.

Lumbering

The lumber industry and the pulp and paper mills are the chief commercial users of our forests. About half of the saw lumber produced in Canada comes from British Columbia. Busy lumbermen cut the tall Douglas fir, cedar, spruce and hemlock. The logs may be made into long structural

LUMBER PRODUCTION IN CANADA
MILLIONS OF BOARD FEET, 1947.

timbers or sliced into thin plywood. More than four-fifths of Canada's wooden shingles are produced on the west coast.

Quebec is the second leading producer of saw lumber, but cuts much less than British Columbia. Ontario and New Brunswick are the only other notable producers of lumber, but in these provinces lumbering has been largely replaced by the pulp and paper industry. Canada cuts much more lumber than she can use at home. We therefore export about half of it to

other countries that are less forested, or have different kinds of trees.

Pulp and Paper

From ground-up pulpwood of our vast softwood forests comes newsprint paper, one of the chief products that we export. Canada's pulp and paper industry pro-

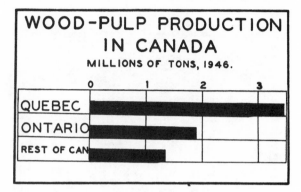

WOOD-PULP PRODUCTION IN CANADA
MILLIONS OF TONS, 1946.

duces about one-third of the world's supply of newsprint, making it possible for many people all over the world to read daily newspapers. More than half the newspapers in the United States are printed on Canadian paper, or on paper made from Canadian logs. At one time Canada used to export the pulpwood and let other countries make it into paper, but now most of the manufacturing is done in Canada and the paper is exported.

It is in the Canadian Shield of Quebec and Ontario that there are the double resources of trees and power needed for the pulp and paper industry. Spruce, which clothes the Shield everywhere, makes the best pulpwood. The many streams and storage lakes provide the hydro-electric power. Moreover, Quebec and Ontario are close to the big market in the United States. Skillful French-Canadian woodsmen are attacking the vast forests north of the St. Lawrence River. The logs are floated downstream to the mills of Quebec which are able to produce about half the newsprint of Canada. Another one-third comes from Ontario, and Newfoundland is also an important exporter.

Production

If we include all three main uses of forests—lumber, pulp and fuelwood—Quebec cuts more timber annually than any other province. It produces more than one-third of Canada's total. British Columbia and Ontario are next, one specializing in lumber and the other in pulp. In

Courtesy Abitibi Paper Company and Ontario Government.

After passing through several heavy rollers the pulp comes out as sheets of paper. Chemicals are used to control the quality and finish of the paper.

addition, Ontario has a larger rural population using fuelwood than British Columbia. New Brunswick cuts less than one-tenth of the annual Canadian total, although the industry is locally important.

Despite the importance of the forestry industry to Canada, and its value in our export trade, only a small percentage of Canadians work directly in the industry. There are about 100,000 Canadians in all the logging camps across Canada, and about as many more in the mills making lumber, pulp and paper. With the aid of excellent and modern machinery these few scattered people are able to make an important contribution to Canadian development.

Canada's vast forests are an important resource. Although only a few Canadians are required to cut the trees, all use the products in some way or another. Although the forests seem unlimited when we see how they cover most of the Canadian Shield, we should not forget that about 15 per cent of the timber removed each year is lost by fires. This brings no return to anyone, and reduces the value of large areas for many years.

Whenever we are in the forest we should be careful with matches and camp-fires. Forest fires not only destroy potential lumber and pulp, they remove cover for fur-bearers, and increase the possibility of floods. In addition, beautiful green woodland scenery is replaced by desolate areas of blackened trunks and scarred stumps. Many of the floods, which cause damage in lowlands which may be far away from the burned over area, are the result of forest fires. The protective value of forests in flood control is explained on page 74. We can all help to preserve one of Canada's great resources by obeying the rules for the prevention of forest fires.

Summary

The forest industry of Canada may be considered in terms of the distribution of kinds of forests. The tall trees of the west coast province produce much of the lumber. The softwoods of the Canadian Shield and of Newfoundland are important for pulpwood. The hardwoods of Southern Ontario and Quebec are the basis for the furniture industry. Throughout rural Canada, local farm woodlots are useful sources of fuelwood for most of the farming population.

Things To Do

1. (a) Where is the nearest saw mill to your home?

   (b) From how far away are the logs brought to this mill?

   (c) For how many months of the year does the mill operate?

   (d) How many board feet of lumber does the mill cut in a year?

   (e) What percentage is this cut of the total cut of your province?

   Refer to the Canada Year Book or the annual report of the Department of Forests in your province for the provincial cut.

2. Write paragraphs describing the different steps between the cutting of a tree and the planing of the final lumber. Tell how the cutting and logging is done, how the logs are floated down the river, and how they are cut into various sized planks and boards.

3. Is there much lumbering carried on in the area where you live? If there is not, try to find out from your history book when the lumber industry cut the forests of your area.

How much of the original forest remains today?

4. (a) List the raw materials or natural resources that a pulp and paper mill needs in addition to logs.

   (b) How many of them are usually found close by?

   (c) How many kinds of finished products may a pulp and paper mill produce?

   (d) Does a mill usually produce more than one grade of paper?

5. Make a poster to help prevent forest fires. Draw a scene which will show the danger from forest fires and print a motto on it which will remind people to be careful.

6. If your school library has the Forestry Lessons booklet issued by the Dominion Forest Service, Ottawa, read the poems at the back of the book describing forests and trees. How many of the questions can you answer at the end of each chapter?

7. Write an essay on the values of preserving our forests. Explain how forests help in the conservation of soil, water and wildlife.

CHAPTER 10

FUR RESOURCES AND FUR PRODUCTION

Fur may be considered a resource of the forest because fur-bearing animals find shelter and food in the vast forested areas of Canada. Even the areas of poor scrub trees, where commercial forestry is not practical, are useful because they can indirectly produce fur, if nothing else.

History

The fur trade is one of Canada's oldest industries. The first French explorers who visited our shores traded with the Indians giving them trinkets for furs. The popularity of these furs in the courts of France encouraged the hardy settlers of New France to do more trading during the winter. Many settlers trapped fur-bearing animals near their farms. Others, more adventurous, became "coureurs des bois" and explored the unknown forests west of the St. Lawrence Valley. With the help of Canada's navigable rivers, and the friendly Indians, these French explorer-traders soon penetrated into the rich fur regions north and west of the Great Lakes.

In the meantime, English explorers who were seeking the Northwest Passage found their way into huge Hudson Bay. This large body of salt water did not prove to be the "Western Sea" for which they were looking. They discovered, however, that the southern shores of the Bay were wooded and less forbidding than the barren rocky coasts of the northern parts. In 1670 the historic Hudson's Bay Company was formed in England, and soon opened trading posts at the mouths of rivers flowing into southern Hudson Bay and James Bay.

After the conquest of New France by Britain in 1763, Scottish traders began to operate from headquarters in Montreal. Assisted by the experienced French "voyageurs", these Montreal traders formed the North West Company and explored the region northwest of Lake Superior. Because of the direction in which rivers flow in central Canada, the Montreal companies had soon crossed to the headwaters of rivers flowing to Hudson Bay and were obtaining furs which once went to the Hudson's Bay Company. This loss forced the English traders to move inland to maintain their trade with the Indians. A race was started between the two chief concerns, the North West Company and Hudson's Bay Company. Each penetrated farther to the west and north to find new fur areas. As a result of their trading competition much of northwestern Canada was explored and became known as a vast area containing numerous fur-bearing animals. (See map on page 22).

In 1820 the two rival companies combined and took the name of the Hudson's Bay Company. Development of the fur trade became more peaceful after that. For many years fur was the only resource which the Company brought out of Canada's large western Territories.

The coming of farmers into the fertile Prairies at the end of the 19th century showed that this region had other and more valuable possibilities. The settlers soon killed off most of the fur-bearing animals in the southern regions. The remaining animals sought refuge in the wooded and rocky country of the Canadian Shield, and in the forested areas of the northern part of the Great Plains. Since their numbers can be depleted easily by over-trapping, the governments insist on closed seasons part of the year to protect the animals.

At the present time most of the fur-bearing animals are trapped by Indians who live in the forested areas of Canada. Fur

Courtesy Manitoba Travel and Publicity Bureau.

An Indian trapper cuts into a muskrat house in the spring and sets his trap. The Manitoba Government built up the muskrat population near The Pas until it now supports many trappers each year.

is still a very important resource to them. In wintertime the Indian trapper laces on his broad, webbed snowshoes and tramps along the snowy trails through the cold, silent, northern forests. He visits each trap, looking for a catch, and often spends the night in a rough lean-to of logs, warmed only by his flickering camp-fire. Trappers trade their winter's catch at one of the many fur-trading posts which are scattered over our little-inhabited northern woods. In return the Indians receive food and utensils which help them to live from year to year. There are also many white trappers who make a living by trapping fur-bearing animals during the winter. Quite often they live in settlements and carry on some other activity during the summer.

Production

Fur production has gradually been increasing in Canada during the present cen-

tury. The provinces that have the largest annual catches are those with large areas of unoccupied forest land. These are Ontario, Alberta and Quebec. Not far behind them are Manitoba, Northwest Territories and Saskatchewan.

The leading fur-producing province changes from year to year because the catches vary from place to place. The reason for the variation in annual catches is the strange cycle of abundance among fur-bearers. For example, lynx become quite numerous every 10 years. They may be plentiful in Quebec one year, but may not become numerous in Alberta until two years later. Similarly, mink have an eight- or nine-year cycle of abundance. The white fox of the Arctic appears in great numbers every three or four years. This cycle seems to be caused either by disease or by a disappearance of the animal's prey. For example, when rabbits, the chief prey of the lynx, die off, lynx have no food and they also die. When rabbits again become plentiful there are many lynx in the woods. In the same way the cycle of the white fox depends greatly upon the abundance or scarcity of lemmings, small Arctic mice. This strange fluctuation in numbers of fur-bearers causes the income of native and white trappers to vary from year to year.

The most valuable fur-bearing animals in Canada are mink and muskrat. Larger numbers of muskrat are trapped, but the fur of mink is the more valuable. Other fur-bearers which are frequently caught by Canadian trappers are silver fox, beaver, white fox, red fox, and ermine.

Fur Farming

At one time all fur-bearing animals were trapped in the woods. As the forests were cleared, enterprising farmers found that they could no longer trap during the winter. Towards the end of the last century, two clever farmers on Prince Edward Island thought of catching foxes alive and keeping them in pens. As these foxes multiplied in numbers the pelts were sold at a good profit. The project soon became popular with other farmers. Fur-farming, or fur-ranching, is now considered a branch of agriculture. At the beginning of the present century Prince Edward Island was the centre of this industry.

Courtesy P.E.I. Information Bureau.

This fox farm on Prince Edward Island is one of many that are found on the "Island Province". The animals are well cared for in clean pens in order to produce good pelts.

Each year the Islanders sold many silver fox pelts and large numbers of high-priced live foxes to people who wished to start fur-farming.

Prince Edward Island was too small to remain the centre for Canadian fur-farming. The industry spread to the other Maritime provinces, and to Quebec and Ontario. Aided by cold winters which give the animals a good thick fur, Quebec soon became the leader in fur-farm production. About one-third of the fur-farms of Canada are located there. Ontario and Prince Edward Island follow as important provinces for fur-farming; Alberta and New Brunswick also have many fur-ranches.

Some of the wild fur-bearing animals cannot be raised successfully in pens on farms. In addition, the fur has to be valuable enough to pay for the cost of feeding and housing the animals. About 90 per cent of the pelts from fur-farms come from

mink and silver fox, which can be raised in captivity and make valuable furs. On many farms throughout the Maritimes and in Quebec one can see the wire mesh of the fur pens.

Although fur-farms increased in number prior to World War II, they never produced as many furs as were trapped in the woods. The percentage from fur-farms varies from year to year, but they usually supply 20 to 40 per cent of the fur production of Canada. The remainder is made up of pelts trapped throughout the thinly-populated, less accessible wooded areas of Canada.

Most of the fur pelts are brought from the widely scattered trading posts and fur-farms to Montreal. There, the furs are graded and sold to manufacturers to be made into clothing, such as coats, capes, neck-pieces, and trimming. Except for the war years, 1939-1945, more than half the Canadian fur catch was exported to London, England, the headquarters of the Hudson's Bay Company. This famous old company still buys much of the fur trapped in the Canadian woods, and sends it to the world market in London.

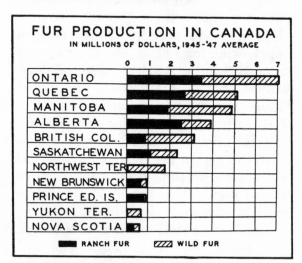

Summary

Canada's fur resources come chiefly from the forested areas where lumbering is not yet possible, but important contributions also come from fur-farms in settled agricultural regions. Although this resource is much less valuable to Canada than mining, forestry or fishing, it is very important to the native Indian and Eskimo trappers. It is also an additional source of income on many farms which might not otherwise be successful. If ranch-fur and wild fur catches are combined, Ontario, Quebec and Alberta are the leading producers of fur wealth. The forested and little-used regions of Manitoba, Saskatchewan, and the Northwest Territories also supply large numbers of pelts each year.

Things To Do

1. (a) From the chapter on Fur Production in the Canada Year Book, make a list of the provinces having the most valuable fur catches for last year.

   (b) Make another list of the provinces with the largest number of pelts caught.

   (c) What provinces are in different order in the two lists?

   (d) Explain why some furs are more valuable than others.

2. Make a bar graph showing the total fur catch of each province. Shade in the amount of each bar which represents fur-farm production. (See page 62). How much of the total fur catch of each province comes from fur-farms?

3. Read again the chapter on "Rivers and Lakes", and then write an essay on "The Importance of Rivers in the Early Fur Trade of Canada".
   Read assigned chapters in your history books for information about the fur-trading days in Canada.

4. Read the article on muskrat trapping in the Mackenzie River delta in the March, 1948, issue of *The Beaver*, published by the Hudson's Bay Company, Winnipeg. This magazine has excellent pictures and stories about modern and past activities in Canada's northern woodlands and Arctic.

Courtesy Canadian Fishing Co.

On the Pacific Coast, large numbers of fishing vessels gather near river mouths during the salmon season. This small crew is pulling in its circular seine net.

CHAPTER 11

FISHING

Fish are another of the natural resources of our country. They are found in coastal waters off the shores of the whole continent, and also in most of the inland lakes and rivers. Fish are an important source of food for people living near the coast. In most fishing areas more fish are caught than can be eaten locally. The excess catch is shipped to inland areas, or to other countries that do not catch enough fish.

Canada is bounded by three oceans, two of which supply us with an abundance of fish for home use and export. The Atlantic fishery of our east coast provinces usually supplies more valuable catches of fish than does our Pacific fishery. British Colum-

64

bia, however, has replaced Nova Scotia as the leading province in the production of fish. Inland fisheries are less valuable than the catches of either coast, and usually make up less than one-quarter of the total annual catch.

The Atlantic Fishery

The fishing grounds of the Atlantic have been known and used for several centuries. It is believed that daring French fishermen were fishing on the Grand Banks off Newfoundland before Cabot reported the discovery of the coast of Canada. Some of them built rough huts on the beaches of this unknown land while they were ashore drying their fish.

For many generations the settlers of the Maritime Provinces and Newfoundland have turned to the sea for a livelihood. In Nova Scotia and Newfoundland, especially, where the rocky nature of the hilly land made farming difficult, people have settled on the shores of the many small but good harbours. The settlers of New Brunswick and Prince Edward Island had better land for agriculture, and never developed the fishing industry as intensively as the Nova Scotians.

In the last century fishing was chiefly carried on in coastal waters close to shore. It was not until 1873 that the first Canadian deep-sea vessel sailed from Lunenburg to join the boats of other nations on the Grand Banks. Even to-day deep-sea fishing makes up a small percentage of the value of the Atlantic catch of Canada.

The centres of the deep-sea fishing industry are at Lunenburg, Nova Scotia, and St. John's, Newfoundland. From these scenic ports, sturdy vessels of 40 to 100 tons set out for the fishing banks. They are usually manned by a crew of 10 to 20 adventurous fishermen. Once out on the high seas, the vessels may remain there for a month or more while the crews fish in small dories in the surrounding waters. Often the catch is salted or frozen aboard.

Sometimes it is rushed back to the harbours for quick sale.

The chief fish caught is cod. They feed in large numbers in the shallow waters which extend off the east coast of North America from Massachusetts to Newfoundland. To many fishermen of Nova Scotia the word "fish" naturally means "cod".

The coastal fishery is the most valuable on the east coast of Canada, and occupies a larger number of persons than deep-sea fishing. It is carried on in the coastal area close to the east coast of Nova Scotia, the shores around the Bay of Fundy, the coasts of the Gulf of St. Lawrence as far inland as northern Gaspé, and as far east as the south coast of Newfoundland. Throughout this region there are numerous small fishing villages scattered along the coasts at the heads of sheltered harbours. The chief catches in coastal waters are cod and haddock.

The lobster industry which developed rapidly prior to World War II, ranks as the second most valuable catch from coastal waters. From 20 to 40 million lobsters are caught annually and there are over 100 lobster canneries in the Maritimes, chiefly in Prince Edward Island and New Brunswick. At one time most lobsters were canned, but now many are shipped alive to the inland cities of Canada and the United States.

Herring are caught along all the coasts, but the largest number are found off the coast of New Brunswick in the Bay of Fundy. Young herring are called sardines when they are packed in oil and canned. One of the largest sardine canneries in the world is at Black's Harbour, New Brunswick.

Pacific Coast Fishery

The Pacific Coast fishery is based largely on salmon. Great numbers of these fish are caught each year at the mouths of the large rivers, such as the

Fish hatcheries help maintain fishing in many inland lakes and rivers in Ontario. When the fish are large enough they are turned loose in the lakes. Only the best kind of fish are released.

Fraser, Skeena and Nass. There are several kinds of salmon, but the most valuable is the sockeye. This red-fleshed fish overcomes many obstacles in ascending the rivers in the late summer to spawn at the place where it was born four years before. In the spring the young fish run down the rivers and disappear into the Pacific. Four years later some unknown instinct brings them back to their birthplace to spawn and die. The salmon fisheries of the British Columbia rivers are protected by the Government. It sees that enough fish are permitted to go upstream each year to maintain a supply for future years. The two cities of Vancouver and New Westminster, at the mouth of the Fraser River, are the centres of the salmon-canning industry.

Coastal fishing, except at river mouths, is not as common in British Columbia as in the Maritimes because the off-shore water is deeper. There is no wide "continental shelf" similar to that off the east coast. The centre of the coastal and deep-sea fishing industry is Prince Rupert, the nor-thern terminal of the Canadian National Railway. Halibut is the chief fish caught off Vancouver Island and the Queen Charlotte Islands. Herring are also very important during the winter months. A few large vessels hunt whales in the North Pacific Ocean off the Queen Charlotte Islands.

Inland Fisheries

Between the Atlantic and Pacific fishing grounds, Canada has a large number of inland lakes. Commercial fishing is carried on in many of these lakes to help feed the inland towns and cities. The fish of the Great Lakes are caught by both Canadian and American fishermen. They fish for six or eight months of the year with nets. After the shores are frozen over many continue fishing through holes in the ice. The chief fish caught are whitefish, trout, perch, pickerel, and lake herring. They are sold fresh and transported rapidly to the cities of the St. Lawrence and Ontario Lowlands.

In the Prairie Provinces, the large lakes

Courtesy Ontario Travel and Publicity Bureau.

Sport fishing by vacationers is an important industry in the many lakes and rivers of the Canadian Shield. These fishermen are relaxing at Red Rock Falls in northwestern Ontario. Their catches are limited in number by the government so that the supply of game fish is not depleted.

along the western edge of the Canadian Shield are important sources of commercial fish. Lake Winnipeg "goldeye" are well known to most travellers. The innumerable lakes upon the Shield supply food for the local and native population. Whitefish and pickerel are the chief fish caught.

Fishing in Saskatchewan and Alberta is carried on north of the North Saskatchewan River. Rainfall is more abundant there and rivers and lakes are larger than in the southern grasslands. Fishing companies gradually have extended their operations farther northward where cold waters give good firm-fleshed fish. Excellent lake trout come from Lake Athabaska,

and in 1945 fishing was begun in Great Slave Lake, Northwest Territories. The fish are shipped southward in refrigerated barges to the railroad at Waterways, Alberta. By rail they are transported to central Canada and the United States.

Hudson Bay, the largest interior body of water in Canada, has no commercial fishing. The valuable cod found off the east coasts of Canada does not enter Hudson Strait any farther than Ungava Bay. Cod fishing is important off the west coast of Greenland, owing to a northward-moving warm ocean current, but the coast of Canada's Baffin Island has a southward-moving cold ocean current, and no cod.

Sport Fishing

Although inland fisheries are not as valuable as the Atlantic and Pacific fisheries in annual catch, they have a product which is important to Canada's revenue. Game fish of northern lakes attract large numbers of tourists from the United States and southern Canada. Sport fishing permits many city dwellers to relax and enjoy a holiday. A few weeks of life in the outdoors amid the beautiful rugged scenery of the many lakes and rivers in Canada's less settled regions attracts many vacationists. The scent of the cool spruce forests, and the fine spray of a rapids in one's face, are as much an attraction as the thrill of landing a fighting fish.

Certain well-known streams in the Maritimes and along the edge of the Canadian Shield are reserved for fishing clubs. Many lakes are re-stocked with young fish every few years by the provincial governments to enable tourists to catch enough fish. It would be difficult to name all the favourite game fish streams in Canada, for each person thinks that he has the best location. Some of the many popular fish are the fighting salmon of the Restigouche River in New Brunswick, the black bass of the Laurentian lakes in Quebec, the shiny trout of Lake Nipigon in Northern Ontario, and the Kamloops trout of British Columbia.

Summary

The most valuable commercial fish caught by Canadian fishermen are salmon, cod, lobster, herring, whitefish, and halibut. Newfoundland, Nova Scotia and British Columbia have the largest number of fishermen, but there are only half as many people employed in Canadian fishing as there are in mining or lumbering. British Columbia has the most valuable fish catch, chiefly salmon, but the combined catch of the Maritimes and eastern Quebec, chiefly cod and lobster, is larger. The inland commercial fishery, consisting chiefly of whitefish, is less valuable than the coastal catches. The inland lakes and rivers, however, have many game fish which are important as an attraction for tourists.

Things To Do

1. Read the labels on the cans of fish at your home or in a store.
   (a) Where was the fish canned?
   (b) How many miles is that from your home?
   (c) Are there cans from both coasts of Canada in the stores?
   (d) Why are cans from one coast more numerous than from the other?
   (e) What foreign countries are represented in the canned-fish section of your grocery?

2. Describe a day's activities if you were a fisherman on a schooner leaving Halifax for the Sable Island banks. Read some of the articles in the Canadian Geographical Journal describing fishing in Eastern Canada, such as in July, 1949, Feb., 1938, July, 1936, Aug., 1934, July, 1931.

3. How many kinds of salmon do you know? Which kinds are the most valuable?

4. If a cod fish is caught off the coast near Sydney, Nova Scotia, how many days would it take before it could be delivered by refrigerated train to Toronto, Ontario? A railroad timetable will help to give you the answer.

5. If you went on a fishing trip to the nearest National Park in your province, what kinds of fish would you likely catch? What kind would you catch at the river or lake nearest to your school? Would they be the same kinds? Ask for information from the National Parks Division, Department of Resources and Development, Ottawa.

Facts For Reference

The value of the chief commercial fish caught in Canada, 1946:

Salmon	$26	million	Halibut	$ 4	million
Cod	22	"	Sardines	4	"
Herring	17	"	Mackerel	2	"
Lobster	14	"	Grayfish	2	"
Whitefish	4	"	Haddock	1	"

The Shipshaw dams on the Saguenay River generate more electrical power than any other area in Canada. Most of the power is used by the aluminum industry at nearby Arvida, Quebec.

CHAPTER 12

WATER-POWER RESOURCES

It may be difficult to think of water power as a resource in the same class as minerals, soil, and trees. And yet the water which flows in our streams, and tumbles over our rapids and falls, is as capable of being used as our copper, wheat lands, or pulp wood. If it were not for the presence of this resource of flowing water, we would not be able to use many of our other resources.

Natural resources have to be manufactured into other forms in order to be useful. The rock containing copper or lead has to be broken into small pieces by

machines before the metal is extracted. Other machines then make it into wires, tubing and sheets for our homes and factories. There must be some easy and cheap source of power to run all these machines. Similarly, the trees in the forest go through many cutting and chopping stages before they become furniture, matches, or paper. Man has found that he can make machines run if he has one of three main sources of power energy. These sources are coal, petroleum, and water power.

In Chapter 8 we discovered that our coal

is not located near our centres of population or manufacturing industries. Although coal can be changed into steam power, it costs a great deal to transport it from the fields in Alberta and Nova Scotia to the factories of Ontario and Quebec. Petroleum is found in the same distant regions of the Great Plains, but does not supply enough oil for gasoline for our cars and trucks. Canada has an excellent supply of water power quite near her factories. Nine-tenths of the electrical power used in Canada is made by water power.

Two important conditions are necessary for the creation of water power. One is steady and plentiful precipitation; the other is a slope down which the water may fall. Water power is, therefore, most plentiful in mountainous or hilly regions where there is much rainfall. Because rugged country is also the location of minerals and forests, nearby water power is used to develop these resources.

Potential Water Power

All water power is not turned into electrical energy. Often there are no industries located in the area to use it. The presence of unused power is called "potential" power. Potential hydro power is measured by the speed of a stream, the volume of water, and the height of the water fall. It gives an estimate of how much power could be developed in Canada if we needed it.

Our knowledge of the physical geography of Canada should help us to locate our water-power resources. The rivers of the southern part of the Canadian Shield have falls and rapids as they spill over the escarpment rising above the St. Lawrence Valley. Aided by the heavy winter snowfall which melts into water in the spring, the southern edge of the Shield has a large amount of available water power. Quebec, which is covered by more of the Shield than any other province, has the greatest potential power resources in Canada.

One area which has both high mountains and heavy rainfall is British Columbia. It has the second greatest potential water power in Canada. Many of the coastal rivers are too short to generate large quantities of water power. In addition,

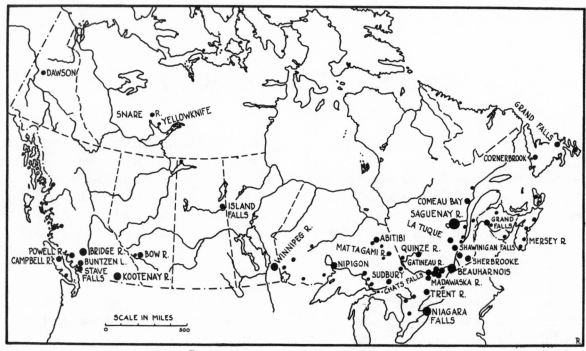

Developed water power sites in Canada.

most of the rainfall comes only during one season and streams may be low in late summer.

Potential water power may become developed if there are industries and factories located nearby to use it. In many cases factories are built near a source of power. The pulp and paper industry needs large amounts of cheap electric power. The plentiful supply of water power in the southern Canadian Shield is one reason why this industry is so well developed in the softwood forests of Quebec and Ontario.

Distribution of Developed Water Power

Quebec has more developed water power than any other province. Since Quebec lacks coal for its industries, it uses the hydro power found in its numerous rivers.

The largest dam in Canada is built on the Saguenay River at Shipshaw, and supplies electric power to the aluminum industry at nearby Arvida. The Beauharnois Rapids, in the St. Lawrence River west of Montreal, supply large amounts of power for Canada's biggest city. Numerous other rivers, such as the St. Maurice and Gatineau, have been dammed so that their power may be used for important industries.

Ontario is second to Quebec in developed water power, although it does not have as much potential power as British Columbia. Ontario has more factories than any other province, and one of the reasons has been the great amount of electricity which is obtained from Niagara Falls, in the middle of the industrial area. The Hydro Electric

Courtesy Ontario Hydro-Electric Power Commission.

Numerous water power sites have been developed in the Ottawa River Valley. At Chats Falls, west of Ottawa, 224,000 horsepower is produced for nearby industries and homes.

Power Commission of Ontario has distributed this power energy over most of the southern part of the province. It is used by cities and factories, and is also delivered to a great many Ontario farmers, who are now able to use electric lights and small power machines. From the many streams of the Canadian Shield the Ontario government is also developing new

DEVELOPED WATER POWER IN CANADA
MILLIONS OF HORSEPOWER, 1947.

	0	1	2	3	4	5	6
QUEBEC							
ONTARIO							
BRITISH COL.							
MANITOBA							
NOVA SCOTIA							
NEW BRUNSWICK							
ALBERTA							
SASKATCHEWAN							
YUKON AND N.W.T.							
PRINCE ED. IS.							

power sites for the people of Northern Ontario. One of the largest of present power plants in Northern Ontario is at Abitibi Canyon, north of Cochrane.

British Columbia ranks third in the development of water power. It has only about one-third of that of Ontario and one-seventh that of Quebec. Although water power is available, people live chiefly in the southwest corner of British Columbia and are not close enough to many of the interior and coastal power sites.

The Prairie Provinces have little developed water power. Since the topography of the Great Plains is flat, and rainfall is scanty, we would not expect to find much water power. One of the few generating plants is located on the Winnipeg River in southeastern Manitoba, but it is operated by water from the Canadian Shield. The Prairies, however, have much of Canada's coal and petroleum and can turn these resources into steam and diesel power.

The Maritimes have developed a large share of their small potential power. Because the provinces are small, power

sites are not far from towns or industries. Grand Falls, on the St. John River, is one of the largest power developments in New Brunswick. The power resources of Nova Scotia are increased by the use of coal from Cape Breton Island. Prince Edward Island has scarcely any water power, since the land is flat and the rivers are short.

The Northwest Territories and Yukon Territory have ample potential power. It is found in the rapids of the northern part of the Shield which drains towards the Mackenzie Valley, and in the water falls of the Yukon mountains. Since few people live in these regions, power is developed only in small plants near Dawson, Y.T., and Yellowknife, N.W.T.

Courtesy Ontario Department of Planning and Development.

The Shand Dam, built across the headwaters of the Grand River about 30 miles north of Galt, will hold back rapid spring run-off and help to prevent downstream floods.

Summary

Water-power resources are very important to Canada, which lacks coal and petroleum in the most desirable places. Water power runs the many industries of the St. Lawrence and Ontario Lowlands, and the pulp and paper and mining industries in the less settled regions of the Canadian Shield. In addition to supplying power, the damming of rivers decreases the flood danger by regulating the periods of rapid run-off. A controlled river may be made useful; an uncontrolled one may cause destruction.

The greatest amount of potential water power is found in the southern part of the Canadian Shield, and a great deal of it is utilized by Quebec and Ontario. Large amounts of water power which could be generated in mountainous and rainy British Columbia may be very important in the future development of that province. The Maritimes have sufficient water power for present industial developments. The Prairies lack water power because the region has little rainfall and a level topography, but they have much of Canada's coal and petroleum.

Things To Do

1. (a) What is the source of the electric power that lights your school?

   (b) How many miles of wire carry it from the power plant to the school?

   (c) How large an area is served by power from the same source?

2. On an outline map of Canada mark the water power plants which were mentioned in this chapter. Add any more that you know of yourself. A map of "Resources of Canada," published by the Department of Mines and Technical Surveys, Ottawa, shows all the potential and developed water-power sites in Canada.

3. Write four paragraphs describing how each of the factors of physical geography—topography, drainage, climate, and vegetation—influences the amount of potential and developed water power in an area. Treat each factor as a separate influence, and in a fifth paragraph show how they are all related.

4. Why does Saskatchewan have very little developed water power, and British Columbia very much? Read the chapter to find the answer.

5. In the Canadian Geographical Journal of November, 1947, read about the building of Shipshaw Dam during World War II.

   (a) For what is the power used?

   (b) Why was the dam kept secret during the war?

   (c) Read about "A River in Harness" (the St. Maurice) in the Canadian Geographical Journal, May, 1950.

6. Re-read Chapter 9 on Forestry.

   (a) Why are pulp and paper mills of Ontario and Quebec located near water power sites?

   (b) In addition to power, name others ways in which pulp and paper mills use water.

Facts For Reference

Potential and Developed Water Power by provinces, 1947:

Province	Potential (h.p.)	Developed (h.p.)
Quebec	8,500,000	5,900,000
Ontario	5,400,000	2,800,000
British Columbia	7,000,000	1,000,000
Manitoba	3,300,000	460,000
New Brunswick	70,000	130,000
Nova Scotia	20,000	130,000
Alberta	500,000	105,000
Saskatchewan	540,000	90,000
Yukon and N.W.T.	390,000	20,000
Prince Edward Is.	3,000	2,600
Newfoundland (1948)	7,000,000	262,000

CHAPTER 13

CONSERVATION OF NATURAL RESOURCES

Directly or indirectly the occupations of most Canadians are dependent on the extraction, production, transportation or processing of some one or more of the products of our natural resources. Each resource is the basis of prosperous industry. Therefore, we should use them wisely.

Can you visualize what our country would be like without some of these resources? Suppose there were few fish in the waters off our coasts or in our lakes. Many of the scenic fishing villages of Nova Scotia, or the busy canneries of British Columbia, would not be there. The people who now sell clothing or other manufactured goods to these places would have to look elsewhere for a market. The tourists who enjoy fishing amid the relaxing beauty of our lakes would go to other countries, and many resorts would close down. Suppose we killed off all the wild animals in the forests. Many native people would be without meat. Fur-trapping, which supports many people in the northern regions, would cease, and the ladies of our southern cities would pay much more for fur coats imported from other countries. Truly, Canada would be a much less attractive country if any of our resources were exhausted.

Resources are limited in amount. As our population grows we are steadily increasing our demands upon them. Every day scientists are finding new ways to use them, or are seeking better ways to use the by-products which were once wasted. Since our lives depend so much on resources we must be careful that our demands do not deplete the supply. There is little value in preserving the raw materials a resource so that no one gets any use from them. On the other hand it is also not wise to use a resource completely so that an industry has to be abandoned.

Some resources are renewable. That is, they produce again and again if some of the original amount is left. Water is one of the easiest resources to replace. As it flows out to the sea, more rain is falling on the land. Although renewable, the proper use of that water after it falls as rain is one of most troublesome problems which man is facing. Forests take a longer period in which to renew themselves. A forest will grow again in 50 to 100 years if some trees are left to seed the area. The rate of growth depends chiefly upon the climate. Soil resources take still longer to renew. The top few inches of soil, which feeds much of the world, can be washed away in a few days. The slow natural process of weathering rock and gradually adding humus may require 200 years.

Soils are lost by too-rapid water erosion or by wind-blowing. If you have ever watched little gullies being cut into a new embankment along a road you know how water can wash away the soil. On most hillsides the soil is protected by tree cover which breaks the force of the rain, and grass cover which absorbs the water gradually. If farmers cut down the trees and plough under the grass, life-giving soil is exposed to the elements. During heavy thundershowers water runs across the bare surface instead of sinking into the coil to become ground water. The running water carries some of the surface top-soil with it and soon small guillies appear. The gullies concentrate the water into little streams which carry still more soil. Soon much of the soil is carried away to the river and the hillside lies bare and useless.

In a few years the farmer notices that his well is going dry. The water which once soaked into the ground and found its way to his well now runs directly off the bare hard surface to the streams. The

Courtesy Ontario Dept. of Lands and Forests.

Because the tree cover has been cut from the lowland of Southern Ontario, erosion is becoming serious in some places. This wise farmer is doing "contour-ploughing" to stop the water from running down the slope too rapidly. Trees will be planted on this slope..

farmer may find it difficult to believe that cutting trees on a slope caused his well to be dry.

If the land is too flat for water to wash away the soil, the wind may do the damage. A strong wind can pick up small particles in the soil. Soon a dust storm is carrying away the food-producing land and depositing it in dust layers in the cities and towns.

Resources are being wasted in many ways. There are, however, many methods of conservation which can help to maintain them in continuous use for generations. Soil erosion and wind-blowing are events which are taking place in Nature all the time. It is only when man does something wrong to speed up this action that we begin to worry about it.

Soil erosion can be prevented by plowing only the lowlands or level lands. If sloping land has to be ploughed the furrows

should be cut across the slope instead of down it. Sometimes fields or strips of grass are left across the slope to help hold the soil in place. The more trees that are left on the slope the less the danger from water erosion. Wind erosion is most serious in dry areas where the particles of soil are loose. Rows of planted trees help to break the force of the wind. If trees will not grow, such as in the southern Prairies, fields of pasture help to hold the soil in place. When we plough under the semi-arid grasslands we are inviting dust storms.

Since what we eat depends largely on how much soil we have, it is important to conserve it. Soils must be kept on the land to produce crops instead of being permitted to fill up our rivers and lakes. Every acre of soil which, due to poor management, is washed away, means less food can be produced, and there is less income for the farmer. The soil must also be cropped properly so that its natural fertility is not depleted. Instead of growing the same crop on the same field every year different crops should be planted, especially the grasses which restore fertility. In Canada each year, because of our one-crop practices, our soils yield fewer bushels per acre unless expensive fertilizers are used.

Three hundred years ago much of southern Canada was covered with dense forests. Our forest resources are slowly disappearing. The rich hardwoods of Ontario and Quebec were cleared away to make farms. The lumbermen began cutting into the forests of the southern Canadian Shield and later into the tall trees of the West Coast. Trains ran through the forests scattering sparks, and fires destroyed more and more timber.

The time has come when we are concerned about the future of our forest wealth. On the coast of British Columbia the great forests may be gone within two generations. The forests of central Saskatchewan are no longer sufficient for local building. In Ontario serious floods each spring are already showing the effects of removing the protective forest cover. Until the small farm woodlots are restored to their former importance in Ontario the water will continue to run off the land in the spring faster than the small rivers can hold it.

The forests have three great enemies: insects, fire and man. The problems of insects and blights are being considered by scientists in their laboratories. Their work is very important to the future of Canada's resources. In some years fire, insects and disease destroy more timber than is used by the whole pulp and paper industry.

Courtesy Ontario Department of Lands and Forests.

Each year thousands of acres of productive forest are burned, despite the efforts of the provincial governments. Many of these fires are due to carelessness of people in the woods.

Since Canada's export trade is so greatly dependent upon forest products, it is our duty as citizens to be careful with fire when travelling or camping in forest areas. Man, through his overcutting of

the forest, is the most serious problem. In our anxiety or greed for the wealth which the forest brings in lumber, pulp or paper we often cut down the trees faster than new ones can grow. Unless the rates of timber cutting are controlled to corres-

Courtesy Ontario Department of Lands and Forests.

This forlorn scene was once a shady, green woodland. No one can use the wood destroyed by a forest fire. There is no underbrush to protect animals. The rains will soon begin to wash away the bare soil. It pays to protect our forests!

pond to the rates of tree growth our forest industry will disappear in a few decades.

Fish are another resource which can be depleted easily if not guarded. Once the habits of the fish are known it is a simple matter for fishermen to be at the right place at the right time to catch them. Our fish resources are protected by limiting fishing to certain short seasons and restricting the numbers caught. Government scientists work to prevent commercial fish from being killed in the streams by pollution, diseases or by other predatory fish. Many of the interior lakes are periodically restocked with game fish from a hatchery. Conservation means more than preventing the use of some resource; it also means active measures to insure the continuing supply of that resource.

Since the uses of our resources are interrelated, the misuse of resources creates growing problems. City people are often inclined to think that conservation is a problem only for the farmer. But when their homes are destroyed by floods, or their lights turned out because of a power shortage, they are feeling the results of the lack of conservation. What happens on the slopes upstream affects those on the river banks downstream. Conservation is a community and regional problem.

The inter-relationships of resources may be noted from the following examples. If forests are cut down wild game and fur-bearing animals are driven away. The removal of forest cover may cause the soil to be washed into streams, and this silt may destroy fish spawning grounds. The waste rock from mining may block streams in which fish migrate, or prevent the flow of water downstream for irrigation or water power. Power dams which are built to use the water resource may prevent the use of the river for fishing. Soil erosion on slopes may fill the dam with silt and decrease its usefulness. Forest fires destroy the wild-life population and change the character of soils.

No resource can be misused without possible harm coming to other resources. Therefore the people concerned with the use of one resource are also interested in what is being done by people working on other resources. Conservation and resource-use need the combined efforts of many people in a region, and they must see that their problems do not stand alone, but are solved by cooperation.

Because the use of resources is the basis of our economy, it seems quite right that we should do much to conserve them. Canada has only a few large resources which supply products to be exported to pay for the materials which we lack. We should guard them carefully. Resources are there to be used, but they are to be used wisely. Generations of future Canadians have to depend on them. The misuse of a few years can be felt for decades.

Things To Do

1. List 3 examples of soil erosion in your neighbourhood. State what methods might be used to prevent it.

2. For class discussion report on some government project which is being, or has been, carried on in your province to conserve a natural resource. For example, read about the work of the Prairie Farm Rehabilitation Act (P.F.R.A.), Maritime dyking projects, the Conservation and River Valley Developments of Ontario, fur conservation at The Pas, Manitoba, or the International Pacific Salmon Fisheries Commission.

3. Give a report on conditions in the "Dust Bowl" of the United States about 1933-35. State why you think such events could happen in Canada.

4. Describe the cycle of events which might occur after a steep hillside has been cut-over and ploughed.

5. Write an account of how your daily life would be changed if any one or two of our natural resources were depleted.

6. Read the articles on Conservation in the Agricultural Institute Review for September, 1947, and January, 1950.

The Alaska Highway was built during World War II through northeastern British Columbia and southern Yukon to connect Edmonton, Alberta, with Fairbanks, Alaska. The gravel highway passes through beautiful scenery north of the St. Elias Mountains (above) in southwestern Yukon Territory.

CHAPTER 14

TRANSPORTATION

In order to obtain food, clothing, and shelter from our natural resources, we must have a good transportation system to move the products from one place to another. Resources are of little value in their natural state. Their products must be carried to sources of power where they are changed into other forms for further use. In manufacturing, many resources and raw materials are brought to factories from far and near. Then the finished products must be carried to the centres of population. Our good network of water, land and air transport is one of the reasons why Canada's natural resources are so useful.

One of Canada's greatest problems has been to overcome her broad east-west extent. The rugged barriers of the Appalachians, Canadian Shield and Rockies divide our wide country into separate geographic regions. These topographic features have greatly influenced the direction and kind of transportation in Canada. Great distances from coast to coast mean that Canada needs a good transportation system that will connect these various sections.

Early Water Transportation

In the early days of French settlement, rivers were the only means of transportation and communication. Vessels from France sailed up the broad St. Lawrence River to Quebec or Montreal. West of Montreal, bark canoes, made from the numerous birch trees of the St. Lawrence Valley, were used to travel into the interior. For many years the water route up the Ottawa River to Lake Huron was an important trail along which the furs of the Great Lakes region were brought out to the coastal ports.

After the conquest of New France, trade with the interior increased, and larger boats were built. Cargo canoes which carried supplies to the traders in the northwest were 30 to 40 feet long and often manned by about 14 paddlers. On the rivers of the prairies these canoes were called "York boats".

There was little transportation by large boats on the Great Lakes until late in the 18th century. Sloops and small schooners then began to carry goods to the new settlements of southwestern Ontario. Decked sailing vessels and square-rigged naval vessels were gradually replaced by steamships early in the 19th century. The Great Lakes are a natural trading route but they could not be fully used until the rapids along the way were by-passed by canals. In the twenty-five years after 1825 the British Government built many canals. These gave the St. Lawrence a nine-foot channel from Montreal to Lake Huron.

Early Road Transportation

While water transportation in Eastern Canada was being improved, roads were also being built. Before the fall of New France there was a rough road along the north shore of the St. Lawrence joining the settlements between Quebec and Montreal. In southern Ontario roads were laid out as townships were surveyed for new settlers. The old corduroy roads, made from the plentiful logs of the surrounding forests, were gradually replaced by smoother plank roads or dirt-surfaced trails.

There were many natural hazards to overcome in building roads in Eastern Canada. The forests had to be cut down to clear a path. There were numerous creeks and streams to be forded and later bridged. Frost pushed up the roads in winter time, and spring thaws turned them into ribbons of mud. Travel in the spring was almost impossible, and in summer was rough, bumpy and dusty. In winter, however, the snow made a smooth surface for sleighs, and travelling was then much more popular.

One of the tasks of the early British colonists was to connect the Maritimes with central Canada during the winter. By 1830 a road built from Fredericton to Quebec was open for mail service during the winter, but much of it was impassable in summer. After 1850 a road built eastward from Levis, Quebec, connected the Maritime roads with those in the St. Lawrence Valley.

In southern Ontario a main road joined Montreal with Niagara by 1855. From there connections could be made to many other roads which had been cut across the colony. By the middle of the 19th century it was possible to travel by water or road across the Canada of that time from Halifax, Nova Scotia, to Windsor, Upper Canada. These were the only means by which the people of Canada could move from one section to another. Canadians were not able to know much about other parts of the new Dominion because of the many difficulties which physical geography placed in the way.

Railroad Transportation

The coming of the railroads marked the next period in the expansion of Canada's transportation system. Fifty years after the first short railroad was built around rapids in the Richelieu River in 1835, Canada had rail connections from coast to coast.

During the decade, 1850-60, Upper and Lower Canada built over 2,000 miles of railroads, linking the principal towns and cities and speeding the movement of products. Montreal and Toronto were joined by railroad, and the western end of the line was continued to the United States through Sarnia.

Although many local railroads were built during these prosperous years, it was after Confederation when the Maritimes were linked with Central Canada. The Intercolonial Railway, which started in Halifax, passed through Moncton to Rivière du Loup on the St. Lawrence River.

Following Confederation, the growing new Dominion in Eastern Canada promised to build a railroad across the wide

Courtesy B.C. Travel Bureau.

Passes through the Rockies permitted the early railroad builders to find a transcontinental route. Along the Thompson river (above) in British Columbia, railways have been carved out of the slopes on both sides of the river.

continent to the tiny colony of British Columbia. It was estimated that only 23,000 persons lived west of Lake Superior at that time. The building of the transcontinental Canadian Pacific Railway is one of the famous stories in Canadian history. Large gangs of workmen were brought in from Europe and the Orient.

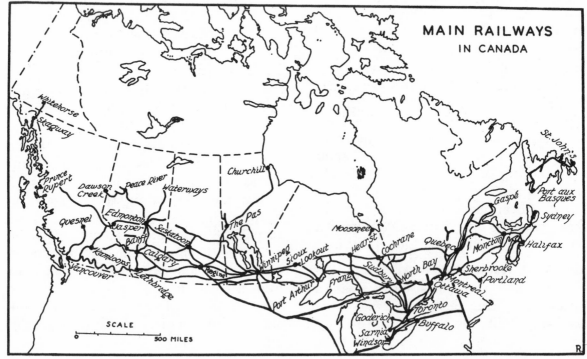

MAIN RAILWAYS
IN CANADA

SCALE

500 MILES

Surveyors struggled through unknown, rough or mountainous country, and hardy workmen pushed the rail lines through behind them. The imagination and enthusiasm of the company's organizers helped to conquer Canada's geographic barriers. The railroad was built in several sections, but it was finally completed as a through line in 1885. Soon the settlers who had been passing through Ontario into the United States were able to take a northern route into our fertile prairie lands.

The rush of settlers to the west resulted in more railroads to ship out the wheat which was grown in increasing amounts. The Canadian Pacific extended branch lines northward to Edmonton and also to Saskatoon and Prince Albert. Golden grain from the prairies was soon filling the railroad cars on the main line which ran to the head of the Great Lakes.

Canada's second transcontinental railroad, the Grand Trunk Pacific, started from Moncton, New Brunswick, in 1905. The western section of the railroad was built from Winnipeg across the northern prairies to Edmonton. It crossed the Rockies through Yellowhead Pass and reached its western terminal at Prince Rupert in 1914. Yellowhead Pass is lower than the Kicking Horse and Crowsnest passes which are used by the Canadian Pacific Railway farther south. The Rockies decrease in elevation to the north, so that the northern passes are lower and the mountains are less of a barrier. In 1915 the Grand Trunk Pacific cut a path westward from Quebec through the little-known central part of the Canadian Shield. This route opened up areas of possible mineral resources in northern Quebec and Ontario, and passed through the agricultural lands of the Clay Belt. The former Grand Trunk Pacific is now part of the main line of the Canadian National Railways.

The wave of prosperity which swept over Canada prior to World War I saw a peak of over 400,000 settlers enter the Dominion in the year 1913. This settlement boom made necessary a third transcontinental railroad, the Canadian Northern. In 1905 it consisted of several small lines on the prairies. By 1908 the lines were linked together, and a new railroad was built westward from Edmonton through Yellowhead Pass and southward to Vancouver. By 1915 the company had constructed the third route across northern Ontario, between the Canadian Pacific Railway to the south, and the Grand Trunk Pacific to the north.

The final stage in the growth of Canada's railroad system was the building of lines northward to the pioneer areas. The agricultural lands of the Peace River country of northern Alberta were reached by rail in 1915, enabling settlers to ship out their wheat. The development of resources in the Mackenzie Valley of the Northwest Territories was helped in 1921 by a railroad built from Edmonton to near the village of Waterways in northeastern Alberta.

The plateau of interior British Columbia was given rail service in 1921, when the Pacific Great Eastern was built from Squamish, near Vancouver, to Quesnel. The builders were unable to complete the railroad to Prince George to join with the Canadian National Railway.

A railroad was cut through the northern forests of Manitoba to The Pas by 1911. The line was continued towards a saltwater port on Hudson Bay, but construction stopped in 1918 when only 90 miles from Port Nelson. The railway, ending in the bush, remained unused for almost ten years. It was then completed to the fine harbour of Churchill in 1931.

A north-south railway was built through Northern Ontario from North Bay to Cochrane in 1902-08. Along its line prospectors found rich silver mines at Cobalt, and productive gold mines at Kirkland Lake. The route, now called the Ontario

Northland Railway, also tapped the farm lands of the Lesser Clay Belt at Lake Temiskaming. In 1932 the railroad was continued northward through unsettled forests to Moosonee on James Bay. The shallow water of this bay has prevented much use of the northern terminal.

As settlement spread over Canada, the railroads also grew. They were the means of bringing settlers into new regions, and they were soon carrying the products of the lands, mines, forests and lakes to the manufacturing centres in older communities. Without these lines of steel to carry the raw materials out and bring back manufactured goods, Canada's development would have been much slower.

Manufactured articles make up one-third of the products carried by our railroads. The products of our mines are almost as important, making up just under

Courtesy Ontario Department of Highways.

The "Queen Elizabeth Way" is one of the best highways in Canada. Ontario has more miles of paved highways than any other province.

one-third of the tonnage each year. Coal is the chief mineral product carried by the railroads, but many other ores are carried from mines to smelters and refineries.

Wheat makes up about half the tonnage of the large amount of agricultural products shipped by railroads. Most of it is carried from the prairies to either the east or the west coast, for shipping overseas. The tonnage of forest products carried by the railroads is not as great as that of

other resources. Most logs are carried downstream to the mills by rivers, and the sawn lumber is carried later by trains.

Present-day Road Transportation

The road network of Canada expanded after the invention of the automobile at the beginning of this century. Few roads are found in the rugged areas of the Cordillera, Canadian Shield and Appalachians. These sections also have fewer people to serve by road. The greatest number of roads are on the level areas of the prairies and St. Lawrence Lowlands. Ontario has almost half the mileage of paved roads in Canada. Some of the best roads are the main highways from Windsor to Montreal, and the modern "Queen Elizabeth Way" from Toronto to Niagara Falls. Saskatchewan has the greatest total mileage of roads. Most of them are non-surfaced roads which are easily constructed across the flat prairies.

The last link in Canada's transcontinental highway was finally completed in 1941, with the construction of a gravel road north of Lake Superior. Although there is only one route through Northern Ontario, there are alternate roads to cross Canada in the other provinces. The National Trans-Canada Highway, the first paved road to cross Canada, is not yet completed.

Great Lakes Waterway

Canada's most important waterway is the Great Lakes system which we share with the United States. The lower lakes were used for commerce for many years before Lake Superior was opened to through navigation. In 1855 a canal was built on the American side of the rapids at Sault Ste. Marie and forty years later a second canal was dug on the Canadian side. As the size of canal locks between the Great Lakes increased, larger boats were built. The St. Lawrence River boats are limited in size by the 14-foot depth of their canals, but the boats on the upper lakes are much bigger. The lar-

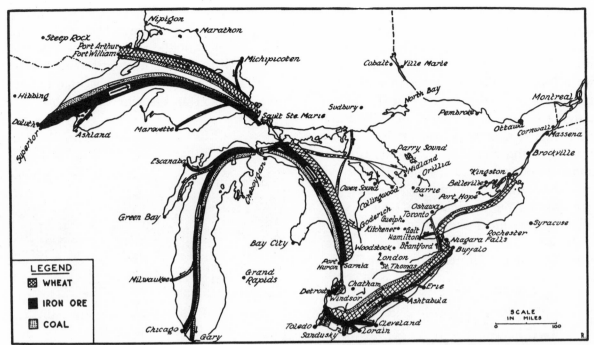

Transportation on the Great Lakes.

gest vessel in use has a capacity of over a half-million bushels of wheat. It takes about 22,000 acres of prairie farmland to raise such a cargo. If the same quantity was handled by train it would take 30 trains of 65 cars each to carry the load overland.

Three chief products are carried on the Great Lakes. They are wheat, iron ore, and coal. Each of these products has great

Courtesy Port Arthur Chamber of Commerce.

Large grain elevators store prairie wheat at Port Arthur and Fort William at the head of Great Lakes transportation. The large lake freighters are loaded with golden grain from spouts at the side of the elevator.

weight and bulk, and needs cheap water transportation to carry it to markets. The wheat comes from the Canadian Prairies to the huge grain elevators at Port Arthur and Fort William. During the eight or nine months' open season it is carried

southward to ports in Ontario such as Midland, Goderich, and Port Colborne, or all the way by water to Montreal. Railroads carry the grain from the Ontario ports to Montreal for shipment overseas during the summer, or to the winter ports of Saint John or Halifax in the Maritimes.

The iron ore carried on the Great Lakes vessels comes from mines in the Mesabi Range in Minnesota and from Steep Rock,, Ontario. Most of it is carried by American boats and is taken to industrial cities on the south shore of Lake Erie. The only Canadian city to receive much of this iron ore cargo is Hamilton, Ontario.

Coal is the main item of cargo carried northward on the Great Lakes. It comes from Pennsylvania and Ohio through the American ports on the south shore of Lake Erie. It is distributed to many Canadian ports in southern Ontario and eastward to Montreal, and also to ports on the Upper Lakes.

The Great Lakes system is the busiest waterway in the world. More tons of freight go through the Detroit River in a year than pass through both the Panama and Suez Canals. There is an average of one boat about every 12 minutes. On a summer's evening one can sit on the well-kept waterfront at Windsor, Ontario, and watch the busy parade of large lake freighters moving up and down the river. The Sault Ste. Marie Canal usually has twice as much traffic as the Panama Canal, despite its shorter season, and in 1940 had three times as much. About 100 million tons of cargo are carried on the lake boats each year. This figure shows the importance of this waterway to the transportation systems of Canada and the United States. In 1942 a

Courtesy Hydro News, Ontario.

Large and rapid machinery is now used at the chief Great Lakes Ports to load and unload the freighters. Here, coal is being unloaded from a freighter directly into small cars.

record of 120 million tons was carried, of which 75 per cent was iron ore from the head of the lakes.

Air Transportation

Air transportation is the newest method of moving goods and peoples. Although at present more expensive than water, rail or road, it is much faster. The first flying machine in Canada was flown in 1909 in Nova Scotia. It was not until after World War I, however, that flying became important. Soon after the war the Quebec and

Courtesy Windsor Chamber of Commerce.

The Detroit River, separating Detroit (right) from Windsor, Ontario (left), is one of the busiest waterways in the world. At the opening of navigation in April, the long freighters start northward for cargoes of iron ore and wheat.

Ontario Governments realised the advantages of float-equipped planes. They organized aerial patrols to help locate forest fires in the wooded sections of the southern Canadian Shield.

Much of Canada's northern regions had no rail or road transportation until after World War I. Aeroplanes soon proved very useful in opening up the country. The first flight into the Northwest Territories was made to the oil field at Norman Wells in 1921. Prospectors began to use planes to reach unexplored areas away from the main northern rivers. When minerals were discovered large cargo planes were used to fly in mining equipment and buildings. For these reasons Canada often carried more air freight than any other country.

Air mail service began in southern Canada in 1927. Two years later mail was carried by air all the way north to Aklavik, near the Arctic Ocean. In southern Canada this service was stopped during the depression years after 1932, but started again in 1938, after Trans-Canada Airlines began operations. Prior to World

War II Canada had its first coast-to-coast airline transportation for passengers and express. This airline, operated by the government-owned company, Trans-Canada Airlines, reached from Halifax to Vancouver by 1941. Two years later the company started trans-Atlantic flights, along the same routes flown by bombers going to Europe.

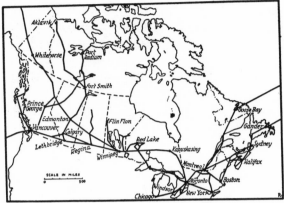
Main air-line routes in Canada.

An air route to Alaska and the Canadian Northwest was opened in 1939. It was called the "Northwest Staging Route", and operated from airfields built by the Canadian Government. When the United States entered the war, they connected these airfields with a road called the Alaska Military Highway. During the war years supplies were carried by truck over the road to Alaska, and planes flew the Staging Route to the Yukon, Alaska, and the Soviet Union. The road became the Alaska Highway after the war, and is maintained by the Canadian Government. Planes follow the airway when flying the short Great Circle route from Central Canada to the Orient.

Summary

Canada's transportation network grew as the country expanded. The Dominion now has a good system of roads, railroads, waterways, and airlines in the settled parts of Eastern Canada and over the southern parts of Western Canada. Each of these methods of transportation played an important part in opening up the country. Each new route meant that new lands could be settled, and additional resources developed. By means of our present transportation system the products of the natural resources of small areas can be distributed and used by people all across Canada.

Things To Do

1. Using road maps, plan an automobile trip from your home to some large city about 200 miles away.
   (a) Mark on the map the route that you would follow.
   (b) Plan two or three side-trips along the way to visit historic sites or parks. Which highways would you have to follow to reach these places and then return to your main road?
   (c) Plan the return trip from the large city to your home by a different road than you took when going. How much longer will it be?
   (d) List the route numbers of the highways on which you would travel.
2. Read Chapter 14 again and in your own words write a short history of transportation in Canada. Emphasize the difficulties caused by the physical geography of Canada, and tell how each means of transport overcame these problems.
3. In your history books read the story of the building of the Canadian Pacific Railway. Tell the story in your own words and describe the different kinds of topography through which the main line passes.
4. (a) On an outline map of Canada draw the Trans-Canada Highway. On the same map draw in the main lines of the C.P.R. and C.N.R.
   (b) Name the chief cities through which the railroads and roads pass.
   (c) Draw in the northern branch lines which serve Canada's pioneer areas, and the Alaska Highway which crosses our Northwest.

5. (a) Read Chapter 4 and compare the use of Canada's rivers with our development of land and rail transportation. Why has Canada not used her rivers very much for transportation?

   (b) Read the section in Chapter 4 describing the Great Lakes system. After reading Chapter 14 improve the map you were asked to make in the exercise at the end of Chapter 4.

6. Trans-Canada Airlines fly planes from coast to coast. Why is it important for them to have weather stations all along the route to report the weather every few hours? If you were a pilot in which direction would you look for storms at Toronto, or Winnipeg or Edmonton? The answer to this question will be found in Chapter 5.

Miles of Highways, by provinces, 1947:

	Surfaced	Non-Surfaced	Total
Newfoundland -	115	2,100	2,215
P.E.I. - - - -	450	3,255	3,705
N.S. - - - -	7,600	8,000	15,600
N.B. - - - -	8,700	3,650	12,350
Quebec - - - -	24,200	16,200	40,400
Ontario - - -	58,000	15,100	73,100
Manitoba - - -	9,000	82,400	91,400
Sask. - - - -	11,700	204,100	212,700
Alberta - - -	10,400	70,000	80,400
B.C. - - - - -	9,800	12,400	22,200
TOTALS - -	139,965	414,105	554,070

Facts For Reference

Table of Miles of Single Track Railroad, by Provinces, 1947:

Newfoundland - - - - -	705
P.E.I. - - - - - - - -	286
N.S. - - - - - - - -	1,396
N.B. - - - - - - - -	1,836
Quebec - - - - - - -	4,764
Ontario - - - - - - -	10,460
Manitoba - - - - - - -	4,832
Saskatchewan - - - - -	8,782
Alberta - - - - - - -	5,687
B.C. - - - - - - -	3,886
Yukon - - - - - - -	58
	42,652

Courtesy Ontario Department of Lands and Forests.

Pulp and paper manufacturing is one of Canada's most valuable industries. This large paper mill in Northern Ontario makes valuable products from our forests.

CHAPTER 15

MANUFACTURING

Manufacturing employs more Canadians than any other industry. The workers in the factories turn the products of our farms, mines, forests and waters into useful articles. Copper is made into wires, sheets and tubes. Wheat is made into cereals, macaroni, and flour. Trees are made into furniture, paper and lumber. Furs must be dyed, trimmed and sewn. Fish must be filleted, frozen or canned. All of these operations employ many men before the final products reach our homes.

Manufacturing depends upon the presence of natural resources. Countries which lack these raw materials, however, may import them from other countries that have more than they need. Canada has several resources in abundance. Our manufactur-ing industries are largely based upon their utilization. We do not have everything we need, however, and some industries use the products of the resources which are imported from other nations.

Agricultural Products

The largest number of people in the Canadian manufacturing industries work upon products from the farms. There are over 10,000 factories in Canada where farm products are being manufactured or processed for our use. Bread and bakery plants are more numerous than any other kind. They are found in all of the large cities, and most towns have one or more bakeries. Flour and feed mills are also very numerous. The sight of these mills in many cities tells us how important wheat is to Canadian manufacturing. Butter and cheese factories are scattered all across Canada, but most of them are in the St. Lawrence Lowlands. Other industries based upon agricultural products are meat-packing and slaughtering, the making of leather goods including boots and shoes, and the canning of fruits and vegetables. One or more of these industries are found near each of Canada's agricultural areas.

Textile manufacturing is one of the large Canadian industries which obtains its raw materials from the farms of other countries. Cotton comes from the plantations of southern United States, wool from the ranches of Australia and New Zealand, silk from the hillsides of Japan, and rayon from the mills in England. These textiles are imported into Canadian mills, located chiefly in Quebec. Many women work in these factories, making clothing, hosiery, and knitted goods. The manufactured products are then transported to the centres of population in other parts of Canada that lack textile raw materials or cheap power and labour.

Mineral Products

The processing of mineral resources requires large factories which employ many workers. During the war years, 1939-45, when armaments were being made in Canada, about half the working population was making manufactured articles from products of the mines.

The most important mineral resource is iron. From it are made all kinds of machinery, tools, and castings, as well as numerous small metal items. Canada's only large quantities of iron ore are in Newfoundland and Northern Ontario, and much is imported. The iron is melted into steel in hot blast furnaces located at Sydney, Nova Scotia, and at Hamilton and Sault Ste. Marie, Ontario. They are not able to make all of the steel needed in Can-

ada, however, and additional steel products are imported from the United States.

Many factories manufacture products from Canada's non-ferrous metals such as copper, lead, and zinc. These small plants make brass objects, many kinds of electrical apparatus, jewellery and silverware. Canada exports a great deal of her non-ferrous metals in their natural state to other countries for further manufacturing.

Non-metallic minerals are not usually as valuable as the metallic minerals, but the number of industries using non-metallics is greater. For example, workmen chip stone into monuments and ornaments; others make clay into dishes and pottery. Limestone rocks are ground into cement products for building. Sands are made into glass of all kinds ranging from windows to bottles. Refineries turn petroleum into gasoline, kerosene, and asphalt. With the exception of petroleum, Canada has

Courtesy National Film Board.

One of the new Canadian industries is synthetic rubber at Sarnia, Ontario. The large spheres store petroleum by-products from which synthetic rubber is made.

ample supplies of most of the non-metallic minerals.

The chemical industry is another important kind of manufacturing in Canada. Its raw materials come from a variety of sources, and many are not found in Can-

88

ada. Salt is one of the important chemical raw materials which Canada has in abundance. The manufactured articles from the chemical industry include medicines, soaps and paints. During the war years the chemical industry made ammunition and explosives. In this period the industry was third—behind aircraft manufacturing and shipbuilding—in the number of Canadians employed.

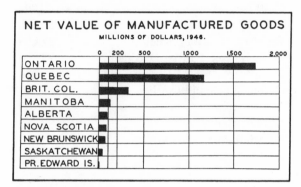

NET VALUE OF MANUFACTURED GOODS
MILLIONS OF DOLLARS, 1946.

	0	200	500	1,000	1,500	2,000
ONTARIO						
QUEBEC						
BRIT. COL.						
MANITOBA						
ALBERTA						
NOVA SCOTIA						
NEW BRUNSWICK						
SASKATCHEWAN						
PR. EDWARD IS.						

Forest Products

There are almost as many industries in Canada depending upon forest products as there are upon farm products. The large pulp and paper mills of Quebec and Ontario and the big lumber mills of British Columbia are well known. Some of these mills employ several hundreds of men. The machinery which they operate changes the logs into lumber or paper. There are also many small sawmills, box companies, and printing firms all over Canada using the resources of our vast forests. In most years the sawmill and pulp and paper industries employ more men than any other single Canadian industry.

Fishing and Fur Products

There are about 500 small industries in Canada that are dependent upon the resources of our coastal and inland waters. They employ a few thousand Canadians. The fishing industry is important only to small sections of Canada. Similarly the manufacture of fish products is important to only a few towns on the Atlantic and Pacific coasts.

The industries which use Canadian fur resources are not numerous, nor are there many people working on these products. Most of the companies which do fur trimming and sewing also make fur coats and neckpieces. Many of the furs produced in Canada's forests and on fur-farms are sent to other countries for manufacturing.

Summary

Canadian manufacturing depends largely upon our natural resources. The raw materials from our farms, forests, mines, and waters are carried by our transportation systems to manufacturing centres, usually located near a source of cheap power.

There are more industries using agricultural products than any other resource, but more people work in the industries depending on mineral and forest products. Fish and fur products are less important in Canadian manufacturing. Many men are needed to make and run the machines which manufacture the products that we buy from the stores. Towns and cities having industries therefore grow larger and larger. These large populations have to be served by stores and businesses, and professional men such as doctors, lawyers, and teachers. Thus, towns which have many industries grow into cities, and are able to enjoy many of the comforts of life which are not possible in most villages or rural areas. Cities often lack, however, the quiet peacefulness, and clean fresh air that is found in small towns and in the countryside. Life in a busy factory may not be as happy or healthy as life on a farm or in a small town.

Things To Do

1. Choose a manufacturing industry in your town or city.
   (a) What are its raw materials—agricultural, mineral, forest or fish?
   (b) How many different kinds of raw materials are used in the factory and from where do they come?
   (c) What means of transportation is used to bring in the raw materials?
   (d) How is the manufactured article transported to markets?

2. Examine the labels on the canned fruits and vegetables at your grocery store. How many agricultural regions of Canada are represented? Why are the products canned near where they are grown?

3. Name a city in Canada where the following articles are manufactured: bicycles, automobiles, furniture, flour, radios, washing machines, agricultural implements, candy, pencils, shirts. Which of these products are also imported into Canada? (Read the labels on these articles in your homes or at a nearby store.)

4. Read certain assigned chapters in the book *"Canadians at Work"* by M. Hallman (Longmans Green, 1950) describing the processes of manufacturing some of the raw materials of our resources.

Facts For Reference

Largest Number of Employees Among the Leading Industries of Canada in 1947:

Industry	Employees
Sawmills	55,500
Electrical Apparatus	52,800
Pulp and Paper	50,000
Bread and Bakery	32,000
Clothing, Women's	31,000
Machinery	30,000
Clothing, Men's	30,000
Railway Rolling Stock	28,600
Primary Iron and Steel	27,000
Hosiery and Knitted Goods	26,600
Furniture	25,000
Cotton, Yarn and Cloth	24,100
Automobiles	23,900
Rubber Goods	23,500
Printing and Publishing	23,200

The excellent harbour at Halifax is one of the best on the east coast of North America. Many Canadian exports go out from its wharves. This aerial view shows the Citadel and part of the Halifax business district.

CHAPTER 16

FOREIGN TRADE

Foreign trade is a means of measuring a country's resources. If world markets are open and transportation is available, a country will export its surpluses, and import what it lacks. Much of the world's trade, however, is controlled or directed by tariffs which countries place upon exports and imports. Thus, the world's products do not always move freely from place to place.

Canada's prosperity is closely connected with foreign trade, for we are one of the world's chief trading nations. Although we have only 1/200 of the world's population, we account for about 1/30 of the value of world trade. Before 1940 Canada was the fourth leading export nation of the world. During the war years (1939-45) our exports increased until only the United States was exporting more than we were.

Exports

Canada's export products come chiefly from our farm, mine, and forest resources. At one time we took the products directly from our forests and mines and shipped

CHIEF EXPORT PRODUCTS OF CANADA
MILLIONS OF DOLLARS, 1949.

	0	50	100	200	300	400
NEWSPRINT						
WHEAT						
WOOD PULP						
PLANKS, ETC.						
FLOUR						
ALUMINUM						
FISH						
NICKEL						
FARM MACHINE						
COPPER						
OTHER GRAINS						
CATTLE						

the logs and ores to other countries where they were manufactured into more valuable things. Now, however, Canada does more of her own manufacturing. We change our natural resources into manufactured forms and then sell the surplus production to other nations.

Products from our farms are the most valuable exports of Canada. Wheat is our chief agricultural export. Canada is known throughout the world as an exporter of good hard wheat, and in most years we export more wheat than any other country. It makes up about two-thirds of the value of all our agricultural exports. Other farm products which are sent abroad are bacon, hams, flour, cattle, cheese, tobacco, and canned fruits and vegetables.

Export products having a mineral origin are usually second to agriculture in value. Canada is one of the world's leading producers and exporters of non-ferrous metals such as nickel, copper, zinc, lead and aluminum. We use some minerals for

our own industries and export about 60 per cent of our mineral production to other countries.

Canada is an important world producer of gold and some of the non-metallic minerals such as asbestos and gypsum. Gold is exported to the United States to help pay for our imports. Asbestos and gypsum, which are also exported, are manufactured into many articles by factories in the United States.

Two other mineral exports, steel and aluminum, come from resources which Canada lacks. We import iron ore from the United States, and then export manufactured products in the form of automobiles, farm machinery, tools, and other metal equipment. Aluminum is made from the ore called bauxite, which is imported from British Guiana. Cheap electrical power is needed to turn the bauxite into alumina powder and then aluminum. Canada has the world's largest aluminum plant at Arvida, Quebec, on the Saguenay River near the huge Shipshaw dam.

Canada's forests are able to supply much of the world's needs for wood products. About half Canada's lumber exports are sent from British Columbia in the form of planks, boards, plywood and shingles. We also export poles, railroad ties and mine props. Much of our wood is ground into pulp for export. Sometimes the pulp is made into paperboard, plastics and synthetic fibres, but most of it is made into newsprint paper which is the chief export from our forests. About 90 per cent of our newsprint is exported. It is used chiefly in making daily newspapers for people in the United States.

Imports

In foreign trade, a country has to balance some exports with imports. Other countries cannot pay for the products which we send them unless they are able to sell something to us in return. The resources of the world are distributed in this

92

The huge aluminum factory at Arvida, Quebec, imports bauxite ore from British Guiana, and exports aluminum products. The factory, the largest in the world, uses hydro-electric power from the Saguenay River.

way. Canada imports the mineral resources which she lacks and also the products which cannot be grown in our climate. Canada's exports consist of large quantities of a few things, but our imports are small quantities of many things.

The two chief mineral resources which Canada imports are crude petroleum and coal. They come from regions in the United States which have more than they need. Other mineral imports are iron, bauxite, tin, antimony, sulphur, and phosphates. Except for iron, none of these is found in any quantity in Canada.

Agricultural imports are chiefly those which cannot be grown in Canada's cool climate. They are tea, coffee, sugar cane, cocoa, oranges, grapefruit, and nuts. Canada imports other tropical products, such as cotton and rubber, that are used in industry.

We often think that our fertile lands could feed us without help, and yet even agriculture needs imports to assist production. For example, petroleum must be imported to run farm machinery. Nitrates and phosphates are used as fertilizers. Jute and cotton are made into bags to hold flour. Quebracho from South America is used to tan hides into leather. Tin and other metals are imported to make cans for preserving fruits and vegetables.

93

Agricultural products are one of Canada's chief exports. Production can be maintained by wise management of our lands. In this picture, taken near Peterborough, Ontario, cover crops are planted in strips around the slope to help hold the soil in place. In the distance, hilly areas are left in forest. Trees are left along the roads to give shade and break the force of the wind.

Canada's other imports are chiefly manufactured products which other countries can produce cheaper or in greater quantities than we can. Such imports are machinery, automobile parts, chemicals, textiles, and goods for our homes such as radios, lamps, dishes, and rugs.

Trade

Canada's foreign trade is mainly with two countries, the United States and the United Kingdom. They have always been the chief countries with which Canada traded. While Canada was still a colony in 1850 almost 50 per cent of our imports came from the mother country. As the nation grew, however, we began to obtain more of our manufactured goods from closer factories in the United States. Shortly after Confederation the United States was sending us more imports than any other country. It has maintained this position throughout our history. The United States supplies about two-thirds of our total imports, and the United King-

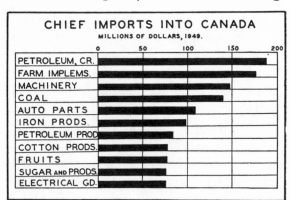

dom, which ranks second, sends only about one-fifth.

Our exports are about equally divided between the United Kingdom and the United States. Before 1920, when we sup-

94

plied the mother country with the food which she could not raise, the United Kingdom was always our best customer. Since then the other Dominions have been helping to feed Britain, and at the same time we have increased our shipments of forest and mineral products to the United States. Our exports to the United States now equal, and sometimes pass, our exports to the United Kingdom.

Summary

Canada's exports come chiefly from farms, forests, and mines. Our chief export is wheat which goes to the United Kingdom along with other food products. Our forest resources—newsprint, pulpwood, and lumber—are sent mainly to the United States. Our mineral resources—nickel, copper, asbestos, lead and zinc—are received by both the United States and the United Kingdom. Canada imports small quantities of many things. These imports consist of products which cannot be grown in our climate, mineral resources which we lack, and manufactured articles which other countries can make more cheaply.

Things To Do

1. Consult the Canada Year Book or the magazine "Foreign Trade", issued by the Department of Trade and Commerce, Ottawa, for figures on Canada's foreign trade. Use the table at the end of this chapter to make a bar graph showing the percentage of our exports received by our chief markets. Make another graph showing how much the different countries send to Canada.

2. (a) Name the chief products which Canada exported in the last year for which you can obtain figures. Which of these are mentioned in this chapter?

   (b) Name Canada's chief imports. Are they the same as those listed in this chapter? Explain the differences.

3. Make a list of all the kinds of food you eat in a day.

   (a) How many items in your list are raised in Canada and how many are imported?

   (b) From what country do each of the imported foods come?

Facts For Reference

Average percentage of Canada's exports

	1935-39	1941-45
United Kingdom	40	37
Other parts of Europe	7.5	5
United States	36.5	37
Other North America	3	4
Asia	4	7
Africa	2.5	7
Oceania	5	2
South America	1.5	1

Average percentage of Canada's imports

	1935-39	1941-45
United States	61	78
Other North America	2.5	3
United Kingdom	18	9.5
Other Europe	6	.5
South America	3.5	3
Asia	5	3
Oceania	3	2
Africa	1	1

Asbestos is mined near Thetford in large open pits. The fibrous rock is crushed in the nearby mills, and the waste dumped in large piles. Workers live in the surrounding town.

CHAPTER 17

THE APPALACHIAN-ACADIAN REGION

The Appalachian-Acadian Region includes part of the Eastern Townships of Quebec, Gaspé Peninsula, and the three Maritime Provinces. In Chapter 3 the region was described as having rough, hilly topography, but with locally important areas of level land.

Topography

The physical features of the region differ from place to place. The Appalachian section has a parallel series of low mountain ridges extending from Lake Cham-

plain in the southwest to Gaspé in the northeast. The rounded mountains rise about 3,000 feet above sea level in the Eastern Townships. The green rolling hills gradually become lower to the west and merge into the St. Lawrence Lowland. The Chaudière River flows northward across a low depression at the northeast end of the Eastern Townships.

In Gaspé Peninsula, rocky hills rise almost directly from the water, leaving very little level land along the north shore. The central part of the peninsula is a plateau which has been cut by several short rapid rivers. Elevations reach 4,000 feet in the rugged areas. The lowland of the southern part of the peninsula is similar to the east coast of New Brunswick.

In New Brunswick, the Acadian region has four major sub-divisions. The Central Highlands occupy the middle and northern parts of the province. They form a rolling, rugged, forested region of flat-topped hills and ridges. Altitudes average about 1,500 feet above sea level, but some peaks are 2,000 feet. The highlands are drained by many rivers which flow either to the broad valley of the St. John River, or eastward to the Miramichi River. Much of the lumbering of New Brunswick is carried on in this area where there are very few settlements.

The Northwestern Plateau is lower. It lies between the Central Highlands to the south and east and the Appalachian region to the north. This flat-topped upland has altitudes of 800 to 1,000 feet, and is cut by the narrow, deep valleys of the St. John and Restigouche rivers. Many French farmers now live in this section, and some of the high valleys have good agriculture.

The Eastern and Central Lowland is found along the east coast, south of Chaleur Bay, and extends inland to the Central Highlands. This sandy lowland continues eastward along Northumberland Strait into Nova Scotia. In many parts of New Brunswick this lowland is swampy, wooded and little used. Settlements are located on the coast or at the mouths of rivers. Around Moncton and continuing eastward over Chignecto Isthmus, however, the rolling lowland has many farms.

The southern Uplands rise to altitudes

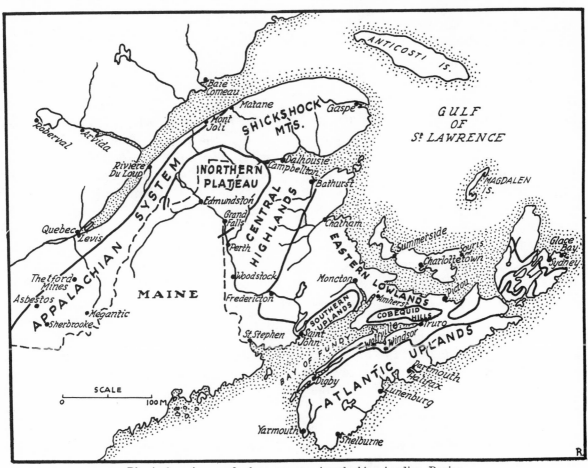

Physical regions and place names. Appalachian-Acadian Region.

of 1,500 feet along the north shore of the Bay of Fundy. They merge with the Central Highlands in a hilly section east of the St. Croix River. Where the St. John River breaks through the narrow line of hills at the city of Saint John, the famous Reversing Falls are found. At low tide the river

The moderate climate of Prince Edward Island encourages agriculture on the rolling hills. Small rural villages and well-kept farms are scattered over the countryside.

spills through the gorge between the hills, forming rapids. When the waters of the rising tide are compressed into the opening a few hours later the rapids are covered by water flowing in the opposite direction.

Most of Nova Scotia is a rocky backbone ridge called the Atlantic Upland. It has altitudes of 500 feet, usually rising directly from the sea along the south and east coasts. The Upland becomes higher to the northeast, having an altitude of 1,000 feet in the Cape Breton Plateau. Lowlands are located on the north side of the Upland along the Bay of Fundy coast, and especially in the tidal marshes of the Minas Basin. The Annapolis-Cornwallis Valley, famous for its apples, is a narrow lowland extending southwestward from Minas Basin.

Prince Edward Island is part of the coastal lowland of eastern New Brunswick and Nova Scotia. The island has no hills over 500 feet above sea level. The south coast is deeply indented with broad bays and inlets. The north shore has been smoothed by waves into broad sandy beaches. The red sandstone of which the island is composed has given its distinctive colour to the fertile soils. There are farms over all the island because there are no rugged areas.

Climate

The Appalachian-Acadian region is close to the sea, but its mild influence is not felt far inland, owing to offshore winds. Summers are cool near the coasts, and in the hills of central New Brunswick and the Eastern Townships. Since lowlands are always hotter than hills in summer, the warmest parts of the region are in the valleys. Summer afternoon temperatures seldom rise above 85° F.

The length of growing season in the Maritimes depends largely on altitude and location. The longest growing season is near the coast where the relatively warm water delays first autumn frosts. There is an average of 160 days during which no frosts occur to kill the crops at the southern tip of Nova Scotia and along the north side of the Bay of Fundy in New Brunswick. The hilly region of central New Brunswick cools off rapidly in the autumn, and the frost-free period lasts for only about 60 days. Prince Edward Island has cool temperatures in the spring when ice is drifting out of the Gulf of St. Lawrence. Planting is sometimes delayed then, but a mild autumn lengthens the growing season to an average of 150 days.

Southwestern Nova Scotia has the mildest winter temperatures in the Maritimes. Its January average temperatures are the second mildest in Canada, after the coast of British Columbia. Because of the mild climate, Halifax and Saint John are ice-free in winter. When the St. Lawrence River is frozen these ports are still used by ships from the Atlantic.

98

On Prince Edward Island February is generally the coldest month. The Islanders feel this cold more than the people on the nearby mainland. The surrounding water and ice increase the humidity and make the cold more penetrating. People have to wear warmer clothes on Prince Edward Island than they do in southern Nova Scotia or southern New Brunswick. Winter temperatures in New Brunswick are coldest in the Central Highlands. Fredericton has an average January temperature which is about the same as that of Montreal or Ottawa, but colder than that of Windsor or Toronto.

The Maritimes have the second greatest amount of precipitation in Canada. The rocky south coast of Nova Scotia is open to rain-bearing winds from the Atlantic and receives about 55 inches of precipitation each year. This is about twice as much as southwestern Ontario receives in a year.

Many rain-bearing winds pass over low Prince Edward Island without dropping

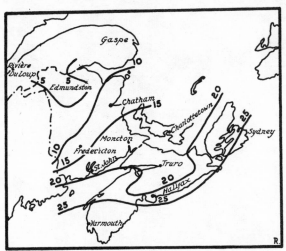

January Temperatures in Maritimes

moisture. Throughout the year, however, an average of 40 inches of precipitation falls. This is quite sufficient for crops. The amount of rainfall is about the same as that of the St. Lawrence Valley in Quebec.

Precipitation in New Brunswick decreases from 45 inches on the Bay of Fundy coast to 35 inches in the Central Highlands and Northwestern Plateau. In the interior, more of the precipitation falls as snow, which usually becomes quite deep in the New Brunswick forests. This snowfall is useful for winter logging.

Agriculture

Farm products in the Appalachian-Acadian region are limited to crops with a relatively short growing season, but production is aided by the adequate rainfall. Natural pastures produce good grass in all of the farming areas, and hay is the chief cultivated crop. Oats are the most important of the grain crops, and potatoes are the chief root crop. Farmers receive most of their money from the sale of dairy products, such as milk, butter and cheese, or from special crops such as apples or potatoes. Dairy products are usually sold to the nearby towns and cities, but the specialized crops are exported to other countries.

Dairying is widespread throughout the lowlands of the Maritimes and on the rolling hills of the Eastern Townships of Quebec. Some areas are more prosperous than others. Among the better dairying sections are the belt in New Brunswick from Saint John to Sussex to Moncton, Colchester and Pictou counties in Nova Scotia, all of Prince Edward Island, and the Sherbrooke region of Quebec.

The Maritime Provinces are noted for their high-quality potatoes. They are the chief cash crop of the farmers of Prince Edward Island, where the red soils are well suited to this product. Table potatoes are exported to other parts of Eastern Canada, and good seed potatoes are sent to southern United States and the West Indies.

The Upper St. John River valley of New Brunswick is another important potato-producing section. In Carleton and Victoria counties, opposite the famous potato region of the Aroostook Valley in Maine, potatoes are the main source of the farmer's income. The good quality of New Brunswick potatoes allows them to be sold even in the potato districts of Quebec and Ontario. The surplus potatoes are sold abroad, chiefly in the West Indies, and also in South America.

Apples of the Annapolis-Cornwallis Valley, Nova Scotia, are another specialty crop of the Maritimes. Many farms in the Maritimes and Eastern Townships have a few apple trees, but this valley is the only centre of production for export. The long, narrow valley produces about one-third of the Canadian apple crop. Only a small part of each farm is in orchards, and the rest of the land is used for general farming. Many of the Annapolis apples are of the cooking variety. The cloudy summer weather does not produce the colour which is typical of Ontario and British Columbia apples. The apples which are not sold to Great Britain are dried, or pressed into apple juice so that the crop can be marketed throughout the year. Many tourists visit the pretty Annapolis Valley in the "Land of Evangeline" during blossom-time in the spring. The valley slopes are covered with blooms and the air is fragrant with their perfume.

Mineral Resources

There are more people occupied in mining in the Appalachian-Acadian region than in the better-known industries of forestry and fishing. Mining is carried on

Courtesy N.B. Information Bureau.

Potatoes are one of the important cash crops in the upper St. John River Valley in northwestern New Brunswick. Their good quality permits them to be sold throughout eastern Canada and abroad.

in two main centres in the region—the coal fields of Cape Breton Island, and the asbestos mines of the Eastern Townships, Quebec. There is no mining on Prince Edward Island, and very little in New Brunswick.

Evangeline's monument and church at Grand Pré, Nova Scotia are reminders of the days when the Acadian French farmers tilled the fertile red soils south of Minas Basin.

Coal mining occupies about three-quarters of the miners of Nova Scotia. Sydney is the largest city in the coal region of Cape Breton, but Glace Bay and New Waterford are also important. Coal is also mined in Pictou and Cumberland Counties on the north side of the mainland of Nova Scotia.

The Cape Breton coal industry is very old. For many years it was the chief producer of coal in Canada. The mines are now very deep and some shafts have been dug out under the sea three or four miles. Since 1940 coal production has gradually declined. The men now have farther to go to work, and skilled miners are not as numerous as they used to be. Despite the decline, however, there are still reserves

of coal there which, it is believed, will last for another 150 to 200 years.

Much Cape Breton coal is used to make steel in the blast furnaces at Sydney. The iron ore for the steel industry is brought across Cabot Strait from Newfoundland. Cape Breton coal is used as fuel in homes in the Maritimes and sometimes in Quebec. The railroads of the Maritimes use it to run their steam engines.

Nova Scotia is one of the leading producers of gypsum in Canada. Men dig the rock from quarries at several locations, the most important being on the south side of Minas Basin. Much of the gypsum is shipped to the United States for manufacturing into wall board, plaster of paris, and other products.

Before 1900 Nova Scotia was one of Canada's leading gold-producing provinces. The veins were gradually exhausted, and by 1920 the miners could find only a small amount of gold. New mines were discovered after 1930 as a result of prospecting, and soon Nova Scotia was producing as much gold each year as she did in the prosperous years before 1900. Production decreased during World War II owing to a lack of miners, but increased again after the war.

The chief salt deposit of the Maritimes is found at Malagash, Nova Scotia, on Northumberland Strait. A new process of purification greatly increased its value and the salt is now used for many purposes in addition to salting fish. The salt is obtained from seams below the earth's surface by mining methods similar to those used to dig coal.

In the same area, at Nappan, near Amherst, another salt mine was opened in 1946. This mine uses the brine method of obtaining salt. Hot water is forced down pipes to dissolve the salt deposits. The briny water is then brought to the surface and after evaporation the salt is left. Since the export of salt fish is very important to Nova Scotia, the province is fortunate to have large salt mines within its borders.

Other minerals which are mined in Nova Scotia include barytes, dolomite, limestone and granite. Bricks are made from the local red clay at several places. Each of these industries employs only a few hundred men.

Mining is not important in New Brunswick. Some coal, mined at Minto in the south-central part of the province, is burned to produce electrical power. A small natural-gas field near Moncton supplies that city with fuel, and a little petroleum is obtained from the same area.

Asbestos is the chief mineral in the Appalachian region. This fibre-like, non-metallic mineral is found in veins in the hard rock. It can be made into fireproof boards and clothing, brake linings, and shingles, among other things. Canada produces about 80 per cent of the world's asbestos, and all of it comes from a belt of greenish rocks passing through Thetford, Quebec.

Asbestos is mined by open-pit methods. Skilled men operate large steam shovels to remove the surface soil and scoop up the rock after it is blasted into pieces. As the hole becomes larger, small railroad cars are run into the pit to carry out the rock. At the nearby mills the asbestos fibres are separated from the rock and most of the raw asbestos is sent to the United States for manufacturing.

Forestry

The value of forest products in New Brunswick is usually greater than those of agriculture. The forest industry ranks third after manufacturing and agriculture in the number of people employed. In Nova Scotia forest products are more valuable than fish products but forestry does not employ as many persons as fishing. Forests are not important on Prince Edward Island because about 90 per cent of the island is cleared for farming. In the Appalachian region there are many small

sawmills cutting spruce and balsam fir for pulpwood, but this forested area of Quebec is not as important as the one on the north side of the St. Lawrence River.

For its size New Brunswick is an important producer of forest products. About 80 per cent of the province is cov-

Throughout Eastern Canada, logging is done during the wintertime. The loggers are often farmers or fishermen in the summer. Logs are carried by sleds to a central area, and are put into the rivers in spring.

ered with productive forest, about half of which is owned by the provincial government. Only about one-tenth of the forest can be reached for logging, however, because of the lack of roads and railroads in the interior of the province.

New Brunswick was an important lumbering province in the days of wooden sailing ships in the last century. Much of the good white pine lumber was exported to Great Britain through the busy port of Chatham on the east coast. The lumbering industry declined with the disappearance of wooden shipbuilding, and has been replaced by the cutting of timber for pulpwood. Logs are floated down the Miramichi River to sawmills located at Chatham. The sawmills at Grand Falls and nearby towns on the upper St. John River use logs obtained from the Northwestern Plateau and Gaspé. Sawmills along the lower St. John River receive timber from the central part of the wooded province.

Trees are usually felled in the autumn, and transported over New Brunswick's deep winter snow to river banks or to roads. In many parts of the Central Highlands horses are used for transportation since roads are difficult to build into the rough country. After the break-up of the rivers in March or April, the logs are floated downstream to the pulp and paper mills. There they are cut into small logs, chopped up by machines into chips. The pieces are dissolved and the fibres put between rollers to become paper.

The products of pulp and paper mills are two or three times as valuable as those of lumber and sawmills. The largest paper mills are located at Dalhousie at the mouth of the Restigouche River and at Bathurst on the south side of Chaleur Bay. At Edmundston, near the water-power of Grand Falls on the St. John River, the pulp mill is on the Canadian side and paper is made across the river at the mill in Madawaska, Maine. Large pipes, through which the pulp is forced, connect the mills which are in different countries.

More than half of Nova Scotia is covered with productive forest, but the area makes up only 1½ per cent of Canada's forests. Most of the forests are owned by companies or farmers, unlike the forests of other parts of Canada which are owned by the provincial governments. Nova Scotia and British Columbia are cutting their timber faster than other sections of Canada. Lumbermen obtain about one-third of their forest products from Colchester and Cumberland counties, in the wooded interior of the province.

About half the value of Nova Scotia's forest production is obtained from saw lumber or lumber products. Most of the lumber is exported, chiefly to Great Britain. About one-quarter of the forest cut is used for pulp and paper, and another quarter becomes fuelwood for farmers'

homes. Nova Scotian forests supply large numbers of Christmas trees which are exported each year to delight the children of the New England States.

Fishing

Nova Scotia has more fishermen than the rest of the Appalachian-Acadian region. In numerous small villages around its rocky shores, fishing is the chief occupation, and the reason for the existence of settlements. This industry was described in Chapter 11.

Most of the coastal fishing between the months of April and November is for cod. The deep-sea fishery, centering around the harbour of Lunenburg, employs fewer men. The income from the fishing industry is not high, and most of the families are poor people who lack many of the conveniences of modern life.

From out of the little villages small boats carry two or three men along the coasts to fish for cod and haddock. Some boats are larger and may contain from five to seven men. They usually return home each night with their catch. In spring and summer the fish are split, dried, and salted at the settlement, and are later sold in the cities. In autumn fresh fish are transported to the cities for immediate sale. During the winter, many fishermen work in the lumber camps or mines.

In New Brunswick fishing is an important seasonal occupation for many of the French settlers along the northeast coast. In the Bay of Fundy commercial fishing, especially for sardines, is carried on off Charlotte County.

On Prince Edward Island there are more fishermen than there are factory workers, but even fishing is minor compared to agriculture. Lobsters are a valuable catch in the region on both sides of Northumberland Strait.

The Gaspé coast of Quebec is quite similar to that of Nova Scotia. Numerous fishing villages, with small garden plots, are hidden in sheltered inlets or at the mouths of short, rapid streams. The French fishermen catch most of their fish close to shore and ship them westward to the Quebec markets.

Manufacturing

The Appalachian-Acadian region is not a great manufacturing area. Its small population does not make a big market for local industries. Many manufactured articles can be made more cheaply in Central Canada and can be transported to the region for sale. Most of the Maritime manufacturing industries are based upon local resources. If an industry makes more than can be used in the Maritimes the surplus is often exported to foreign countries rather than to the rest of Canada. It is often cheaper to export their products by ship than it is to transport them by railroad to Central Canada.

In Nova Scotia the iron and steel industry at Sydney is the most valuable one in the province. Other important industries are shipbuilding, fish curing and packing, the manufacture of lumber, pulp and paper, and the making of butter and cheese. Local industries at Halifax are petroleum refining and chocolate manufacturing. At Sydney coke and gas are produced from the nearby coal.

The manufactures of New Brunswick are quite similar to those of Nova Scotia with the exception of steel manufacturing. The leading industry, both in value to the province and number of people employed, is the production of pulp, paper and lumber. Other people in New Brunswick work in industries which depend upon fishing and agriculture. Special industries of the province include a sugar refinery at Saint John, a railway car factory at Moncton, a cotton mill at Marysville, near Fredericton, and a chocolate factory at St. Stephen.

Manufacturing is unimportant in agricultural Prince Edward Island. Fish curing and packing is the most valuable in-

dustry. Because of the importance of agriculture, other industries are the making of butter and cheese, and meat slaughtering and packing.

The Appalachian region has only a little manufacturing. The people in the small fishing and agricultural villages of Gaspé Peninsula make handicraft articles for the tourist trade. In the Eastern Townships the manufacture of butter and cheese, and cotton and rayon textiles are the chief occupations. The former industry is due to the good dairying pastures on the rolling hills. The textile industry uses the many small water-power sites on the rivers flowing through the long valleys.

Cities

Halifax, the capital of Nova Scotia, is the largest city in the Appalachian-Acadian region. As Canada's far easterly winter port, it receives many of the export

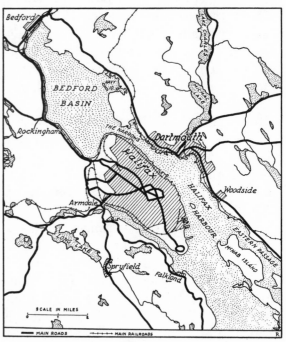

Halifax Area.

and import goods of the Dominion in its warehouses and over its wharves. The people of Halifax, in addition to running a port, work in important manufacturing industries, and carry on much of the business of the province. The best view of the sheltered harbour and busy wharves may be obtained from the historic citadel, an old British fort crowning the highest hill in the centre of the city. On the east side of Halifax harbour the city of Dartmouth is an industrial and residential suburb of Halifax.

Saint John is Canada's second winter port and the largest city of New Brunswick. The industries and businesses of Saint John are similar to those of Halifax, but the city has not grown as large. Most of the products of the St. John River Valley are exported through this fine port. The manufactures of the city supply many of the small towns in the south-central part of the province. Visitors always plan to see the famous Reversing Falls while in Saint John.

Sherbrooke is the largest city in the Eastern Townships and the seventh manufacturing city of Quebec. The city is located on the steep slope above the St. François River. Textile mills, using local water power, are important. The processing and canning of foods make use of the agricultural products of the farms in the surrounding fertile hills. Sherbrooke is a supply centre for the farms and rural villages of the central Eastern Townships.

Sydney is the only city in the Appalachian-Acadian region producing iron and steel. The city is an important port for the export of coal, and is a railway terminal for Cape Breton Island. Many vessels from the fishing fleets use Sydney as their home port. *Glace Bay*, near Sydney, is almost as large. Coal mining is the chief occupation of the people living there.

Moncton, the second largest city of New Brunswick, is located along the east bank of the Petitcodiac River. It has an important position as a railway centre for the Maritimes. Workers in the city make lumber, textiles and stoves. One of Moncton's tourist attractions is the Tidal Bore. This wall of foaming water is caused by the tidal waters rushing up the Petitcodiac River at the head of the Bay of Fundy.

Charlottetown, the capital of Prince Edward Island, is the only city on the Island. This pretty city, known as "The Cradle of Confederation", is chiefly a residential centre, but also has the largest stores and businesses on the Island.

Fredericton, the capital of New Brunswick, is a picturesque residential city located on the St. John River. Its tall, stately trees and pretty riverfront drive, are among the remembered sights of the scenic St. John River Valley. Many people work in the government offices, but others work in factories manufacturing boots and shoes, and canoes. The University of New Brunswick, the oldest in Canada, is located on a hill overlooking the southern edge of Fredericton.

Parks

City people like to get away from the crowds and closely-packed buildings of our communities. Working people with a few weeks' vacation enjoy sights which are different from those which they see all

Courtesy National Parks Bureau.

The rocky coast of Cape Breton Island is of little use for agriculture or forestry, but its rugged beauty attracts tourists.

year. In order to assist these people in their recreation, and also to attract tourists from other countries, the Provincial and Dominion governments have established several parks in each region of Canada. Natural scenic beauties are preserved in them and accommodation is supplied to visitors. Wildlife, birds and animals are protected.

Cape Breton Highlands National Park occupies the rugged plateau and forested hills of the northwestern tip of Cape Breton Island. Along the good roads of scenic Cabot Trail, much of the original wild beauty of the coast of Nova Scotia is presented to the touring visitor.

Prince Edward Island National Park is a sandy strip along the north shore of the Island noted for its broad beaches and excellent bathing. Within the park is the "Green Gables" farm which is known in Canadian literature.

For many years New Brunswick was the only province without a National Park. In 1948 a site was selected on the Bay of Fundy coast near Alma, between Saint John and Moncton. The rolling hills, cool woodlands and good fishing will soon be attracting visitors to this area.

In order to preserve some of the well-known. sites which were famous in early Canadian history, small parks have been made around their ruins. Near Annapolis Royal, the first real settlement in Canada, are Fort Anne, Port Royal and Champlain's "Habitation." Fort Beauséjour, overlooking the Chignecto Isthmus and the Tantramar marshes of New Brunswick, and the Fortress of Louisbourg on Cape Breton Island, are famous French forts built during the 18th century. Tourists who visit these parks learn something about the history of Canada.

Courtesy National Parks Bureau.

This is a model of the historic fort at Louisbourg, Nova Scotia, which faced out to the Atlantic Ocean. A small village was built inside the walls. There are many interesting historic sites in the Maritimes.

Gaspesian Park is the only provincial park in the region. It has been set aside by the Quebec government to save the last herds of caribou on the south shore of the St. Lawrence River. The scenic road which circles the shores of Gaspé Peninsula, passing by picturesque Perce Rock at the eastern tip, also brings visitors to Gaspesian Park.

Things To Do

1. Make a copy of the map showing the chief topographic regions of the Appalachian-Acadian region. (a) On this map place the names of the chief cities and dots for their locations. (b) How many of the dots are in lowland areas? (c) Explain the reason for the location of some of the cities in highland sections?

2. Draw or copy an outline map of the Appalachian-Acadian region. Trace the coast line and main rivers. On this map place symbols or colours indicating the position of all resources which are mentioned in the chapter. For example, if you used red for agricultural resources, you would colour the Annapolis Valley red and put a letter "A" beside it for apples. Similarily, use another colour for mineral resources and a letter standing for the resource. For example, "C" for coal.

3. After reading other assigned reference books for information, write a short essay on one of the following topics:

   The Forest Industry of New Brunswick
   Fur Ranching on Prince Edward Island
   Deep-sea Fishing from Nova Scotia
   Asbestos Mining in Quebec.

4. Write a description of one of the cities of the Appalachian-Acadian region. (a) Tell what you would see if you were a tourist and had only one day to visit the most interesting places. (b) Describe what people do in the city. (c) List the chief industries and occupations. (The Tourist Bureau of your chosen city may send you information.))

5. Read your history reference books and find out what happened at the places which are now Historic Site parks in the Maritimes. (a) Name the Historic Site park nearest your home. (b) Write a short essay about some historic event which happened at a Historic Site park. Tell how geography influenced some of the events at that place.

Facts For Reference

What people do in Nova Scotia (1941)

Agriculture	37,597
Manufacturing	29,251
Mining	16,791
Fishing and Trapping	10,849
Forestry	6,538
Service	35,746
Trade	20,308
Transport and Communication	14,782
Construction	12,549
Total	184,411

What people do in New Brunswick (1941)

Agriculture	41,798
Manufacturing	21,421
Forestry	13,418
Fishing and Trapping	4,276
Mining	1,753
Service	26,108
Trade and Commerce	14,031
Transport and Communication	12,482
Construction	6,800
Total	142,087

What people do in Prince Edward Island (1941)

Agriculture	16,672
Fishing and Trapping	1,559
Manufacturing	1,421
Forestry	215
Mining	11
Trade and Finance	1,786
Service	1,412
Construction	1,208
Transport and Communication	1,176
Total	25,460

Chief Cities of Appalachian-Acadian Region (1941)

Halifax	70,488	Dartmouth	10,847
Saint John	51,741	Truro	10,272
Sherbrooke	35,965	Fredericton	10,062
Sydney	28,305	New Waterford	9,302
Glace Bay	25,147	New Glasgow	9,210
Moncton	22,763	Magog	9,034
Charlottetown	14,821	Rivière du Loup	8,713
Thetford Mines	12,716		

CHAPTER 18

NEWFOUNDLAND AND LABRADOR

Newfoundland lies on the eastern side of the Gulf of St. Lawrence. The island is 70 miles northeast of Cape Breton Island across Cabot Strait, and 100 miles by ferry from Sydney. Only 12 miles separate Newfoundland from Labrador and the mainland of Canada across the Strait of Belle Isle. The new island province has a population of about 330,000. Labrador includes all of the coast long governed by Newfoundland, and the interior country as far back as the headwaters of the rivers. This inland area of the Canadian Shield was granted to Newfoundland in 1927 following a boundary dispute with Canada.

Topography

Newfoundland is a rough plateau which is highest on the west and slopes down to the east and northeast. In most places the rocky coast rises steeply from the water, much like the eastern coast of Nova Scotia. Tiny fishing villages are nestled at the heads of numerous inlets which cut into the coast.

The Long Range which extends up the west coast of Newfoundland is the highest part of the island, having an elevation of 2,000 feet. This barren, flat-topped range becomes lower to the north near Belle Isle Strait. The lake-dotted interior plateau of Newfoundland is about 1,000 feet above sea-level. Many ridges cross the plateau from southwest to northeast, dipping down into the sea around Notre Dame Basin. Narrow lowlands are found between the bare ridges along this northeast coast.

The plateau is lower on the east. Avalon Peninsula, which is connected to the rest of the island by a narrow neck of land 4 miles wide, is rolling hilly country of about 500 feet elevation. There are more settlements and roads in the central part of the peninsula than in the interior of the main part of the island. The rivers of the Avalon Peninsula are not as large or deep as those cutting into the plateau to the west.

Labrador is part of the great Canadian Shield which is described in Chapter 19. The rocky coast is lowest in the south and increases in elevation northward. The Torngat Mountains in northern Labrador have steep-sided, scenic peaks of about 5,000 feet elevation. The rough, little-known interior of Labrador is similar to the rocky, lake-covered Canadian Shield in northern Quebec and Ontario.

Climate

The climate of Newfoundland is influenced by the cold Labrador Current off the northeast coast and the warm Gulf Stream off the southeast coast. The north coast of the island is therefore the coldest section, owing to the ice-floes which lie off the coast most of the winter and spring. The south coast is the warmest part of Newfoundland in winter, but the west coast, which faces the Gulf of St. Lawrence, is warmest in summer.

Because of the influence of cold waters around its shores, no part of Newfoundland becomes as warm in summer as the Maritimes or St. Lawrence Lowlands. Crops do not grow well in Newfoundland because of the short frost-free period. Climate forces Newfoundland to import much of the food needed by the residents.

Labrador is cooler than Newfoundland

in summer and colder in the winter. Northern Labrador, which has no summer, is within the Arctic region of Canada. It is inhabited by Eskimos. Summer days in the interior of Labrador can be hotter than 80°F., and the usual temperatures

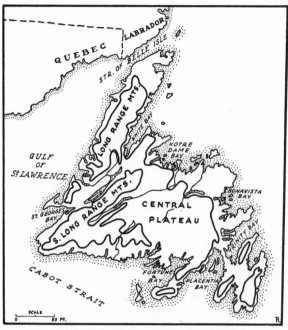

Physical Regions of Newfoundland.

are similar to those of central Quebec or the Clay Belt of Ontario.

The south coast of Newfoundland is the wettest part of eastern Canada, having more than 60 inches of precipitation. This is due to southerly winds picking up moisture over the warm Gulf Stream, and depositing it when the air rises over the steep south coast. Northeastern Newfoundland is noted for its deep snows. This area, which receives cold winds from the Labrador Current, has as much snow as the Laurentians, north of Quebec City.

Fishing

Three hundred miles to the southeast of Newfoundland stretch the shallow waters of the Grand Banks. This broad region, which is part of the North American continent, is covered by the ocean. It is one of the world's best fishing areas. The mixing of warm and cold waters in this area results in the growth of fish food for the

larger fish. The Grand Banks have been used by fishermen since the early days of the first explorers to the New World. European fishermen still come to the Banks each summer and share the catch with Newfoundlanders and Americans.

Courtesy Newfoundland Tourist Development Office.

The steep, rocky coast of Newfoundland rises sharply from the sea. Small fishing boats anchor in the sheltered inlets. Fish "stages" built on the steep cliffs hold drying cod.

Fishing has been the chief industry of Newfoundland throughout its history. Settlers who came to the island in the 17th century were primarily fishermen. To this day fishing is still the chief occupation of most Newfoundlanders. More than 1,000 tiny fishing villages scattered along the coasts of Newfoundland hold about three-quarters of the population of the island. Most of the villages are small. Perhaps 50 to 100 families live at the head of a sheltered inlet. The men fish near the coast during the day, returning home in their small boats at night. Women and girls split, clean, and salt the fish on racks near the beach. The cod then hangs on these racks to dry before being taken to the larger towns for sale.

About three-quarters of Newfoundland's fish are caught in coastal waters, within a few miles of the shore. The chief catch is cod, but herring are found off the west coast. Some lobsters are caught off the south coast, and Atlantic salmon are netted at the mouths of rivers on the northeast coast. The fisherman usually does not re-

109

ceive much money for his fish, and therefore living conditions are often poor in the little villages. His livelihood depends greatly on the world price of fish and the amount of competition from other fishing regions. This dependence on one product, cod-fish, was one of the weaknesses of

Numerous small fishing villages are scattered around the coast of Newfoundland. The square frame houses are perched on the rocky hillsides. There is very little soil for gardening. In the foreground cod fish are drying.

Newfoundland when it was a separate Dominion of the British Commonwealth before 1932.

Few fishermen go to the Grand Banks compared with the number fishing near the coast. Large schooners are needed to go out to the Banks, and most fishermen cannot afford such expensive boats. Schooners make about three trips between March and September. They usually bring their catch of cod back to St. John's or some other east-coast port.

Each summer a few thousand fishermen move northward to the coast of Labrador. Some of them, called "floaters", live on their schooners throughout the fishing season. Other fishermen build temporary houses on the rocky shores and fish from small boats along the coast. They are called "stationers".

Seal-hunting off the coast of Labrador in the spring was a major occupation at the beginning of the century. It is much less important now because the hair seals have been killed off. The sealing fleet sailed from St. John's in late winter, and pushed into the ice floes off the Labrador coast. Seals were killed on the floes and their skins and blubber taken back to the ships. So many were killed, however, that the seals became hard to find. Now only a few vessels make the trip into the dangerous ice. This depletion illustrates what happens to a resource if it is not conserved or used carefully.

Forestry

The forest industry is only about 40 years old in Newfoundland, but sometimes has passed fisheries as the most valuable resource of the island. Only one-third of Newfoundland's area is forested, but the valuable spruce, balsam and pine make excellent pulpwood. Because of the island's plateau character, and cool summer climate, much of the upland is covered with grassy meadows or scrub trees. The best forests are found on lowlands and interior valleys of the west and northeast coasts.

The deep-sea vessels bring several weeks' catch from the Grand Banks. The fish are split and dried on the shore. After being piled, they are covered to await transport to markets.

Many fishermen work at logging in the winter time and return to their fishing villages in the summer. Logs are floated down the Humber River to Cornerbrook on the west coast, and down the Exploits River to Grand Falls in the northeast. Both towns have plenty of water-power nearby to run the mills. Newsprint is one of Newfoundland's most valuable exports. It is sent chiefly to the United

Kingdom and the United States. Despite its value to Newfoundland, however, we must remember that there are fewer people in this industry than in fishing.

Mining

The Wabana iron-ore deposits of Bell Island, in Conception Bay, are among the largest in the world. The iron has been mined since the beginning of this century, but production has never been very high. Some of the mine shafts are now 2 or 3 miles under the sea on the west side of the island. Most of the iron is transported to the blast furnaces at Sydney, Nova Scotia. Newfoundland has no steel industry because there is not enough good coal on the island. Although iron is a valuable export of Newfoundland, the mining of it employs only a few thousand people.

The other mines in Newfoundland are small. At Buchans, in the interior, a zinc, lead and copper mine produces for export to the United Kingdom. A little-known, but valuable mineral, fluorspar, has been mined at St. Lawrence, on Burin Peninsula on the south coast, since 1933. This mineral is used to help make aluminum, and became important during World War II. Most of the ore was shipped to Arvida, in the Saguenay Valley of Quebec.

The geology of Newfoundland is not very well known. Some of the rocks are similar to the Canadian Shield, which has yielded rich minerals in Quebec and Ontario. Minerals such as the rich iron-ore deposits that have been discovered in Labrador, along the Hamilton River, near the Quebec boundary, may be found when the rocks are more fully studied.

Both forestry and mining need large amounts of water-power, which Newfoundland has in abundance. The heavy rainfall and deep snows supply plenty of water for the rivers. When these rivers tumble over the edge of the plateau to the coast, they become possible power sites. The present developed power is used chiefly for the pulp mills at Cornerbrook and Grand Falls, but also for St. John's and the towns on the Avalon Peninsula. If new mineral resources are found in Newfoundland there will be water-power nearby to aid in development.

Agriculture

There are few farmers in Newfoundland or Labrador. Although many fishermen cultivate small gardens near their homes, few people make their living wholly from the land. Much of the rocky upland of Newfoundland lacks soil, and the summer climate is too cool for most crops. Because of these limitations the island does not produce enough food to feed itself, and much is imported.

The Avalon Peninsula has more farms than any other part of the province. Dairying is carried on to supply milk to St. John's and the towns along the coast. Much of the cultivated land is therefore in hay and pasture. Most farms also grow some vegetables to sell to the towns. The best soils and mildest climate are found on the west coast. Land is being cleared in some of the valleys, and agriculture should expand there when more people settle along the west coast area.

Cities

St. John's is the only large city in Newfoundland. About one-sixth of the population of the island lives in this city on the east side of the Avalon Peninsula. St. John's has a long, narrow, well-sheltered harbour, with an entrance between high hills. The city is the chief port of the island and the supply centre for the fishing fleets. Most of the businesses and manufacturing of Newfoundland are located in St. John's. The main business section of the city is found at the foot of the rocky hills, at the head of the harbour inlet. Homes are built on the slopes, and back in the hills around the harbour.

Of the other towns of the Avalon Peninsula, *Carbonear* and *Harbour Grace,* on

111

Conception Bay, are the largest. Both have good harbours and some manufacturing. There are a few towns around Bonnavista Bay on the northeast coast. *Bonnavista* has a fish storage and refrigeration plant. *Port Union* is a ship-building

Courtesy Newfoundland Tourist Development Office.

St. John's, the capital of Newfoundland, is the largest city on the island. The sheltered harbour is visited by numerous trans-Atlantic vessels. The buildings of the city cover the hills around the harbour.

centre for the fishing fleet. Each of these towns has a few thousand people.

Grand Falls is the largest town in the north-central part of Newfoundland. It is the centre of the pulpwood and newsprint industry of that area. Pulp is also produced at *Bishop's Falls,* 9 miles away, and pumped by pipeline to the paper mill at Grand Falls. Hydro-electric power is produced by falls at both places. *Botwood* is the port for this area, and is connected by railroad to the main trans-island railroad. Pulp and paper products and mineral products from Buchans mine are exported through Botwood.

The chief settlements along the south coast are on Burin Peninsula. Several small towns are connected by road. Roads are generally lacking on the rest of the island outside of the Avalon Peninsula.

Cornerbrook is the chief town on the west coast. The pulp and paper mill was started there in 1925 and the town has grown and prospered since then. The town has a good harbour, and electric-power is supplied

from Deer Falls on the Humber River. Since the west coast has valuable forests and good soils, Cornerbrook should continue to grow in the future when more settlers come to the area.

Port aux Basques, on the southwest coast, is noted as the western terminal of the trans-island railway, which was built in 1897.

Most of the population of Newfoundland lives on the coast in numerous small villages. These communities have no connection by land, but are served by coastal steamers throughout the long navigation season. Because of the lack of transportation each village is isolated, and the people have little connection with the outside world.

There are only about 5,000 people living in Labrador. Villages such as Northwest River, Nain and Cartwright have only a few hundred people. The residents usually

Newfoundland and Labrador.

fish off the coast during the summer and hunt and trap in the forest in the winter. The large airport at Goose Bay, on Lake Melville, is operated by the Canadian Government. It is a very important base for trans-Atlantic flying. Since there are no roads or railroads in Labrador, all travel is by boat in summer and dog-team in winter. There are about 700 Eskimos living along the coast of northern Labrador, and about 300 Indians hunting and trapping in the interior forests.

Things To Do

1. (a) Draw a map of Newfoundland and Labrador and name on it all the towns and cities mentioned in this chapter.

   (b) Write a short essay explaining why there are no towns along certain parts of the coast, and hardly any in the interior.

2. Make a map of the North Atlantic Ocean showing Labrador, Newfoundland, Greenland, Iceland, British Isles, and France. Draw lines showing the chief trans-Atlantic air routes from Goose Bay and Gander in Newfoundland.

3. Explain how the fishing industry of Newfoundland is similar to that of the Maritime provinces. In what ways does it differ? Read Chapter 11 and the fishing section of Chapter 17 before writing your answer.

4. If your parents had to move to Newfoundland in which part of the island would you like to live if you had your choice? Explain why you would choose to live in that part. What would your father probably be doing for an occupation if you lived there?

Facts for Reference

What People do in Newfoundland (1948)

Fishing	33,000
Forestry	10,000
Manufacturing	9,000
Agriculture	4,300
Mining	3,500
Service	15,000
Transport and Communication	8,000
Trade and Finance	7,000
Construction	5,500
Total	95,300

Automobiles are made in the huge factories at Windsor, Ontario. Similar American models are made across the river in Detroit. Many small industries, making automobile parts and accessories, are located in the upper left of the picture.

CHAPTER 19

THE ST. LAWRENCE LOWLANDS

The St. Lawrence Lowlands lie between the Appalachians and Great Lakes to the south and the Canadian Shield to the north. They are separated into two sub-regions by a rocky arm of the Canadian Shield, called the Frontenac Axis, which extends southward across the St. Lawrence River at the eastern end of Lake Ontario. The eastern sub-region lies along the St. Lawrence River in Quebec, but includes the lower Ottawa River valley, part of Eastern Ontario, and extends southward along the Champlain Valley into the United States. The western sub-region, called the Ontario

114

Lowland, is bounded on the north by the Canadian Shield and Georgian Bay, and on the south by Lakes Erie and Ontario.

Topography

The land, although called a lowland, is not everywhere level. Gravel and loose rocks, left behind during the Glacial Age, form low ridges and rounded hills over parts of the lowlands. Along the shores of the Great Lakes former beach lines of old glacial lakes rise in terraces from the water's edge. In places, such as Mount Royal (770 feet) at Montreal, hills of old rock jut through the covering of soil and gravel.

The lowland is quite flat on both sides of the St. Lawrence River west of Quebec. It becomes wider to the westward. The flatness is broken by several rivers which cut across the valley to empty into the St. Lawrence. From the north, the St. Maurice is the largest; from the south the Richelieu, Nicolet and Chaudière Rivers wind across the lowland. The Monteregian Hills, a line of ancient volcanic necks, rise steeply above the level lowland between Montreal and Sherbrooke. The lowland in Eastern Ontario slopes from elevations of about 500 feet within the Canadian Shield to about 200 feet at the junction of the Ottawa and St. Lawrence Rivers.

The Ontario Lowland is more hilly than the plain along the St. Lawrence. North of Lake Ontario the lowland rises in gradual steps from 300 feet at the lake to over 1000 feet in Algonquin Park in the Canadian Shield. The escarpment over which Niagara Falls tumbles continues to the northwestward around the western end of Lake Ontario. There it is known as the "Hamilton Mountain". The line of hills, marking the eastern side of the escarpment, extends from Hamilton across the rolling lowland to Bruce Peninsula, between Georgian Bay and Lake Huron.

West of the escarpment the rolling hills of the upland of Southwestern Ontario have elevations of 1600 feet north of London. This scenic countryside slopes gradually down to about 600 feet, which is the level of Lakes Erie and Huron. The lowest and flattest part of the region is in Essex and Kent Counties at the far southwestern corner of the province. This southwestern section was once the bottom of a glacial lake, and for many miles across its surface not even the smallest hill rises above the plain.

Climate

Parts of the St. Lawrence Lowlands are the hottest sections of Canada in summer, and can become quite cold in winter. Temperatures can range from almost 100 degrees on hot summer days to 30 degrees below zero in winter.

Winters have changeable weather. Sev-

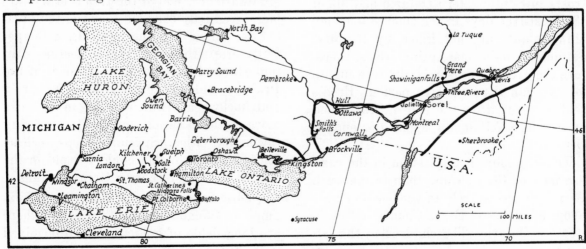

St. Lawrence Lowlands.

eral cold, clear days are followed by a few days of mild, cloudy weather. This succession of cold and cool days continues throughout the winter, with each day a little different from the one before. January is usually the coldest month, and by the end of March the snow is beginning to disappear.

The people in Southwestern Ontario have the third mildest winters of Canada. It becomes colder north of London, in Central Ontario, but the coldest section of the Lowland is usually along the St. Lawrence River from Montreal to Quebec. The average winter temperatures at these places, however, are not as cold as they are in the Prairie cities.

Summers in southwestern Ontario are the warmest in Canada. Since the cool influence of the Great Lakes is felt for only a few miles from the shores, many people go to the lakes on Sundays or for summer vacations. As far east as Montreal, temperatures above 80°F are common during summer days. The residents of Quebec, at the eastern end of the region, do not have as many warm days. Average July temperatures there are about the same as those of Winnipeg on the Prairies.

The frost-free period for crops is longer in the St. Lawrence Lowlands than in the lowlands of the Maritimes. There is an average of about 175 days between killing frosts in Southwestern Ontario and about 135 frost-free days in the Quebec lowland. Many plants are not killed by the first autumn frosts or last spring frosts, therefore the growing season is almost a month longer than the frost-free period. Frosts seldom occur after the end of April, and usually are felt again about the end of October.

There is more precipitation in the eastern part of the Lowland than in the west. About 40 inches falls in Quebec and only about 30 inches in Essex County in Southwestern Ontario. The children in the latter region also have less snowfall to enjoy during the winter. Heavy snows are more usual east of Lake Huron, south of Georgian Bay, and north of Montreal.

Agriculture

The St. Lawrence Lowlands are fortunate in having level topography, good soils and mild climate. They were developed as the first important agricultural area of Canada. Louis Hébert started the first farm at Quebec City in 1617. In the following years other French settlers cleared their long, narrow farms back from the St. Lawrence River. Under the old seignorial system the French colony raised enough food for its own needs. By the end of the French period (1763) about 45,000 people (three-quarters of the population) were living on farms between Quebec and Montreal on both sides of the river.

The first farmers settled in Ontario about 1760. Within 100 years there were more than 100,000 farms, and much of the lowland had been cleared of forest and was producing crops. Until about 1850 the farmers of both Quebec and Ontario were concerned only with raising enough food for their own use. Wheat was the chief grain crop, and it was ground into flour at home or at a nearby mill. Other grains were fed to the few head of livestock. Each farm grew vegetables and often had a few fruit trees.

Towards the end of the 19th century farmers gradually changed towards the present-day mixed farming methods, with specialty crops for sale. Wheat decreased in importance following the settlement of the Prairies, and was replaced by oats, barley and buckwheat. Farmers began to raise more cattle to supply milk to the growing towns and cities. Specialty crops such as fruit, tobacco, or flax could be sold in the United States or sent to Great Britain.

Quebec farms are probably the best example in Canada of mixed farming. There are long fields of golden grain intermixed with green pastures and forage crops

116

Courtesy G. M. Dallyn and Canadian Geographical Journal.

Long, narrow fields, separated by rail fences, are characteristic of the farms of Quebec.
They stretch back from the river or road to wooded hills.

which are stored for winter. A small vegetable garden is located near the house and an old orchard is nearby. A few acres of potatoes may be on the other side of the garden. The back of the farm probably has a woodlot where the farmer cuts his winter's fuel. The woodlot also helps to delay spring run-off of melting snows and prevents soil erosion. In the bush there may be a sugar shanty where the sap from the maple trees is boiled into syrup or maple sugar in the spring. A big stable behind the house will shelter two or three horses, about a dozen cows, a half-dozen

sheep and the same number of pigs. Nearby will be a hen-house with 50 to 100 poultry which supply the family with eggs for breakfast and with fowl for holiday dinners.

Dairying is one of the chief sources of income of Quebec farmers. The province is known for its good butter and is second to Ontario in the making of cheese. Much of the fresh milk is shipped to Montreal to feed the million people there.

Quebec is noted for only a few specialty crops. Tobacco is grown in the Joliette-Berthier district northeast of Montreal.

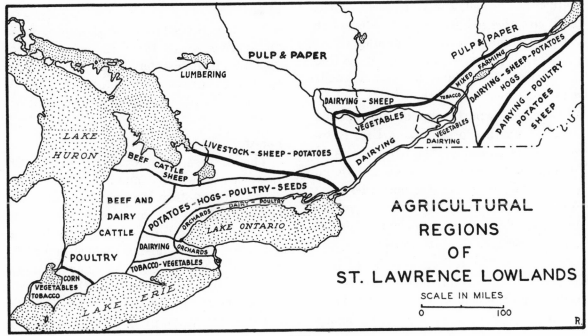

AGRICULTURAL
REGIONS
OF
ST. LAWRENCE LOWLANDS

SCALE IN MILES

0   100

Many commercial gardeners raise strawberries on Montreal Island. The province produces about 80 per cent of Canada's maple sugar and much of the fibre flax. Quebec farms raise more potatoes than any other part of Canada, but most of the crop is eaten locally.

Many farmers on the Ontario Lowland raise products for sale rather than for home use. About three-quarters of the average farm is in field crops which are used chiefly to feed dairy cows. The other one-quarter of the farm grows specialty crops such as fruit and vegetables which may be canned for later sale all over Canada. Cultivated hay is the field crop with the greatest acreage on the Lowland, and it is followed in importance by oats, winter wheat and barley.

Certain sections of the Lowland specialize in the production of one or two crops. Essex and Kent counties have the longest growing season of the region. The small garden-farms in this section have ripe vegetables a few weeks earlier than farms in other parts. They are then shipped to the east and north for sale before the local vegetables are ready. One of the largest vegetable-canning factories in Canada is located at Leamington on Lake Erie. These counties are the main producers in Eastern Canada of corn for canning. Other specialty crops raised on this flat section are tobacco near Lake Erie, and sugar beets northwest of Chatham.

The chief export crop of the section along the north shore of Lake Erie is tobacco. It is grown on the sandy soils of Norfolk County around Simcoe and Delhi. Many of the labourers are men who have come to Canada from Central European countries. This small area grows most of Canada's tobacco used in cigarettes.

Farmers on the rolling uplands of central southwestern Ontario specialize in the production of livestock. Those east of Lake Huron keep many beef cattle, but sheep and dairy cattle are also raised. Dairying is carried on over the whole Ontario Lowland, but it is especially important to the farmers of Oxford County, east of London. Ingersoll, in the centre of this section, is noted for its fine cheese.

The Niagara Peninsula, between Lakes Erie and Ontario, is the chief fruit region of the Lowland, and one of the most important in Canada. Peaches and grapes are the best known fruits of the area which also produces apples, pears, plums, cherries, and berries. The fruit farmers also raise early vegetables for sale to nearby Hamilton and other cities. Most of the commercial orchards are located on sloping land near the shores of Lake Ontario where frosts are not as frequent as on the upland.

Farmers along the north shore of Lake Ontario raise almost the same crops as farmers in Southwestern Ontario. Orchards are located on slopes and terraces near the lake. Truck gardening produces vegetables for the many towns and cities along the lake, and is especially important in the peninsula of Prince Edward County. The raising of dairy cows for milk, butter and cheese is important on nearly all farms of this section.

Farther north from the shores of Lake Ontario general farming is practised. Nearly all farms have dairy cows, and some grow grains. Some farmers specialize in the production of potatoes or clover seed.

Forestry

The first settlers to arrive in the St. Lawrence Lowlands found the region covered with a thriving forest containing many hardwoods. To these settlers who wanted to clear farms and set up homes, the forest was a nuisance which had to be removed. Often the settlers burned down valuable trees and rendered the ash into potash which could be exported in barrels. Much of the value of the tree was lost by these methods because there was no local market for wood.

Gradually, however, the settlers found uses for hardwoods and a prosperous lumbering industry grew up in the last century. Hickory and elm were tough, hard trees. Their wood could be used for tool handles, spokes and rims for wheels, baseball bats, skis, and other articles of which rough use was expected. Maple and oak were used for furniture, flooring, and the interior finishings of houses. Other trees also had their special uses.

The people in the forest industry and the farmers soon cleared most of the forests from the Lowlands. The region is now covered with farmlands and only patches of woodlots are left to indicate what the country used to look like. The furniture industry is still important west of Toronto, around Kitchener and Guelph, but the wood is often brought many miles to the factories.

Lumbering in the St. Lawrence Lowlands is not a mechanized industry as it is in other forested parts of Canada. Farmers cut most of the wood during their spare time in the winter. Fuelwood is the chief use of woodlands in the rural areas, but some trees are cut for lumber by many small mills scattered over the Lowland.

The high spring floods, which are one of the problems facing the people of the Lowlands, are partly caused by the removal of trees. In forested areas the rainwater soaks into the ground and takes longer to drain towards streams. On open, cultivated land the water runs off directly to the nearest streams, raising their levels very rapidly. The removal of the forest took away the protection from rapid floods. Now melting snows and spring rains soon raise the level of rivers above their banks, especially in the Ontario Lowland. Homes and crops are damaged by the resulting floods.

The Ontario Government is encouraging people to replant trees in the Lowlands.

Many areas of poor sandy soil that are not fitted for agriculture are being put back into forest by provincial or county authorities. This reforestation will prevent the soil from being blown away and will decrease the danger from floods farther downstream.

Mining

The flat-lying rocks of the Lowlands do not contain the rich metallic minerals. The minerals produced are salt, petroleum, natural gas, gypsum, marble, limestone, and clay. Since most of these are found in small and bulky quantities, they are not shipped far. There are not many people engaged in mining in the region.

Salt is the only mineral found in quantities large enough for sale across Canada. Large deposits are located under the shores of Lake Huron and the St. Clair and Detroit rivers. The large factories at Goderich and Windsor obtain salt by the brine method of dissolving the salt seams with hot water. This salt deposit is said to be large enough to supply the whole world for over 2,000 years.

Prospectors drilled the first oil well in Canada east of Sarnia in 1862. This petroleum field in Southwestern Ontario supplied the region for many years, but is now largely used up. Natural gas is found at several places along the north shore of Lake Erie. It is used by many people in Southwestern Ontario for heating and cooking in their homes, and supplies fuel and power for several industries.

A few companies mine small quantities of gypsum along the Niagara escarpment west of Hamilton. Limestone is quarried at several places throughout the Lowlands and is used in the manufacture of cement. Good clay is also widespread and small factories make it into bricks and pottery.

Manufacturing

Over three-quarters of Canada's manufacturing is done in Ontario and Quebec. The factories of Ontario alone produce about one-half the manufactured goods of Canada. Most of the factories are located in the St. Lawrence Lowlands, and the remainder are found to the north near water power sites along the edge of the Canadian Shield. One has only to look at the names on the labels in the stores to see how many products come from cities of the Lowlands.

There are many reasons why manufacturing is concentrated in this area of Canada. Some of the reasons are historical, others are geographical. The region was had a good transportation system these products were brought to cities in the Lowlands where factories were already established. The St. Lawrence Lowlands thus remained the centre of Canadian manufacturing.

In Quebec many of the industries are located along or near the southern edge of the Canadian Shield, in order to be near water power. The manufacture of pulp and paper, using the forests of the Shield, is the most valuable industry of the pro-

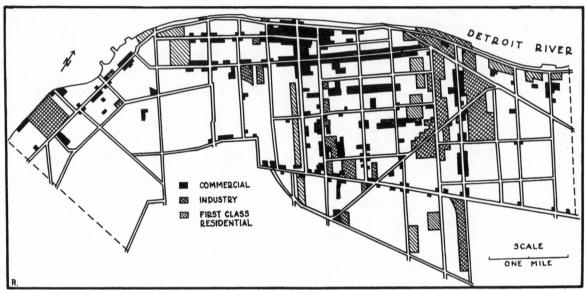

Functional areas of Windsor.

others are geographical. The region was settled early in Canada's history and many small factories were started then to make products for the local population. Factories were located in the Maritime region also at this time, but the population there did not increase as much as it did in the Lowlands and therefore manufacturing did not expand. As the cities grew, other industries were started. They, in turn, hired more people and this made the cities still larger.

Factories must have nearby raw materials, and people to buy their products. The St. Lawrence Lowland had the advantage of having a good supply of local resources. Other resources were located in the Canadian Shield. As soon as Canada

vince. It is followed by the smelting and refining of non-ferrous metals, chiefly aluminum, and the making of a variety of chemical products.

Many factories manufacture textiles. About three-quarters of Canada's cotton yarn and cloth is woven in Montreal and other nearby cities. Mills of the same region also make over half the men's and women's factory clothing, and many leather boots and shoes. Most of the Canadian cigarettes, cigars, and pipe tobacco are made in the Quebec section of the Lowlands.

The factories of the Ontario Lowland make large products which are meant to last for a long time. Some of these manufactures are automobiles, farm machinery,

120

electrical goods, factory machinery, furniture, and rubber goods. The automobile industry is the most valuable one in the province, but there are more people employed making general iron and steel products and electrical apparatus.

Other industries of the Ontario Lowland are the smelting of non-ferrous metals from the Canadian Shield, and the making of pulp and paper. The industrial workers in this section make over half the hosiery and knitted goods of Canada, and three-quarters of the rubber goods. The agricultural resources are used by workers in flour and feed mills, slaughtering and

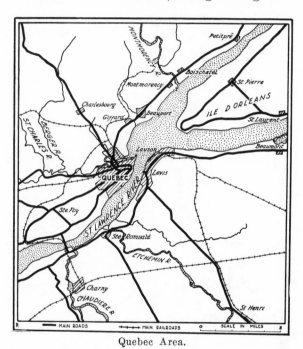

Quebec Area.

meat-packing plants, leather tanneries, and fruit and vegetable canneries.

Cities

Since over half the population of Canada and over half the manufacturing are found in the St. Lawrence Lowlands, we would expect many large cities to be located there. Thirteen of the 25 largest Canadian cities are located in this small region. These 13 cities total 2,500,000 people or about one-fifth of the population of Canada. There are 40 cities with popu-

lations of over 10,000 in the St. Lawrence Lowlands compared with 8 such cities in the Maritimes and 11 on the Prairies.

Montreal is the largest city in Canada. If the surrounding cities on Montreal Island, such as Verdun, Outremont, and Westmount, are included, there are over a million people, one-tenth of Canada's population, in this huge urban centre. The city is Canada's chief port, and has miles of dock space for ocean liners. It is a transportation centre for railroads from all directions. Montreal has an ideal location at the head of ocean navigation, and in the middle of a rich agricultural and manufacturing region.

Factories of all kinds are busy there. They manufacture everything from large ships, aeroplanes and railroad cars to small pieces of clothing and leather goods. Much of the business and commerce of Canada is carried on in Montreal where there are many large banks and insurance companies.

Montreal is a tourist attraction for Canadians and people from other countries. Not only does it have the colour and excitement of Canada's largest city, but it has many large, beautiful parks and fine churches and museums. The city is bilingual and signs are printed in both French and English. This is something which visitors always remember.

Toronto is Canada's second largest city. It is situated on a scenic harbour on the north side of Lake Ontario. Numerous rail lines and good highways connect it with other parts of Ontario. Toronto has many businesses, factories, parks and churches. Most of the manufacturing firms in Canada have their headquarters in Toronto. The city is known for its fine stores and large hotels. It is four times as large as Hamilton, the second city of Ontario, but did not grow as large as Montreal because it does not have the same advantages of location. Queen's Park, with the picturesque Parliament Buildings

121

and nearby University, is one of the scenic views for visitors.

Hamilton is an industrial city. It is the chief iron and steel city of Canada and most of its manufactures are heavy products such as farm machinery, refrigerators, stoves, and elevators. The city has good water transportation on Lake Ontario and through the Welland Canal, and is also served by excellent roads and railroads over the surrounding rich countryside. Hamilton's raw materials for manufacturing come in by water and finished goods are sent out by road and rail. The city is situated along the slope at the base of "Hamilton Mountain", the escarpment at the western end of lake Ontario.

Ottawa, the capital of Canada, is chiefly a residential city. Most of the people work for the government or in stores and businesses supplying the needs of the civil servants. Ottawa used to be an important lumber city when logs were floated down the Ottawa River. Thousands of people each year visit the stately Parliament Buildings in Ottawa, and admire the red-coated "Mounties" who patrol the grounds. The French-speaking city of *Hull*, across the Ottawa River in Quebec, and at the mouth of the Gatineau River, is a manufacturing centre noted for its paper and matches.

Quebec City, the capital of Quebec, is located on a high rocky bluff overlooking the narrowing of the St. Lawrence River. The city, with its walled fort, the Plains

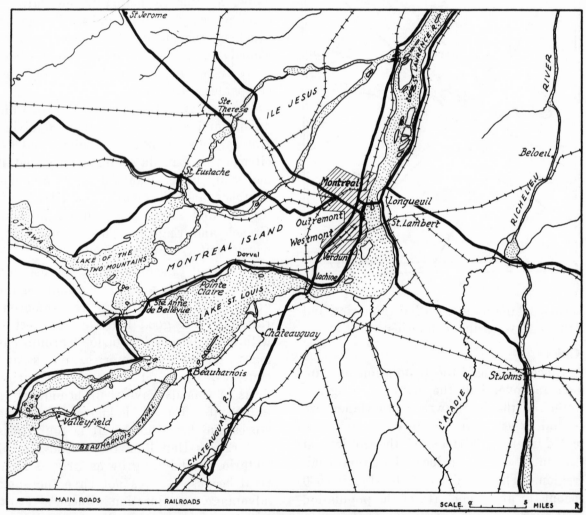

Montreal and area.

122

Looking westward over the Ottawa River from the Parliament Buildings at Ottawa. Some of the government buildings are on the left; in the centre a match and paper company uses the water power of the Chaudière Rapids. The city of Hull, Quebec, lies to the right.

of Abraham, and Wolfe's Cove, is rich in history. Its narrow winding streets are reminders of days gone by, and resemble those of ancient European cities. As well as being a centre of government, Quebec is an important ocean port and has many manufacturing industries on the lowland east of the old city.

Windsor is the automobile centre of the British Commonwealth. It is located across the Detroit River from Detroit, the American automobile capital. There are many American branch plants established within the city. Many iron and steel products, as well as automobile parts and accessories, are made in Windsor. The city also has a large salt and chemical industry and manufactures drug supplies. More tourists enter Canada through Windsor than at any other border city.

London, located on the Thames River, is a city of small industries of many kinds. The factories are unlike the large factories of Hamilton or Windsor. Among the many products made are hosiery, shoes, plastics, and cereals. London is in the centre of a rich agricultural district and has good transportation lines in all directions. The University of Western Ontario is located on a beautiful campus at the northern edge of the city.

Parks

Most cities and towns in the St. Lawrence Lowlands have beautiful parks and recreation facilities within their city limits. There are very few provincial or national parks within this region since it is flat or gently rolling and lacking in spectacular scenery. Most of the parks, visited by people from the Lowlands and tourists from abroad, are located in the rugged beauty of the Canadian Shield to the northward.

There are no National Parks in the Quebec section of the Lowland, but Forts Chambly and Lennox, near Montreal, are maintained as small Historic Site parks. They illustrate to visitors what forts looked like during the French and early English periods. Quebec's other famous parks, noted for their winter sports, are located in the Canadian Shield, but are close to the Lowland cities.

Ontario has three small National Parks, two Historic Site parks, and two Provincial Parks within the Lowland region. St. Lawrence Islands National Park, in a scenic location among the beautiful "Thousand Islands" of the St. Lawrence River, is noted for its camping and bathing. Georgian Bay Islands Park, including peculiar Flowerpot Island, is a similar park of 30 islands in the southern part of Georgian Bay. Point Pelee Park is the

123

Courtesy Ontario Travel and Publicity Department.

The St. Lawrence River has many islands where it crosses the Canadian Shield at Thousand Islands Park. The level lowland, most of which is farmed, stretches off to the right..

most southerly mainland part of Canada, and is noted for its fine beaches. Its marshes are an important stopping place for migratory birds flying north and south.

Two Historic Site parks preserve forts built by the British in Upper Canada. Fort Wellington at Prescott has the blockhouse and earthworks of an old fort which protected the road from Kingston to Montreal.

Fort Malden, at Amherstburg, south of Windsor, was one of the early frontier posts important in the War of 1812-14.

Two Provincial Parks, at Rondeau on Lake Erie and Ipperwash Beach on Lake Huron, are equipped for camping and bathing. Each year they are visited by thousands of city dwellers and vacationists from Southwestern Ontario.

Things To Do

1. Study the average temperatures for cities in the St. Lawrence Lowlands as shown in the table at the end of Chapter 4. Compare the summer temperatures there with those of other large cities in Canada. How many degrees warmer are the Lowlands' cities in winter than cities on the Prairies?

2. (a) List agricultural crops grown on the St. Lawrence Lowlands that have little acreage elsewhere in Canada.

124

(b) Why is it possible to produce these crops there?

(c) Many of the canning factories of Canada are located in this region. Why is this so?

(d) Name the crops they use.

3. Most of the cheese of Canada comes from this region.

(a) Read the labels on boxes of cheese in your grocery store and list the cities or towns where it was made.

(b) Are they all in the same local region?

4. From books in your school library read about the fruit-growing region of the Niagara Peninsula in Ontario.

(a) How is it similar to that of the Annapolis Valley in Nova Scotia?

(b) Are the same crops raised?

(c) How do the two regions differ?

5. (a) Does the furniture in your home come from the St. Lawrence Lowlands?

(b) List the cities from which the different pieces of furniture come.

(c) Of what species of tree are they made?

6. List some of the Conservation projects and River Valley developments being carried on by the Ontario Government. Reports may be obtained from the Department of Planning and Development. Write an essay describing the main purposes of one of these projects.

7. (a) Read the section on manufacturing and list all the industries of the St. Lawrence Lowlands.

(b) Which ones are also found in Appalachian-Acadian manufacturing regions?

(c) After each of the industries listed for the St. Lawrence Lowlands name the natural resources which supply the raw materials.

(d) Which of these raw materials are found within the region?

8. (a) On an outline map of the St. Lawrence Lowlands locate and name all the large cities listed at the end of this chapter.

(b) Using a road map of southern Ontario and Quebec draw the important highways on your map in (a).

(c) List the cities that are not on one of the highways.

(d) From the population chapter in the Canada Year Book list the next 10 largest cities in this region.

(e) Locate them on your map also.

(f) List those located on the main highways.

(g) Why are some of them not located there?

Facts For Reference

1. What People do in Quebec (1941)

Manufacturing	330,775
Agriculture	254,383
Forestry	34,933
Mining	13,725
Fishing and Trapping	8,041
Service	244,376
Trade and Finance	123,065
Construction	73,216
Transport and Communication	68,026
Total	1,150,540

2. What People do in Ontario (1941)

Manufacturing	446,872
Agriculture	269,577
Mining	32,125
Forestry	16,563
Fishing and Trapping	5,470
Service	279,589
Trade and Finance	178,188
Transport and Communication	84,605
Construction	77,584
Total	1,390,573

3. Cities of the St. Lawrence Lowlands (1941)

Montreal	903,007
Toronto	667,457
Hamilton	-166,337
Ottawa	154,951
Quebec	150,757
Windsor	105,311
London	78,264
Verdun	67,349
Three Rivers	42,007
Kitchener	35,657
Hull	32,947
Brantford	31,948
Outremont	30,751
St. Catharines	30,275
Kingston	30,126

Arvida, Quebec, has beautiful curving streets and modern homes. It is a company town for the large aluminum factory. French-speaking farmers in the Saguenay valley supply food to the workers of the town.

CHAPTER 20

THE CANADIAN SHIELD

The Canadian Shield is the largest region in Canada. It covers one-half of Canada's area, but has only a small percentage of its population. It stretches around Hudson and James Bays like a huge horseshoe from Hudson Strait and Labrador in the northeast to Mackenzie District in the northwest. It covers Labrador, and much of Quebec and Ontario, extending as far south as the St. Lawrence River and Georgian Bay.

Topography and Drainage

The Shield is a low pleateau of the oldest rocks known in the world. It has been worn down from high mountains to rolling hills by millions of years of rain, snow and ice. The last Continental Ice Age scraped the rock ridges bare of soil and filled the valleys with rock and gravel.

Lakes have formed in depressions all over the region. They are connected by rivers with numerous rapids.

The plateau has an average elevation of about 2,000 feet above sea level. The difference in elevation between valley bottoms and hill tops, however, is only about 200 to 500 feet. The highest part of the Shield is in northern Labrador where mountain peaks of 4,000 to 5,000 feet rise directly from the coast.

In Quebec the Shield rises as a wooded escarpment north of the St. Lawrence River. From the Lowland it looks like a mountainous region, but within the hills the peaks are all about the same level, and stretch in flat-topped ridges to the northward. The plateau gradually slopes down to the north to a narrow lowland around Ungava Bay.

The main rivers draining the northern part of Quebec are the George, Kaniapiskau, Koksoak and Leaf. The southward flowing rivers of the Shield are shorter, and often have waterfalls where they spill over the escarpment edge. Among the largest southern rivers are the Saguenay and the tributaries of Lake St. John, the St. Maurice, Gatineau, and Ottawa rivers. Much of the dense forest cover of the Shield is being cut and floated down these rivers.

The rocky, wooded surface of the Shield in Northern Ontario is similar in appearance to that of Quebec. It merges gradually into the rolling lowland of Southern Ontario. Pasture lands are cleared in the small lowlands between the rocky hills along the southern borders. The rocky shoreline of Georgian Bay and Lake Superior marks the southern boundary in that area.

The central part of the Shield contains a vast lowland which was once the bottom of an old glacial lake. The waters long ago

THE CANADIAN SHIELD

drained away leaving behind a broad, flat area known as the Clay Belt. The lowland lies in both Ontario and Quebec, with the larger section in Ontario. It is crossed from east to west by the Canadian National Railway which helped to bring settlers into this new farming region. The surface of the Clay Belt is a rolling, wooded plain, with swampy lowlands and low gravel ridges. Much of it is poorly drained, but there are sections of good soil which are being farmed.

Most of the Shield in Ontario drains northward through long rivers which make excellent canoe routes. The Moose, Albany and Attawapiskat Rivers drain into the western side of James Bay through a flat, swampy lowland near the coast. The Winisk and Severn Rivers empty into the shallow waters of southwestern Hudson Bay. These northern rivers all flow in the wrong direction to be useful in the pulp industry for floating logs.

Southward-flowing rivers in Ontario are much shorter than those of Quebec. French River, draining Lake Nipissing, is the main stream flowing into Georgian Bay. This waterway once formed the link in the historic portage from the Ottawa River to the Great Lakes. Many singing voyageurs dipped their paddles into these waters, forcing their fur-laden canoes along forest-lined streams. Lake Nipigon, the largest lake in the Shield north of Lake Superior, empties southward. Rainy River drains northwestern Ontario into the Lake of the Woods, and forms the International Boundary with the United States. It flows through beautiful lake-dotted country which attracts many tourists each year.

The Shield is lower and less rugged in Manitoba than in Eastern Canada. It is cut up by numerous rivers and dotted with many irregular-shaped lakes, but the hills are less rocky and more rounded. The route of the Hudson Bay Railroad between The Pas and Churchill passes through wooded country. The train stops at small settlements consisting of a few stores and a cluster of Indian cabins. The low rocky hills are partially hidden under a blanket of evergreen trees. Most of these trees are too small for lumber, but they shelter many fur-bearing animals.

Short rivers drain into Lake Winnipeg on the southwestern edge of the Shield in Manitoba. The rest of the province drains northward to Hudson Bay. Nelson River empties Lake Winnipeg and cuts through the Shield to Hudson Bay. Several rapids along its course prevent any use by boats, other than canoes. The long Churchill River drains northern Manitoba, and much of the Shield region of northern Saskatchewan. It broadens into lakes at several places.

The low hills and ridges of northern Saskatchewan form the drainage divide for rivers flowing in two directions. Some of the streams flow westward to join the Athabaska River and Lake Athabaska in the wooded region of the northern Great Plains. Many rivers, and large Reindeer Lake, drain into Churchill River and empty eastward. There are very few people living in this rough part of Canada.

Topography in the Northwest Territories is noted for its rocky, barren hills east of Great Slave and Great Bear Lakes. Bare rock ridges and gravel-filled valleys are characteristic of the central section around Lake Dubawnt. The Shield slopes to the northward, drained by Back River, to a low, grassy plain along Queen Maud Gulf. Coppermine River in the northwest flows through rough rocky country all the way to the coast. To the east the plateau merges with a broad, lake-dotted, swampy plain along the west side of Hudson Bay. This latter section is drained by the Kazan, Dubawnt and Thelon rivers which empty into Chesterfield Inlet.

The Shield covers such a big area from north to south, as well as from east to west, that the northern parts are not as well forested as the southern sections. Suppose we make an imaginary flight northward from the little town of The Pas, in northern Manitoba. We would notice that the spruce trees become smaller and smaller, and the patches of grassland and tundra between the trees larger and larger. Soon we would be above country which had very few trees, and in Keewatin District there would be none at all. This barren part is different from anything we know in the inhabited southern regions of Canada.

We cross mile after mile of rock ridges looking very uninviting, and coloured only by patches of grass and low bushes in the valleys. We are amazed at the number of lakes that we see below. In places there appears to be more water than land, and the lakes have every size, shape and form that we can imagine. Geologists tell us that the lakes are caused by the permanently frozen ground of this treeless region. They explain that in southern regions the rain soaks into the ground and gradually works its way through the soil to drain finally into streams and lakes. In the frozen tundra of the north, however, the water cannot soak down. It collects in every little basin or low place to form lakes, ponds and muskegs. This lake-dotted country of the northern Shield is almost impossible to travel over in the summer when water is everywhere. In the winter, on the other hand, the lakes are frozen smooth, and the rock surface is covered with snow. Then the Eskimo inhabitants can travel easily in any direction with their sleds and dog-teams. This is an example of how the physical features of a region influence movement and transportation.

Climate

Since the Canadian Shield covers such a large area its climate is not the same throughout. From north to south the region stretches for a distance of about 1700 miles. This is about the same distance as from Winnipeg to New Orleans and there are many differences in climate in that space. From east to west the Shield also extends about 1700 miles. This is about the same distance as from Fort William, Ontario, to Victoria, B. C.

128

In wintertime the whole Shield is cold. The area northwest of Hudson Bay is probably the coldest part of Canada, but there are not yet enough meteorology stations there to prove it. Temperatures of –50°F. to –60°F. are recorded during the winter in Keewatin District, west of Hudson Bay. This is not much colder than the temperatures of –30°F. to –40°F. which are known north of Lake Superior and north of the St. Lawrence River. In the northern parts cold temperatures occur every day and the thermometer reading seldom rises above zero. Eskimos wear warm skin clothing to keep out the cold. In the southern parts, however, there will occasionally be a few days of mild weather when the thermometer may record above freezing.

In summertime the region is cool. The northern parts are the coolest, being within the Arctic region of Canada. Temperatures seldom rise above 70°F. in the afternoons in the section west of Hudson Bay. Since the growing season is too short for crops there are no farmers in the region. In southern sections like the Upper Ottawa River Valley, evenings are pleasant and cool. Days are warm, and the mercury in the thermometer may reach 90°F. or more. Usual daily temperatures, however, are around 70°F. in the southern Laurentians, and provide welcome relief for people from the hot lowlands. Many city people spend their summer vacations in the beautiful lakes and woods in the southern part of the Shield.

The amount of annual precipitation decreases to the northward in the Shield. The southern slopes receive 30 to 40 inches of precipitation yearly, about half of which falls as snow. The northern sections receive less than 10 inches, most of which falls as hard powdery snow during the long winter. The snow is not deep in the northern part. Some of the rock ridges remain bare, but there is always enough snow in the valleys for the Eskimos to travel by dog sled.

The frost-free period is long enough for growing hardy grains in most places within the forested area of the Shield. In the Clay Belt of Ontario and Quebec there are 75 to 95 days, on an average, without frosts. At Churchill, on Hudson Bay, there is an average of 60 days between last spring frosts and first autumn frosts. Crops can usually be matured in the Clay Belt during the short growing season, but sometimes cold air from the Arctic sweeps down over the region earlier than usual and nearly all the crops are frozen.

Mining

The Canadian Shield is one of the richest mineral regions in the world. Although most of its wealth has been discovered only within the present century, it already has produced many millions of dollars' worth of minerals. New rich strikes are being uncovered every year. As soon as more transportation lines are built into the region, more wealth and raw materials undoubtedly will be obtained.

Most of the minerals found in these ancient rocks are the rich metallics. Gold, silver, copper, lead, zinc, cobalt, nickel, platinum and iron are all known throughout the region. Some sections have larger quantities than others. If we flew over the Shield we would see that little towns composed of frame and log houses have grown up around the mines. Small farms nearby supply part of the food for the miners.

There are several mining regions across the Shield. On the Labrador-Quebec boundary iron ore has been discovered in large quantities. The cost of mining in this remote section is high, but transportation lines will be built to ship out the ore. Since Canada lacks iron ore this region may become very important.

The chief mining region in Northern Quebec is the Noranda-Rouyn area, south of the Canadian National Railway. Prospectors explored the section after World War I, but it was not until 1927 that the rich gold and copper mine at Noranda began to yield its wealth. The small mining area is only 120 miles long by 50 miles wide, and yet in 20 years after 1927, it produced 27 gold mines, 6 copper mines, 4 zinc mines, and 2 molybdenite mines. Over 10,000 miners are working in this region, digging out the ore which becomes the raw material for industries.

Other minerals that are mined in Quebec include zinc from Calumet Island in the Ottawa River, magnesite from Grenville and Harrington townships, and mica and aptite from the Gatineau and Lièvre rivers. Aluminum is manufactured at Arvida on the Saguenay River and at Shawinigan Falls on the St. Maurice River. Bauxite, which is the ore from which alumina powder is obtained, is brought in from British Guiana. Electricity from the water power of the Shield is used to make the alumina powder into aluminum.

The building of railroads helped to uncover some of the mineral wealth of northern Ontario. In 1884, workmen laying rails for the Canadian Pacific Railroad discovered copper ore at Sudbury. A few years later the same ore was found to contain the world's largest supply of nickel. Since its discovery the Sudbury area has produced over a billion dollars' worth of nickel, copper and platinum. Large reserves are there for future use.

While the Temiskaming and Northern Ontario Railroad was being built from North Bay, silver was discovered at Cobalt in 1903. Prospectors rushed to the new strike and Cobalt became the centre of a busy, optimistic mining industry. From there prospectors went into the surround-

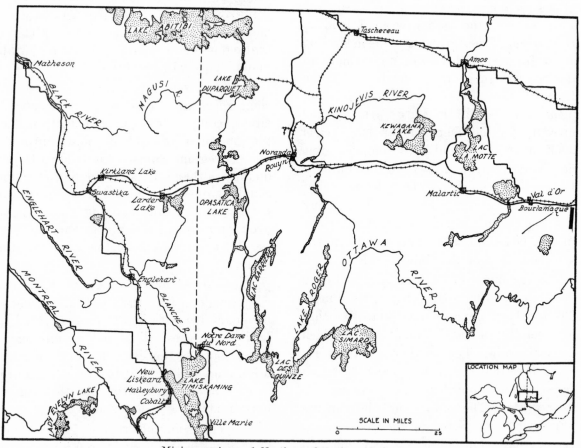

Mining regions of Northern Ontario and Quebec.

130

ing areas. The town became the fourth largest silver producer in the world, and miners also found large amounts of cobalt, for which the town was named. After 1925 production gradually declined, the mines closed down, and people moved away. In 1906 gold was found at Larder Lake and in the following year the wealthy Hollinger Mine at Porcupine was discovered. By 1911 rich gold mines were producing at Timmins and Kirkland Lake, and some of them are still operating. More than one billion dollars' worth of gold was mined from the Kirkland Lake-Timmins district in the 40 years after the first strikes.

Other sections in Northern Ontario are also producing minerals. Iron ore is mined at Michipicotin, north of Sault Ste. Marie, and at Steep Rock, near Rainy River, west of Lake Superior. Gold mines are producing at Red Lake and other places in northwestern Ontario. There are many mines in the belt from Lake Nipigon to Lake of the Woods and north of the Canadian National rail line. Many of these mines depend wholly on air transportation to bring in supplies and equipment. Except for the mining towns and villages along the railroads there is very little settlement in northwestern Ontario.

Less valuable minerals are found along the southern edge of the Shield. Graphite is mined near Renfrew, west of Ottawa; talc is quarried at Madoc, near Kingston; and mica deposits are worked at several places north of Kingston.

Mining in the Canadian Shield of Manitoba and Saskatchewan has not progressed as far as in Quebec and Ontario. There are fewer transportation lines into these sections. Prospectors have not been looking for minerals for as long as they have in Ontario and Quebec. Gold has been found at several places in northeastern Manitoba, especially around God's Lake. This section is probably a continuation of the gold mineralization belt of north-

western Ontario. The other mines are near the western boundary of the province. Copper, zinc and gold are obtained from mines in the Flin Flon-Sherridon area, and nickel has been discovered farther north. The provincial boundary runs through the mining field, and the larger

Courtesy Manitoba Travel and Publicity Bureau.

The mine shaft and mill at Sherridon is the sign of another pioneer town in northern Manitoba. A railroad was built through the northern woods to bring out the rich ore from Sherridon.

share of minerals comes from the Saskatchewan side.

Saskatchewan's Canadian Shield also has been only partially explored for minerals. When new mines are found in northern Saskatchewan, water power can be developed nearby. The people of Saskatchewan have great hopes that the Shield area in their province will yield minerals. These will encourage new industries in addition to those now based on agriculture.

Minerals of the Canadian Shield in the Northwest Territories have been mined since 1930. Gold is mined at Yellowknife on Great Slave Lake and pitchblende at Port Radium on Great Bear Lake. Although these minerals are obtained from the western edge of the Shield they will be discussed in the chapter on the Mackenzie Valley, since their problems are related to those of the Valley.

Very little prospecting has been done in the treeless region west of Hudson Bay. Nickel ore was found south of Chesterfield Inlet in 1928, and gold occurrences have been noted in the interior of Keewatin District. No mining is carried on, however, since the costs of transportation to this remote area are very high.

Forestry

The Canadian Shield now supplies most of the timber for the pulp and paper industry of Canada. In the last century

Courtesy Ontario Lands and Forests.

In spring lumbermen roll logs from the river banks into swollen rivers. The current then carries the logs downstream in rafts to a mill.

lumbering was the chief industry and white pine was the most valuable tree of the forest. Lumbermen penetrated into the headwaters of rivers flowing from the southern edge of the Shield. Before the decline of lumbering the centre of the industry was along the Ottawa River. Strong French-Canadian lumbermen, in spiked boots, rode the logs as the booms were led through the rapids to the mills between Ottawa and Montreal. These were the exciting days of "The Man from Glengarry," so well described in novels by Ralph Connor.

The white pine was greedily cut down with no thought of conservation. The industry then turned to the vast stretches of spruce and balsam. These softwoods are cut during the wintertime, and dragged by truck, tractor or horses to the many rivers. After the ice breaks up in the spring they are floated downstream. At the mills the trees are chopped up and ground into wood

pulp. In some mills the pulping process is continued until finely-ground pulp is pressed out into long sheets of paper. It is then shipped away in heavy rolls. Other mills, usually located within the Shield, send the pulp directly to paper mills in Toronto or Montreal, for example, which are located near markets in the St. Lawrence Lowlands.

Quebec is the leading producer of pulp and paper in Canada, and most of the logs are cut in the Shield. The logging region extends from the Saguenay River on the east to the Ottawa River on the west. Lumber camps are scattered as far north as the headwaters of the southward-flowing rivers. Many French-Canadian farm boys work in the lumber camps in the winter and on farms in summer. Among the many towns manufacturing pulp and paper along the edge of the Shield are Shawinigan Falls, Three Rivers and Hull.

Ontario has very few long rivers flowing southward towards the pulp and paper

Courtesy Ontario Travel and Publicity Department.

The comfortable town of Abitibi in Northern Ontario lies on the Ontario Northland Railroad. In the foreground pulpwood is being piled up for later use in the mill.

markets. Much of the logging must be carried on along railroad lines. At company towns such as Kapuskasing and Iroquois Falls paper is manufactured from logs brought by rail, or from logs floated

132

from the headwaters of northward-flowing rivers. Much is done to make life in the woods comfortable for the workers and their families. Well-equipped loggers cut pulpwood along the shores of Lake Superior, especially in the Nipigon River—Thunder Bay area. New towns are arising as hydro-electric power is supplied by the Ontario government. Large reserves of timber remain untouched in the district west of Lake Superior and north of Lake of the Woods. Mile after mile of dense spruce forests stretch across the Canadian Shield into the uninhabited northern parts of Manitoba.

Forestry is not very important in Manitoba despite the fact that three-quarters of the province is wooded. Most of the people live on farms or in towns in the narrow grassland strip between Lake Winnipeg and the United States border. Small sawmills operate in the Shield east of Lake Winnipeg and a mill on the Winnipeg River makes paper.

Prince Albert, Saskatchewan, was the centre of a busy lumbering industry from 1905 to 1920. The big trees were soon cut, however, and forest fires destroyed other sections. The lumbermen then moved to other areas. Too often this has been the story of exploitation of timber resources in North America. The timber of central Saskatchewan will soon be cut. The province will then have to import more lumber or cut poorer grades of trees in the north.

North of the Churchill River there are no forests of commercial size in the Canadian Shield. The trees are more stunted and are often twisted by the winds. In the Northwest Territories the woods of the Shield are useful only for firewood or for log cabins.

Agriculture

The rocky Canadian Shield is not well suited to agriculture. On the hill tops and steep slopes the soil has been carried away by the continental ice-cap of long ago. The soil in the valleys usually contains much gravel and large stones, and is often poorly drained and swampy. The best soils are found in the beds of former glacial lakes which were formed by the melting waters of the ice-cap. With the exception of the large Clay Belt of northern Ontario and Quebec most of these pockets of good soil are small and scattered.

The Clay Belt was at one time the bottom of old glacial Lake Ojibway. It was formed when the ice-cap melted back to the north of the front edge of the Shield. Since the Shield sloped down to the north the water could not drain southward. To the north drainage was blocked by the ice barrier. The water therefore spread over the land and formed a large lake which was about 350 miles from east to west, and about 200 miles from south to north. When the ice finally melted away to the north, the lake drained into Hudson and James Bays leaving a broad, level lowland.

The lowland of the Clay Belt covers about 30 million acres. This is about the same area as the lowland of Southern Ontario. The gently rolling surface of the Clay Belt is broken here and there by long ridges of gravel. The soils that are a mixture of clay and sand are very fertile. They are especially suitable for agriculture near river banks where they are well drained. There are many sections within the Clay Belt, however, which have infertile sandy soils or swampy land.

The southern part of the Clay Belt, around Lake Temiskaming, was settled as early as 1880. Farmers in the area were able to supply some of the food to the mining camps when mining developed at the beginning of this century. After the Grand Trunk Pacific crossed the northern part of the region in 1910-14, settlers came into this section and began to clear farms in the northern woods. Soon small farming communities grew. More people settled in the Clay Belt following World War

I, and the provincial governments helped others to start farms there during the economic depression years after 1930.

Many of the settlers who came to the Clay Belt were not real farmers. They found that farm life was too hard, clearing took too long, and crops were difficult to sell. In Quebec four out of every ten farms were abandoned after a few years.

area. Pioneers such as these settled southern Ontario and Quebec over a hundred years ago. Canada is fortunate to have these modern pioneers to settle her northern areas.

Clay Belt farmers raise chiefly hay, oats and potatoes. The growing season is too short for most other crops. Farmers sell milk and meat to the nearby towns, and

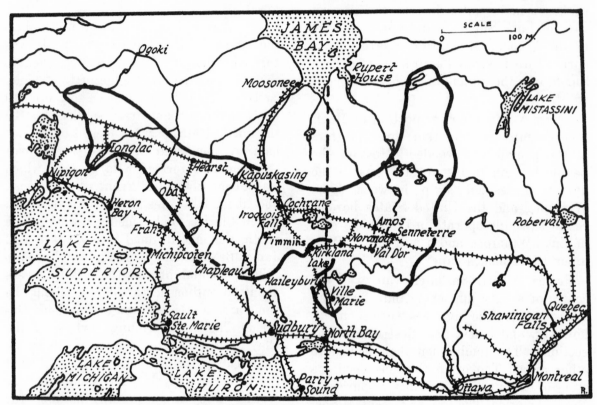

Clay Belt of Northern Ontario-Quebec.

In Ontario seven out of every ten families again moved southward.

Present-day agriculture is well developed in the Lake Temiskaming area. Towns such as Haileybury and New Liskeard in Ontario and Ville Marie in Quebec are prosperous agricultural communities. Farther north, around Cochrane and Kapuskasing in Ontario, and east of Lake Abitibi in Quebec, many farms are still in the pioneer stage. They lack such things as electricity, radios, telephones, pumps and washing machines. The settlers are hard-working, however, and believe strongly in the future of this

raise most of their own food. This region could support a much larger agricultural population. As more roads are built across the Shield, and mining and lumbering towns grow, the farmers will have additional markets for their crops.

Other small agricultural areas are scattered across the Shield, chiefly in Quebec and Ontario. In Quebec the lowland around Lake St. John and the head of Saguenay River has several agricultural towns and happy, contented farm settlers. Milk and vegetables are sold to the mining, lumbering and industrial settlements nearby.

134

In northern Ontario, crops are grown on the small plots of level land near the main cities. There are small farms producing dairy products, poultry and potatoes around Sudbury and Sault Ste. Marie. Near Port Arthur and Fort William

R. W. Harrington photo, courtesy Ontario Travel Bureau.

Agriculture in the Canadian Shield is limited to small pockets of level land and good soil. The rocky hills are never far away. A view of a chicken farm near Port Arthur, Ont.

similar crops are grown. There are a few farmers in the less settled area around Kenora and Rainy River. Settlement in this section is usually along roads or railways. Many of the settlers live in white-washed log houses. They often work for logging companies in the winter to get enough money to run their farms.

In the rest of the Canadian Shield in Manitoba, Saskatchewan, and Northwest Territories, there is no general agriculture carried on. Crops can grow, however, wherever there is soil and settlement. Gardens are producing at nearly every trading post and tiny settlement throughout the area. As far north as Yellowknife, on Great Slave Lake, excellent gardens supply fresh vegetables throughout the summer to the mining population.

Trapping and Fishing

The Canadian Shield is the home of a large share of Canada's Indian population. These people obtain their living following the old methods of hunting and

trapping wild animals in the forest. The chief game animals are moose, deer and caribou. They are killed for meat in the winter, and sometimes the skins are tanned and made into clothing. Whitefish, lake trout, bass, and many other fish are caught in the numerous lakes and rivers during the summer, and through holes in the ice in winter.

Indians today are chiefly trappers. They use the game of the lakes and forests as additional sources of food. Fur-bearing animals such as fox, lynx, ermine, beaver, muskrat and mink are trapped during the winter when their fur is long and glossy. The Indian then brings the pelts to one of the several lonely trading posts scattered throughout the Shield. He trades his furs for food, clothing, utensils and weapons. The use of these articles means that the native does not have to depend upon game and fish as much as he used to a century ago.

The Eskimos who live north of the tree-

Courtesy Manitoba Travel and Publicity Bureau.

An Indian woman is hanging up muskrat pelts to dry in northern Manitoba. The pelts are turned inside-out. Organized trapping is prosperous in the lake-covered lowland near The Pas.

line in Keewatin District and northern Quebec are also hunters and trappers. Since there are fewer animals on the tundra than in the woodlands, Eskimos have to keep moving about throughout the year in search of food. About one thou-

135

sand Eskimos in central Keewatin District kill caribou for food in the autumn as the animals are migrating southward into the woodlands. In the winter they hunt for small wandering herds which remain out on the tundra, and also catch fish through holes in the ice. In spring some Eskimos may come out to the coast of Hudson Bay to hunt seals on the sea-ice. They live in caribou-skin tents in the summer and snow-block igloos in the winter.

Another thousand Eskimos live along the coast of northwestern Hudson Bay. These people make only occasional trips inland for caribou and, throughout most of the year, live on seals hunted off the coast. About two thousand Eskimos living north of the tree-line in Quebec are also coast dwellers. They obtain their food and clothing from the mammals of the sea.

The white fox is the only fur-bearer which the Eskimo can trap. It lives on the tundra, unlike its furry brethren who dwell in the forests. During the winter the Eskimo drives his dog-team and sledge along the coast visiting his traps. The white fox pelts are later taken to fur-trading posts located on the coast.

Since foxes, like the other animals of the tundra, are not numerous, the hardy Eskimo sometimes has trouble in finding enough furs to trade for food and other necessities. The Eskimo is a skilful and patient hunter, however, and if he is not able to trap foxes, he tries all the harder to kill seals or caribou for himself and family.

Cities

Large settlements are located only along the southern edge of the Canadian Shield. Most of them are in rich mining or lumbering districts. Some are important transportation cities and supply centres. All are located in Ontario and Quebec where transportation lines are better developed.

Most of the world's nickel is obtained from mines in the rich area around *Sudbury*. Mining is the chief activity of workmen in the city. Sudbury is also a railroad division point and distributing centre for the surrounding area. *Sudbury* is surrounded by barren rocky hills since the vegetation has been killed by fumes from the ore-roasting ovens. The nickel refineries are located nearby at the towns of Copper Cliff and Coniston.

Fort William and *Port Arthur* are called the "Twin Cities". They are located at the head of Lake Superior where grain from the Prairies is trans-shipped to lake boats. The cities have large grain elevators for storage, flour mills, and many excellent wharves with modern loading equipment. The two cities together form the largest group of people in the Shield. The busy merchants sell supplies to the surrounding mining and logging camps.

The importance of *Timmins* is based upon gold mining. This progressive city is located on a branch line west of the Ontario Northland Railway, and is served by road to the Trans-Canada highway. Several rich gold mines are located in the surrounding area. Some of them have been producing large quantities of gold for more than 40 years. The city has a modern and clean appearance since it has been built within the last few decades.

Sault Ste. Marie is noted for the large locks in the "Soo" canal. The city is an important link in the transportation system of the Great Lakes. Many people work in the blast furnaces of the iron and steel industry. These furnaces obtain some of their iron ore from the nearby Michipicoten area, and coal is imported from the United States.

Shawinigan Falls is an important industrial city on the St. Maurice River. Water-power, obtained from a large dam nearby, has attracted several industries to the city.

French workers have moved in from the farms to help in the making of aluminum, chemicals, and pulp and paper.

Activities at Shawinigan Falls are similar to those carried on at several other smaller cities located on rivers at the southern edge of the Shield in Quebec. The chief cities of the Saguenay Valley are *Chicoutimi, Jonquière, Kenogami* and *Arvida*. North of Shawinigan Falls on the St. Maurice River are *Grand 'Mère* and *La Tuque*. The largest city in the mining region of northwestern Quebec is *Rouyn*. The chief city of northwestern Ontario is *Kenora*. All of these cities are new, and have active, energetic populations which are eager to see the resources of the Canadian Shield developed.

Parks

Many rugged and wild sections of the Canadian Shield have been set aside as parks to preserve their native beauty for tourists. In this way scenery is just as much a resource of a region as are minerals or forests. Thousands of dollars are spent each year by visitors who come in winter and summer to relax and enjoy the unspoiled beauties of Nature. The parks are administered by the provincial governments, and in addition there are many resorts operated by private persons.

Laurentide Park is a large area of wild rivers, quiet lakes and dark forests north of Quebec City. Numerous wild animals roam the area, but no hunting is allowed. Camera enthusiasts are rewarded with many beautiful pictures of unsettled woodland country. A canoe trip along some of the narrow lakes, is a holiday which many people enjoy in the Laurentides.

Mount Tremblant Park, north of Montreal, is typical of Canadian Shield scenery. Cool, forested hills roll to the northward into the wilds of central Quebec. South of the park are some of the finest skiing sections known in Canada. Places

such as Ste. Agathe and Ste. Jovite are famous winter resorts known throughout the world. In winter the week-end ski-trains from Montreal are packed with colourfully dressed skiers and hikers going into the hills to enjoy the fresh clear air and healthful exercise.

La Verendrye Provincial Park is located along the road joining Montreal and the Abitibi area. This road is the only one crossing the central section of the Canadian Shield in Quebec. Visitors come to the park for excellent fishing and take canoe trips through the many lakes and connecting rivers. The lakes are kept stocked with fish so that tourists may make good catches.

In Ontario, Algonquin Park is well known to people from the Lowland. It is a large wilderness area between the Ottawa River and Georgian Bay. Wild animals are protected in their natural state so that city people can see how they

Courtesy Ontario Lands and Forests Department.

Algonquin Park, between the Ottawa River and Georgian Bay, is a shelter for wild animals of the forest. Two inquisitive deer (above) approach the camera man.

live. Algonquin Park is one of the favourite vacation places for people of eastern Ontario. Many a boy or girl is lucky enough to spend a few weeks at one of the well-organized camps in the Park.

Quetico Provincial Park is another wild

section on the international boundary, west of Lake Superior. Few people are able to visit this isolated section, but excellent fishing is the reward for those who come. Since there are not many Canadians living near the park most of the visitors are from the United States.

Whiteshell Forest Reserve is the only park which is set aside in the Shield section of Manitoba. The first white man to enjoy the beauties of this region was La Verendrye, who explored the Winnipeg River in 1734. Volcanic rock cliffs rise directly from the waters of numerous lakes, giving the area the name "Land of Granite Cliffs". Many people from the flat prairies in Manitoba enjoy vacations amid the trees, lakes and hills of Whiteshell Park.

Things To Do

1. Make an outline map of the Canadian Shield from a base map of Canada. Trace on it the largest rivers. Note how the long rivers flow northward or inward and the short ones southward or outward. Draw in the main railroads and roads that cross the Shield.

   (a) Which province has the most transportation lines?

   (b) Which part of the Shield has no roads?

   (c) Are there any large towns in the Shield that are not located on railroads?

2. Read the weather reports in your daily newspaper every day for a week and note the temperatures recorded at towns in the Canadian Shield.

   (a) How much colder or warmer are they than temperatures of cities on the Prairies or St. Lawrence Lowlands?

   (b) Select one city from each of these three regions and each day plot their temperatures on a graph. At the end of the week join the points together with lines or curves. Is the line for the Shield city always at the bottom of the graph?

3. (a) List all the minerals mined in the Canadian Shield. After each mineral name as many places as you can that produce it.

   (b) Are some of these minerals produced at only one place?

   (c) Are there any mines in the Shield not served by railroads? Where are they?

4. In the population chapter of the Canada Year Book find the number of Indians in Ontario, Quebec and Manitoba. Since most of them live in the Canadian Shield, estimate how many square miles each Indian has for hunting grounds. In order to do this, find the area of each province from your text book. Draw the Canadian Shield on a map of Canada and estimate what percentage of each province the Shield covers. How many square miles would this area be? Divide the number of Indians in each province into the area of the Shield in that province to determine how many square miles each Indian has. (In Quebec you should also add the number of Eskimos because they sometimes hunt on the Shield.)

5. (a) How many of the large cities listed in the table at the end of this chapter are in northern Ontario?

   (b) Why are the towns in northern Quebec not so large?

   (c) Why are there no towns from Manitoba in this list?

6. Write an essay describing the changes that have taken place in Canada's use of her forests. Describe the exploitation of the lumbering period, and list several places where forests are almost all cut down. Read chapter 9 again, and the sections on Forestry in each of the regional chapters.

Facts For Reference

Cities of the Canadian Shield, 1941

Sudbury - - - - -	32,203
Fort William - - - -	30,585
Timmins - - - - -	28,790
Sault St. Marie - - -	25,794
Port Arthur - - - -	24,426
Shawinigan Falls - - -	20,325
Chicoutimi - - - -	16,040
North Bay - - - -	15,599
Jonquière - - - - -	13,769
Rouyn - - - - - -	8,808
Grand'Mère - - - -	8,608
La Tuque - - - - -	7,919
Kenora - - - - - -	7,745
Kenogami - - - - -	6,579
St. Joseph d'Alma - - -	6,449

Courtesy Ontario Travel and Publicity Department.

Indian boys play outside their tents at Moose Factory on James Bay. The trading post and mission are located on an island at the mouth of the Moose River. The railway terminal of Moosonee is nearby.

CHAPTER 21

THE HUDSON BAY LOWLAND

The lowland west of Hudson and James Bays is a poorly developed and less important region of Canada. Very few people live there and the known resources are not many. The region is cut off from the rest of Ontario and Manitoba. To the south the sparsely inhabited Canadian Shield separates the Hudson Bay Lowland from the other, well-settled lowlands. A low escarpment forms the northern boundary of the hilly Shield, which is very different topographically from the level Lowland. North of the Lowland the waters of Hudson Bay are frozen over for much of the year, preventing communication in that direction. At some future date the Lowland may play a part in the development of Canada, but at present its geography indicates many difficulties.

The Lowland is a flat, swampy plain stretching west of the shallow waters of southwestern Hudson and James Bays. The rivers, which run rapidly and tumble over the rocks of the Shield, are slow and winding as they cross the level Lowland. Marshes are common between the rivers,

140

but lakes are not as numerous as on the Shield. Much of the area is wooded with stunted trees, except along the barren coast.

Since this region is close to the large area of ice covering Hudson Bay, the climate is cold in winter. It is about as cold as in the Canadian Shield to the southward. Summers are cool near the coast because the water of Hudson Bay is cold. Some days, however, may become quite warm, especially when the wind blows from the land.

Furs are the chief resource of the Hud-son Bay Lowland. The few Indians who live in the area trap fur-bearing animals during the winter and trade them at the posts located at the river mouths. Some of the fur-bearing species have almost dis-appeared. This is not surprising, for they have been trapped for almost 300 years since the coming of the Hudson's Bay Company. In order to maintain a fur sup-ply the Company has organized beaver preserves on some of the islands in James Bay, and also on the mainland of Ontario and Quebec. Only the excess animals are killed each year.

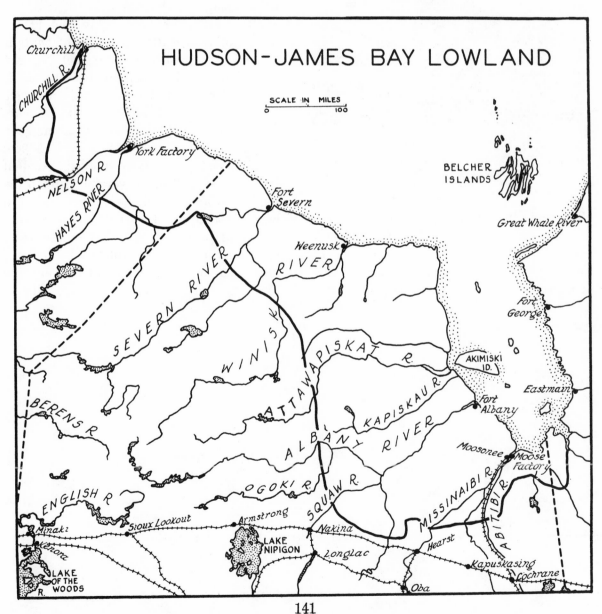

Gardens are kept at most of the post settlements for fresh vegetables. The growing season is long enough for hardy crops to ripen in most years. The residents raise only enough in their gardens for their own needs, however, and are usually too busy with other work to look after farms.

The largest settlement is Churchill, Manitoba, the terminal of the Hudson Bay

Courtesy J. L. Robinson.

The huge grain elevator at Churchill, Manitoba, holds 2½ million bushels of wheat. The village is a rail terminal for northern Manitoba, and is also an ocean port for vessels using the Hudson Bay route.

Railroad. This town of about 200 people is quiet in the winter, except for the activity at the army base located nearby. In summer Churchill is a wheat-exporting port for two or three months. The large grain elevator, which holds 2½ million bushels of wheat, is filled chiefly from the grain fields of northern Saskatchewan. After the floe ice drifts out of Hudson Strait in late July grain ships are able to steam in from the North Atlantic Ocean.

Most other settlements are solely fur-trading posts, but some also have police barracks or missionary buildings. Moosonee, Ontario, is the rail terminal for the Ontario Northland Railway. It is little used because its shallow harbour is not as good as that at Churchill. The trading post of Moose Factory is located nearby on an island in the river. Because of the shallow water in James Bay and at the mouth of Moose River the size of boats is limited to those of five or six feet draught.

A Historic Site Park has been set aside at Fort Prince of Wales, opposite Churchill. It took the English almost 40 years after 1733 to build this strong stone fort. It was captured easily by a French fleet in 1782 and partially destroyed. Ancient iron cannon still peer over the gaps in the parapet walls, which have been restored by the Canadian Government. Each year a special tourist train takes hundreds of visitors through the woods of northern Manitoba to see the huge old fort and the towering grain elevators at Churchill.

CHAPTER 22

THE GREAT PLAINS

Between the Canadian Shield on the east and the Cordillera on the west lies a broad lowland which is part of the Great Plains region of North America. The Canadian section is about 800 miles wide at the International Boundary on the south. The lowland narrows to the north owing to the northwest trend of the Canadian Shield which cuts across the northern part of the Prairie Provinces.

The Great Plains are sometimes called the Prairies because the southern parts, where most of the people live, are grasslands. Settlers came to the grassy area first and were soon growing fine fields of grain. Although most settlement is in the prairie section, the plains region also includes the parkland belt of scattered trees to the north, and the bush country of central Saskatchewan and northern Alberta.

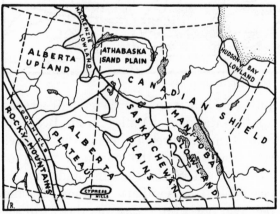
Landform Regions of Prairies.

The forested Mackenzie Valley is also part of the Great Plains region, but you will read about it in a separate chapter because its problems are different from those of the southern section.

Topography

Although there are broad stretches of very level land in the Great Plains region, there are also hilly sections. The land rises in three levels from the flat Manitoba Lowland around Winnipeg to the rolling foothills of the Rockies in Alberta.

The Manitoba Lowland, having elevations of about 850 feet above sea level, is the lowest part of the region. It is the bottom of old glacial Lake Agassiz and is very flat across the centre where the Red River now winds its way. This lowland is the best farming region in Manitoba. To the east the plain merges gradually with the Canadian Shield. Low rocky hills, marking the edge of the Shield, rise slightly above the flat plain. When there are more rocky hills than there are small lowlands one is out of the Plains and into the Shield. The northern part of the Manitoba Lowland is occupied by that province's "Great Lakes"—Winnipeg, Winnipegosis and Manitoba.

To the southwest the Manitoba Lowland slopes to elevations of about 1200 feet in the Pembina Hills. The slope to the westward is gradual along the course of the Assiniboine River. Northwestward the former gravel beaches of old Lake Agassiz rise sharply in steps above the lowland to elevations of over 2000 feet in the Riding Mountains, west of the town of Dauphin.

The surface of southern Saskatchewan is gently rolling where glacial deposits have been left scattered over the plain. Streams have cut deep, narrow valleys down into the plain. In some places streams have disappeared and small dry valleys are left behind. The plain, which extends to the northwest across the South Saskatchewan River, is the best wheat-growing region in Canada. The western boundary of this second level is a hilly escarpment near the Saskatchewan-Alberta boundary.

The third level of the Great Plains has

plain is wooded around Edmonton, except where farms have been cleared. In the northern part of Alberta several flat-topped hilly areas rise above the surrounding, uninhabited bush country.

Climate

The Great Plains are cold in winter and hot in summer. The region can become

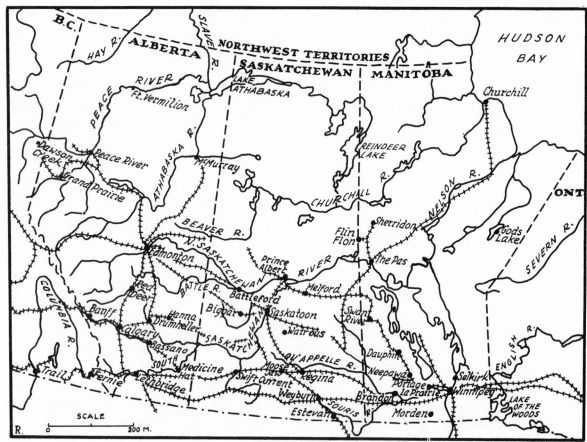

Place names and railroads of Prairie Provinces.

several hilly sections rising above the rolling surface. Near the Saskatchewan-Alberta boundary, Wood Mountain and the Cypress Hills have elevations of more than 4,000 feet and are higher than the surrounding dry plains. Many large ranches are located on their grassy slopes. The plain slopes up to the west where the foothills of the Rockies are about 4,000 feet above sea-level.

West of Edmonton the plain sometimes appears hilly because rivers have cut 200 to 500 feet below the upland surface. The

quite cold in winter when Arctic air sweeps up the Mackenzie Valley from Beaufort Sea. Temperatures as low as –60°F. have been recorded in the northern parts of Alberta and Saskatchewan, and –50° is possible in the southern sections. During the average winter day on the Prairies, temperatures rise to 10° to 25° above zero during the afternoon and drop to 10° to 15° below zero at night. The combination of clear bright days and invigorating dry cold is weather which prairie people like.

Summer days may become quite hot on

the prairies when the bright sun beats down from a clear blue sky upon the level land. The green wheat fields seem to shimmer in the heat haze. Temperatures may rise to over 100° F., but these days are not common.

The farmers of the southern Great Plains do not have as long a growing season without frosts as the people in the St. Lawrence Lowlands. Grains have to ripen rapidly before the first autumn frosts. The Red River Valley of Manitoba has an average of about 115 days each summer without serious frosts. To the northwest

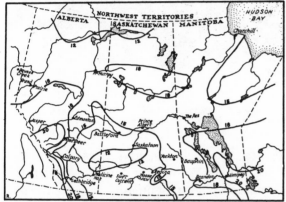

Precipitation areas in Prairie Provinces.

the growing season decreases to 90 or 100 frost-free days around Edmonton.

Prairie farmers are always worrying about the lack of rain. Less than 20 inches of precipitation falls throughout the region in a year. In places where less than 10 inches is received annually it looks almost like a desert. Fortunately for farmers, about half of the precipitation falls as rain during the four growing months of April to July. The dryness of March and April permits the prairie farmer to cultivate his land early and to plant his crops. If the spring rains start too early, the land is turned into sticky mud and there are many difficulties with machinery. The drier period of August and September, with bright sunny days, is excellent for harvesting.

The prairies do not receive the same amount of precipitation each year. Four

or five years of ample rainfall are followed by several dry years when crops do not get enough rain. One of these dry cycles occurred in 1932-36, just when the world was in a great business depression. Many prairie farmers had to borrow money to run their farms, or moved away to new farming regions farther north. More rain fell during the years of World War II, enabling the prairies to grow large amounts of grain to feed much of the rest of the world.

Agriculture

Agriculture is the chief occupation of people in the Prairie Provinces. There are more people on farms than there are engaged in manufacturing. Even the manufacturing industries on the prairies chiefly use agricultural products.

Wheat is the main agricultural crop on the Great Plains. The prairies have about 60 million acres of cultivated land. This acreage is almost seven times that of Ontario farmland. About 7 out of every 10 acres is in wheat. Other cereal crops such as barley and oats cover most of the rest of the farms. In addition to cultivated land there are 30 million acres of grassland in the dry region of southwestern Saskatchewan and southeastern Alberta.

Courtesy Alberta Government.

A characteristic prairie scene has sheaves of golden wheat ripening under sunny Alberta skies. The dark grain elevators stand like sentinels along the railroad in the background.

This is about the size of Nova Scotia and New Brunswick combined. Big ranches raise thousands of cattle and sheep in this largest grazing section in Canada.

145

Almost one-third of the prairie lands lies unused in summer fallow each year. This method of crop rotation is necessary in the dry regions to conserve one year's moisture in the soil for next year's crop. In the wetter sections, land is left fallow every few years in order to plough under the weeds, which grow rapidly along with the grains.

The chief soil zones of the prairies have different crops. The brown soils of the dry region are used chiefly for grazing. There is not as much cultivated land in this section as there is farther north. The ranches are very large. Those of the Cypress Hills and Sandhills section of Saskatchewan average 5,000 to 15,000 acres each. Almost 100 farms from the St. Lawrence Lowlands could be placed on one large prairie ranch. Cowboys work on the ranches, and one of their main jobs is to round up the cattle in the fall. Some of the cattle are then driven to the nearest railroad to be shipped to slaughter houses for meat. Others are transported to pastures in southern Manitoba for

A group of cowboys ride over a small sand dune in the dry southern prairies. Part of southwestern Saskatchewan and southeastern Alberta is too dry for agriculture.

further fattening. The smaller ranches of the Alberta Foothills average about 5,000 acres in size. The Foothills ranches are more prosperous than those of the dry land areas because they receive more rain and have a longer grazing season due to the warm chinook winds.

Many sections of the dry lands have

been made productive by a few large dams controlling the water of the main rivers, or by many small earthen dams holding back the spring run-off on the tributaries. "Dug-outs", or shallow ponds, are often dug in the rolling land to hold the ground water during the summer. The fertile soils can then produce excellent crops of

Ranches are very large on the grasslands of the Alberta Foothills. High quality beef cattle, watched by a lone cowboy on the hill, graze on the treeless prairie.

alfalfa, sugar beets, and vegetables. Alfalfa is used for winter feed for the cattle ranches. After the juice is squeezed from sugar beets, the remaining pulp is also good cattle feed. These irrigation projects cost much money, and need everyone's co-operation to be successful. They make green fields and happy homes where once there was only brown grass and dusty sagebrush.

Farmers on the dark-brown prairie soils raise most of Canada's wheat. About 70 per cent of the cultivated land produces wheat, and the remainder is chiefly in oats and barley. Since this soil zone is widest in southern Saskatchewan, that province produces more wheat than its neighbours. The large grain farms usually cover a section (640 acres) of rolling prairie. Some farms, with machinery such as automatic threshers and big disks for turning the soil, may occupy more than one section. One man and his family, and sometimes a hired man, usually run the farm alone. At harvest time, in August or

September, when extra help is needed, special trains sometimes bring workers all the way from Eastern Canada.

The black-soil zone is the mixed-farming region of the prairies. The farms in this zone keep a great deal of livestock, which are fed on the grains. The farmers raise more wheat than any other crop. Five out of every ten acres are producing wheat. They also raise oats, barley, and flax. Much of the bacon, hams and beef that we eat in Canada, or ship overseas, comes from the mixed-farming zone.

The parklands are the pioneer regions

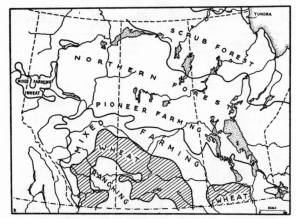

Agricultural and Vegetation Regions of Prairie Provinces. (Compare with soil map on page 36)

of the Great Plains. The first settlers to enter the region started their farms on the grasslands, where clearing of trees was not necessary. After the best grasslands were occupied, settlers made clearings in the parklands—the region of mixed grass and forest. This migration was speeded up during the dry years after 1930. Many farmers from the dry grasslands gave up their farms, which could not produce at that time, and moved northward into the wetter parklands. A few roads and railroads have gradually been built into the fringe of pioneer settlement, but the zone is still sparsely settled and lacks transportation.

Wheat is also the chief crop grown by farmers in the pioneer areas. Barley and oats are becoming more important. These grains are used to feed livestock, which are later sold for meat. Some dairying is carried on to supply milk to the local population.

Settlement in the parklands is advancing slowly compared with the rapid development of the southern prairies. The pioneer has to clear the land of trees, and remove stumps. It then takes a few years before the soil begins to produce well. A farmer is fortunate if he is able to clear five or ten acres of new land each year, and therefore his farm grows slowly. Since he is far away from large towns, his crops are hard to sell. He often has to work part-time at trapping, lumbering, or road construction to make enough money to buy new equipment and tools. In spite of these difficulties there still are hardy men and women in Canada who are willing to work hard to have their own land. These are the people who are settling Canada's northern frontier.

The Peace River country is north of the main agricultural region of the prairies. When settled by pioneers after World War I it was the last large area in Canada where free land was still available. Some of the edges of the area could still be called pioneer land, but the sections around Grand Prairie are now prosperous, established farming regions.

Until about 1910, the Peace River country was settled only by traders and missionaries. The first homesteaders moved into the area by way of Indian trails from Edmonton. The railroad finally reached the Peace River area in 1916, and allowed the settlers to ship out their products. New settlers came in on the railroad and the population jumped from about 10,000 in 1910 to almost 60,000 in 1945. The settling of the Peace River area was part of the last wave of the tide of settlement which swept over our Prairie Provinces early in this century.

The Peace River country is a rolling upland with elevations of 2,000 feet sloping to the east and to the north. Rivers flowing through the area have cut deeply into the upland. For example, Peace River town is 800 feet above the water of the river. Although the frost-free period is only 85 to 90 days, fast-maturing grains ripen in the long summer days.

Most farms carry on mixed farming, except in the Grand Prairie area where excellent hard wheat is grown. Small grains and livestock are raised on all farms. The farmer usually feeds the grains to livestock and obtains his money from the sale of meat. Clover seed is a specialty crop, especially around Dawson Creek.

The best lands in the Peace River country are now occupied, but there are still large areas of good soils which could support farming. The new pioneer sections are located west of Hines Creek and Spirit River in Alberta and along the Alaska Highway in the British Columbia part of the district. North of the Peace River block there is more good land available around Fort Vermilion. However, lands located farther south with better transportation lines, will probably be occupied before settlement reaches this area.

Mining

The sedimentary rocks of the Great Plains contain non-metallic minerals, similar to those mined in the St. Lawrence Lowlands. Coal, petroleum, natural gas, salt, gypsum, sodium sulphate, and clay are all obtained from the region.

There is more coal mined in Alberta than in any other province. The fuel is located in four main north-south belts of coal-bearing rock. Several small coal-mining towns are located along the foothills of the Rockies, and in the western part of the plains from Lethbridge to Drumheller to Edmonton. About half the coal is mined at several places in the belt near the British Columbia-Alberta boundary.

Coal of poorer quality is mined at Estevan in southeastern Saskatchewan. It supplies fuel and power to that part of the province and to part of Manitoba. The people in central Saskatchewan import their coal from the fields around Edmon-

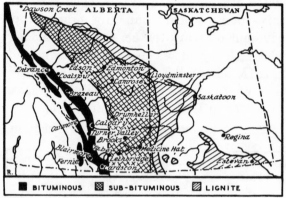

Coal Fields of Western Prairies.

ton. Prairie miners have dug out over 200 million tons of coal since production started in 1886. There are still millions of tons in reserve to be mined in the future as the demand increases. Alberta could be producing much more coal now if there was a larger population in Western Canada, and if the cost of transporting coal to Eastern Canada was less.

Most of Canada's petroleum comes from Alberta. The Turner Valley field, near Calgary, became the largest producer in Canada after 1936. It reached its peak of production in 1942, with over 10 million barrels of oil, and has gradually declined. Several oil companies have found new fields in the zone between Lethbridge and Edmonton and east to the Saskatchewan boundary. One of the results of exploration was the discovery of the petroleum fields at Leduc and Redwater in the Edmonton district. Alberta now produces more petroleum than the Prairie Provinces can use.

Natural gas is often found near petroleum fields. The people in Alberta have large reserves of natural gas which they use for heating. The large field at Medicine Hat began producing gas in 1890 and

148

still supplies homes and industries in southern Alberta. The Viking and Kinsella fields, east of Edmonton, have been used by that city for over 20 years. The field continues eastward into Saskatchewan at Lloydminster.

The bituminous oil sands at McMurray, northern Alberta, may be capable of producing about four times as much petroleum as the whole world has at present. The sands cover an area of at least 10,000 square miles around McMurray, at the junction of the Clearwater and Athabasca Rivers. The problem is to separate the oil from the sand. A suitable method of obtaining this oil cheaply has puzzled scientists for many years. The area produces asphalt, fuel oil, and some gasoline at present, but there are few people nearby to use them.

Salt has been found at several places in the Great Plains. At McMurray, the large field was not producing as much salt as possible because transportation costs for shipment southward are high. The mine was therefore closed and the company started a new mine at Unity, Saskatchewan. Potash has also been discovered at Unity. It is possible that much of central Saskatchewan is underlain by a huge salt bed which could supply all the needs of the prairie people. A smaller salt mine has been producing at Neepawa, Manitoba, for many years. It supplies the people of the southern Manitoba section.

Some of the less valuable minerals of the Great Plains include gypsum, which is mined at several places in Manitoba between Winnipeg and Lake Manitoba. Sodium sulphate is obtained from dried-up alkali lakes in southern Saskatchewan. These are the only natural deposits in Canada. At Lake Chaplin one of the largest alkali plants in the world operates. The sodium sulphate is shipped to Ontario for use in the kraft paper industry, nickel refining, the making of glass, and as a chemical in soapless cleaning powder.

Several brick-making factories, which use local clay, are located throughout the Great Plains. Clay, which is made into fire-resistant bricks, comes from the Dirt Hills section, south of Moose Jaw, Saskatchewan. The white clays of the Cypress Hills are of good quality and are made into heavy-duty dishes and sewer pipes.

Courtesy Saskatchewan Film Board.

Sodium sulphate is a valuable mineral resource in Saskatchewan . The water from alkali lakes is pumped into large flat basins (above) and allowed to stand. When the water is drained off in autumn, the white sodium sulphate can be shovelled from the bottom of the basin.

Lumbering, Fishing and Trapping

The occupations of lumbering, fishing and trapping are not followed by many people in the Great Plains region. Since much of the region is treeless, lumber is cut only in the parkland areas to the north. Some men operate small sawmills for local needs, and pioneer settlers cut fuelwood in the forests. Most lumber and wood materials needed in the prairie cities must be imported from the forested regions of the Cordillera or Canadian Shield.

Commercial fishermen catch whitefish, lake trout, pickerel, and the famous "Winnipeg Goldeye" in the "Great Lakes" of Manitoba. These fish are shipped frozen to prairie cities and into the United States. Few fish are caught in the southern prairies because there are no large lakes, and most rivers are shallow. In the northern Great Plains fish are obtained from Lesser Slave Lake and Lake Athabaska.

A few white men and many Indians trap in the northern forested section of the Great Plains. The same fur-bearers that are trapped in the Canadian Shield are also obtained from these northern forests. In some years the trappers of Alberta obtain more furs than trappers of any other province. Many settlers in the frontier sections carry on trapping as a part-time winter activity. As settlement pushes northward, however, the animals are retreating into the Canadian Shield and Mackenzie Valley.

Courtesy Manitoba Travel and Publicity Bureau.

Meat-packing is an important industry at several prairie cities. The huge stockyards at St. Boniface, Manitoba, hold thousands of head of cattle for slaughtering or shipment to Eastern Canada.

Manufacturing

Manufacturing is not as important as agriculture in the Prairie Provinces. Most of the manufacturing plants obtain their raw materials from the farming industry. The most important of the five leading prairie manufacturing industries is slaughtering and meat-packing. Cattle, and to a lesser extent swine and sheep from the grasslands and mixed-farming regions, are brought to the large prairie cities to be killed. The meat is then shipped in refrigerated railway cars to all parts of Canada and some is sent overseas. The second and third leading industries of the prairies are also based on agriculture. People in flour-and-feed mills, the second leading industry, turn out products slightly more valuable than the

butter and cheese industry, which holds third place. These industries are scattered across all three provinces. Each factory is in the centre of a small farming district.

The manufacture of petroleum products is important in each province because of the large amount of machinery used in the cities and on the farms. Alberta produces more gasoline, fuel oil, kerosene and other petroleum products than the other Prairie Provinces since it has most of the oil wells. Some is imported in tank cars from the United States and manufactured into petroleum products.

The making of railway rolling stock is the fifth industry of the Great Plains. The workers in the rail centre of Winnipeg produce railway cars, locomotives, and parts. There are more people occupied in this industry in Manitoba than in the more valuable one of slaughtering and meat packing.

Other manufactures, which supply the local population, are about the same as those found in each region of Canada. They include clothing factories, bakeries, breweries, printing and publishing plants, sawmills, and bag and box factories.

Cities

Winnipeg, the fourth city in population in Canada, contains over twice as many people as any other prairie city. It has an excellent location at the junction of the Red and Assiniboine Rivers, in the middle of the fertile Red River Valley. Winnipeg is like the mouth of a funnel for all transportation lines in Western Canada. Roads and railroads between Eastern and Western Canada have to pass through the narrow space between Lake Winnipeg and the International Boundary. In the middle of this area lies Winnipeg. The city has large railroad yards and repair shops. Trains from the east or west stop there; locomotives are changed and left there to be checked over; passengers have a chance to rest before continuing their journey in new trains. Besides being a transportation centre, Winnipeg is the chief manufacturing city in Manitoba.

The people of Winnipeg are a mixture of numerous races and nationalities. At one time twenty-two foreign-language

Winnipeg is the largest city on the prairies. This view looks West over its business district along Portage Avenue. The well-planned city has wide main streets for its busy traffic.

newspapers were published in the city. One of the scenic views of Winnipeg is lovely Assiniboine Park, located along the winding, wooded banks of the river. The

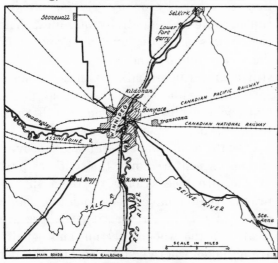

Winnipeg area.

Parliament Buildings and the University of Manitoba are also located in Winnipeg. *St. Boniface*, noted for its meat-packing plants and large stock yards, is a separate

city on the east side of the Red River. It is really a part of "Greater Winnipeg".

Edmonton is called "The Gateway to the North." People pass through it going northwest to Yukon Territory via the Alaska Highway, or northward to the Mackenzie Valley. Supplies and equipment are usually bought at Edmonton and shipped northward. The city has a beautiful setting on the level upland high above the North Saskatchewan River. The main business district and many of the industries are located on the north side of the

The city of Edmonton is divided into two sections by the North Saskatchewan River. Looking north from the University grounds the "high level" bridge leads to the Alberta Parliament Buildings.

river, while some of the residential areas and the University of Alberta are on the south side. The city serves the rich mixed farming area of central Alberta, and is in the centre of a growing petroleum industry.

Calgary is a busy industrial city as well as a centre for transportation lines leading westward into the mountains. Oil refineries are located there, using oil from nearby Turner Valley and other fields. Cattle from the surrounding ranches are brought to Calgary for slaughtering and shipping. The cattle-pens at the railroad yards are very large and are usually full. The city is famous for its "Calgary Stampede", where every summer thousands watch riding, roping, and bucking bronchos. St. George's Island Park in Calgary is noted for the models of prehistoric animals that roamed this area millions of years ago.

Regina is the capital of Saskatchewan, and the chief distribution centre for the southern part of the province. It is the only large prairie city that is not located on a river. Regina has had space to grow in all directions and few tall buildings have been necessary. Large grain elevators and flour mills show the importance of wheat to the people of the city. Meat packing is also a busy industry. From across Regina's artificial lake the beautiful stone of the Parliament Buildings makes one of the finest sights in the city.

Saskatoon, located on the South Saskatchewan River, is the chief city in central Saskatchewan. Its industries are similar to those of Regina, and are based on the rich agricultural lands in the surrounding district. Dairying is especially well developed. The scenic campus of the University of Saskatchewan is located near the river in a pretty part of the city. Several bridges connect the old and new parts of the city which are on opposite sides of the river.

Parks

The people of the Great Plains have built or preserved many beautiful parks within their region. Most of the parks are located north of the grasslands within the cool shade of the parkland forests. There one finds excellent facilities for boating, bathing, and relaxing. Fishing is nearly always good. The surrounding wild woodlands promise excellent pictures for the person with a camera. The parks of Jasper, Banff and Waterton are really within Alberta, but being located in the mountains, are described in the chapter on the Cordillera.

Riding Mountain National Park is a rolling woodland area rising above the plains west of Lake Manitoba. From the escarpment a beautiful view of the checker-board pattern of farms on the fertile prairies stretches away for miles. Big game, including deer, elk, moose and bear, live in the park. A summer resort has been developed at Clear Lake where visitors may enjoy boating, swimming and outdoor recreation.

Courtesy Alberta Department of Economic Affairs.

Wheat has been the chief crop of the prairies since the days of first settlement. Since wheat takes the minerals from the soil without putting anything back, yields per acre on the prairies have slowly been declining.

Prince Albert National Park is in the wooded lakeland country of central Saskatchewan. Thousands of crystal lakes are tied together by many rivers, making canoe routes of hundreds of miles. The region was once the hunting grounds of the Cree Indians and many of the lakes still bear strange Indian names. Beautiful white sand beaches attract vacationists, and sport fishing brings many fishermen for a few days or weeks of relaxation.

Saskatchewan has several small provincial parks scattered over the southern part of the province. Some of them in the prairie region have trees and are shady places of rest and recreation. Others are located in the wooded section and usually are on lakes where swimming and boating can be enjoyed.

Alberta has a larger area set aside in National Parks than any other province. Wood Buffalo Park, on the Alberta-Northwest Territories boundary, is the largest big-game preserve in North America. This huge unfenced park contains Canada's largest herds of woodland and plains buffalo. The latter were moved there from Wainwright Buffalo Park when it was closed. Only resident Indians can hunt or trap in Wood Buffalo Park.

Alberta has another animal reserve at Elk Island Park, east of Edmonton. It is a fenced reserve for a large herd of plains buffalo, and also shelters many elk, deer and moose. A recreational area has been cleared there for visitors from central Alberta.

In addition to large National Parks, Alberta has a great number of provincial parks. More than a dozen small parks have been opened near cities throughout the province. They provide facilities for fun and rest for tourists and people on vacation. Some of the parks are noted for their picnic grounds, others for fishing or game. Some parks simply preserve the natural beauty of the country so that man cannot spoil or destroy it.

Things To Do

1. Read about the settlement of the Prairie Provinces in your history books. As you read, think about the topography, vegetation and climate of the southern prairies.

   (a) Explain how the physical geography of this region was favourable to the first settlers.

   (b) Pretend that you are a settler entering the Great Plains of Canada about 1890. Describe what you would see as you travelled by train to Calgary from Ontario.

   (c) If you had come from England describe your impression of your first winter on the prairies.

2. Describe the seasonal activities of a wheat farmer on the prairies. Start with spring planting in March or April and show how the farmer's work throughout the year is closely connected with the weather and his one crop. Describe what he does when the rain is sufficient, and what he does when his farm receives too much or too little rain. What activities does the prairie farmer carry on in the winter time?

3. On a map of the Great Plains region mark in all of the areas of pioneer agriculture. Draw a heavy line across the map indicating the present northern limit of prairie agriculture. How far north of this line are the pioneer regions? Draw in the chief railroad lines extending northward. Do all of the pioneer regions have rail transportation?

4. (a) List the minerals of the Great Plains that are the same as those mined in the St. Lawrence Lowlands.

   (b) Are any minerals of the Canadian Shield found in the Great Plains?

   (c) Read Chapter 8 on Mining and compare the importance and value of the Great Plains' minerals with the other minerals of Canada.

5. Suppose that you lived in each of Winnipeg, Edmonton, Calgary and Regina for a few years, and are writing a letter to a friend in Southern Ontario telling him of the advantages which each city has. In your letter explain how their locations helped the cities to grow. What disadvantages do the cities have in their locations? Which of the cities have played important parts in the history of the West? Which city do you think will grow faster than the others in the future? Why do you think so?

Facts For Reference

What People do in Manitoba (1941)

Agriculture	92,230
Manufacturing	34,317
Fishing and Trapping	5,193
Mining	3,417
Forestry	1,634
Service	50,380
Trade and Commerce	34,380
Transportation and Communication	21,830
Construction	12,355
Total	255,736

What People do in Saskatchewan

Agriculture - - - - - - - -	187,396
Manufacturing - - - - - -	15,241
Fishing and Trapping - - -	2,687
Mining - - - - - - - - -	1,053
Forestry - - - - - - -	1,036
Service - - - - - - - -	50,685
Trade and Commerce - - -	25,167
Transportation and Communication	18,785
Construction - - - - - -	6,574
Total - - - - - - - -	308,624

What People do in Alberta

Agriculture - - - - - -	141,196
Manufacturing - - - - - -	22,767
Mining - - - - - - - -	9,951
Fishing and Trapping - - - -	2,991
Forestry - - - - - - -	1,163
Service - - - - - - - -	48,483
Trade and Commerce - - - -	26,284
Transportation and Communication	18,027
Construction - - - - - -	10,372
Total - - - - - - - -	281,234

Cities of the Prairies:

	1941	1946
Winnipeg - - - - -	221,960	230,000
Edmonton - - - - -	93,817	114,000
Calgary - - - - - -	88,904	100,000
Regina - - - - - -	58,245	60,300
Saskatoon - - - - -	43,027	46,000
Moose Jaw - - - - -	20,753	23,000
St. Boniface - - - - -	18,157	21,600
Brandon - - - - - -	17,383	17,500
Lethbridge - - - - -	14,612	16,500
Prince Albert - - - -	12,508	14,500
Medicine Hat - - - -	10,571	13,000
Portage la Prairie - - -	7,187	7,700
Flin Flon - - - - -	....	7,600
Weyburn - - - - -	6,179	7,000
Swift Current - - - -	5,594	6,400
Yorkton - - - - - -	5,557	5,700

Courtesy Consolidated Mining and Smelting Co.

The huge chemical and fertilizer plant at Trail, B.C., uses by-products of the lead and zinc smelter and refinery. The ore is brought by rail from Kimberley.

CHAPTER 23

THE CORDILLERA

The far-western part of Canada is a series of north-south mountain ranges and plateaus. It is part of the larger Cordilleran system which extends through North America from Mexico to Alaska. Between the mountain ranges are sheltered valleys where people live. More than half the population of British Columbia lives in the valley near the mouth of the Fraser River in the southwestern part of the province.

The Cordilleran region in Canada contains the province of British Columbia and Yukon Territory. The Territory is north of 60 degrees latitude, and its main rivers flow northward into Alaska. It will be discussed in a separate chapter since its development is more like that of Northern Canada than that of the provinces. British Columbia's outlook is towards the

west where its rivers empty. The mountain barrier tends to cut it off from the rest of Canada.

Topography

The Rocky Mountains are the most easterly range of the Cordillera. Sometimes the name "Rockies" is incorrectly given to the whole series of mountain ranges in British Columbia, but the Rockies are really only one of several ranges. They rise abruptly above the Alberta Foothills as a solid wall of rocky peaks. Snow-covered crests of over 10,000 feet altitude tower above the Alberta ranches. Mount Robson (12,972 feet), near Jasper Park in the Rockies, is the highest.

Banff and Jasper National Parks have been set aside in the Rockies so that the wonderful scenery may be enjoyed by everyone. There one may see glaciers, ice-caps, rushing mountain streams, quiet lakes, broad valleys and steep slopes. Similar features are found in the Rocky Mountains throughout their length. The Rockies decrease in elevation to the north-

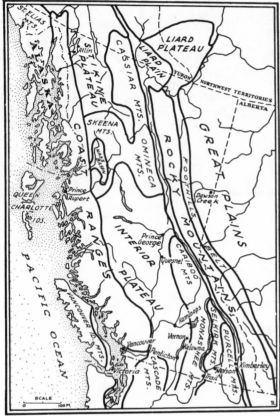

Mountain Systems of British Columbia.

ward and end at the Liard River in northern British Columbia. Other ranges continue into Yukon Territory.

The deep Rocky Mountain Trench separates the Rockies from the Columbia Mountain System in the south and the Cassiar Ranges in the north. The Selkirk Range lies in the southern part of the System and is bounded on the east, north and west by the Columbia River. The Selkirks are jagged, sharp-peaked mountains which are similar in appearance to the Rockies. Peaks of over 11,000 feet rise boldly above green, forested slopes.

The western part of the Columbia Mountain System includes the Cariboo Mountains in the north and Monashee

Mountains in the south. These ranges are not as jagged or high as the Rockies or Selkirks, but still are rugged masses of rock which are of little use to man. The discovery of several rich minerals in these mountains has resulted in some important mining towns in the valleys. The Cassiar Range is a jumbled group of mountains situated in central northern British Columbia. Although prospectors found gold there in the last century, very few people live in the area now.

Between the mountain ranges are several long narrow valleys where people are able to live either by farming or by mining. The East Kootenay region extends from the town of Cranbrook in the south to near the "Big Bend" at the north end of the Columbia River. The Kootenay River drains the southern part of the valley, and the Columbia drains the northern section. The West Kootenay section

Courtesy R.C.A.F.

Glaciers are beautiful rivers of ice as they flow down from the Coast Range, inland from Knight Inlet, B.C. Westerly winds which rise over the Coast Range drop their snowfall on the western slopes. The packed snow turns to ice and begins to move.

extends north from the farming town of Creston through long and narrow Kootenay Lake. The area is drained southwesterly past Nelson into the Columbia River.

The West Columbia Valley has the

smelting and refining town of Trail at its southern end. To the northward the Upper and Lower Arrow Lakes are broadenings of the river. The railroad centre of Revelstoke is the chief settlement in the northern section of the Columbia. The amount of level land for farming or settlements is quite limited in the narrow valleys of the Cordillera.

The Interior Plateau includes most of central British Columbia between the Coast Range on the west, and the Columbia Mountain System and Rockies on the east. The plateau has a rolling upland surface. Rivers have cut deep gashes into the plateau, however, giving it a hilly or mountainous appearance close to the waterways.

The Okanagan Valley, in the southern part of the plateau, drains southward into the United States. Much of Canada's fruit is grown along the slopes of Okanagan Lake, and in other small valleys in the southern plateau. The south-central part of the plateau is cut from east to west by the Thompson River which empties into the Fraser. The first railroads followed the smooth grade of the Thompson through the rugged plateau, and along the valley of the Fraser through the mountains to the sea.

The northern part of the Interior Plateau is drained southward by the Fraser River. Around the town of Prince George the level upland stretches for hundreds of miles. Vast acreages of pioneer agricultural land are found in this sparsely settled section along the Canadian National Railway, and southward to the grazing country near Williams Lake.

The Coast Range rises directly from the Pacific Ocean to heights of about 6,000 feet. Peaks of 7,000 to 10,000 feet are found inland. In the northern part of the province several peaks of this range, such as Mount Waddington, 14,000 feet, are higher than Mount Robson in the Rockies. The Fraser, Skeena, Nass, and Stikine Rivers cut through the high mountains from the interior, and have often been used as transportation routes. Numerous long, narrow, twisting fiords penetrate the mountains from the coast. They are former glacial valleys which have been filled with ocean water after

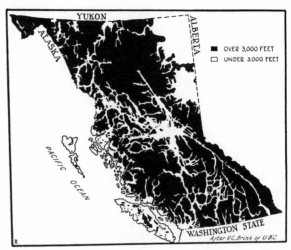

Elevations in B.C.

the land slowly sank thousands of years ago. Many offshore islands mark the peaks of submerged mountains which are now being attacked by waves from the ocean.

Vancouver Island and the Queen Charlotte Islands are the tops of another mountain range which is now under the sea. High mountains, dense forests and heavy rainfall make the western coast of Vancouver Island a difficult place in which to live or travel. Forestry is the chief occupation of people in the small coastal settlements.

Climate

Because of its mountainous character, British Columbia has great differences in climate within short distances. The western side of a mountain may receive heavy rainfall while the eastern side has very little. Valley bottoms may be hot and dry, but slopes receive more rainfall and are usually cooler. Cold, snow-capped mountain peaks may be found a few miles from mild coastal cities. All these varieties of

157

climate show that it is difficult to describe the climate of British Columbia because every section has its exceptions.

The warmest part of British Columbia in winter is the west coast. The coastal lowlands and sheltered valleys are warmer than the coastal mountains. The winters in Victoria or Vancouver are very different from the winters that people in the rest of Canada know. Snow falls there only occasionally and soon melts away. The temperature has never dropped below zero. The Interior Plateau, however, may become quite cold. Prince George, in the northern interior, has recorded –30°F., or more, many times. The high mountains and valleys of eastern British Columbia are also cold throughout the winter.

Summers are cool and bright along the west coast. Victoria's large amount of annual sunshine is among the highest recorded in Canada. Temperatures seldom rise above 75° F. during the summer months. In the valleys of the Interior Plateau, however, the days become quite warm, and temperatures often rise to over 90°F. Clear summer days are common over the Interior Plateau, but mountain peaks are often cloud-covered.

The frost-free period decreases inland from the coast and to the northward. There are about 7½ months without frosts

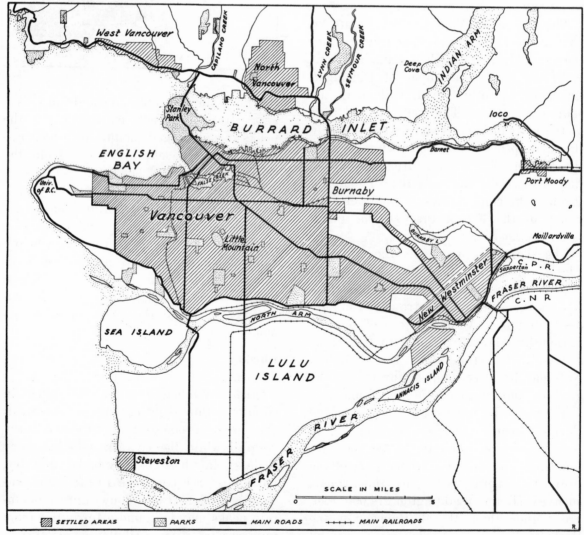

Vancouver Area.

in the Fraser delta in the southwest, and only about 2 months at Prince George in the Interior Plateau. The fruit-growing region of the Okanagan Valley has an average of more than 6 months that are frost-free, and the East Kootenay Valley has about 3 frost-free months at Windermere.

Precipitation is heavy along the west coast. Warm, moist winds from the Pacific Ocean drop their moisture as they are forced to rise over the coastal mountains. More than 200 inches of rain are recorded on the west coast of Vancouver Island, and almost as much on the open coast near Prince Rupert. Vancouver receives 58 inches of precipitation, most of which falls as a steady light rain during the winter months. Vancouver's annual rainfall is twice as much as that of Victoria since the latter is on the leeward, or "rain shadow", side of the mountains.

The Interior Plateau, and especially the deep valleys, receive very little rainfall. The winds usually pass over them without dropping their moisture. Most of the area receives less than 20 inches in a year, and some sections are almost deserts with less than 10 inches of rain. Western slopes of mountains, however, receive more rainfall which can be used to irrigate the valley bottoms.

Forestry

Forestry is the most valuable of the primary industries of British Columbia. The heavy rainfall and mild climate are excellent for forest growth. The tall Douglas firs and red cedars have heights of 200 to 300 feet and may be 5 to 7 feet across. The trunk of the Douglas fir is straight and free from branches almost to its top. Large timbers of more than 100 feet in length and 3 or 4 feet square can be sawn from the tree and used for bridges or large buildings. Among the other trees used in British Columbia are western hemlock **and** Sitka spruce.

British Columbia is the leading lumbering province of Canada. About half of Canada's lumber is cut there. Much of it is exported to foreign countries that do not have the same kind of trees. Port Alberni is a lumbering centre on Vancouver Island, and Port Alice at the north

J. Cash photo, courtesy Seaboard Ltd.

The forests of British Columbia have very tall and straight trees, which make excellent lumber. This tree is being "topped" and later may be used as a "spar" tree.

end of the Island is important for newsprint. Rafts of logs cut from the eastern side of the Island, and from the mainland north of Vancouver, **are** towed across Georgia Strait to the large lumber mills at Vancouver and New Westminster. The huge sawmills at the mouth of the Fraser River employ hundreds of people. They operate machines that make many wood products out of the logs. Most of Canada's shingles are cut from the tall and strong western red cedar of southwestern British Columbia.

Pulp and paper has been secondary to lumber in British Columbia but is increasing in importance. Powell River, on the coast about 75 miles north of Vancouver, and Ocean Falls, farther north, are the largest paper centres. New mills are being

Courtesy Canadian Geographical Journal.

Powell River is a company town built up around a large pulp and paper mill about 75 miles north of Vancouver. It has an excellent sheltered harbour from which paper can be exported directly to the United States.

built, some of which plan to use the waste from lumbering operations.

In the Interior Plateau, timber is felled for many small sawmills scattered over the forested region and usually located close to the railroads. Lumbermen are also cutting into the forests on the slopes of the Selkirks wherever there are transportation lines. Trees which are used are Engleman spruce, lodgepole pine and western larch.

Lumbering methods on the west coast are different from those in Eastern Canada. Lumbermen use more machinery and work continues throughout the whole year. Lumbering areas are usually cut over completely and all trees removed or knocked down. This is different from the "selective cutting" methods of Eastern Canada where trees are cut in strips, and sections

are left for later years. Since the good lumber of the West Coast is being cut down faster than it is growing, the government is now insisting that the companies practise conservation and reforestation.

One method of logging in British Columbia is by use of the "sky-line" or "high lead". A steel cable, called the sky-line, is stretched between two high trees some distance apart. From a trolley on this line another cable is dropped down into the forest and is attached to trees which have been felled by power saws. The cable then drags the tree-trunk through the forest to the base of the sky-line where it

J. Cash photo, courtesy Seaboard Ltd.

The "sky-line" is one of the main methods of logging in B.C. Logs are pulled by a steel wire and pulley to a central "spar" tree, where they are piled. All small trees are knocked over by this method.

is piled up with others. This method can be used on rough, rocky ground and on steep slopes where trucks and tractors cannot move. If the land is more level, loggers drive tractors over rough roadways, towing the trunks to a central collecting station.

After the logs from one section are all assembled they are transported by narrow-gauge railroads or trucks to the coast. There, sawmills either cut them into lumber and boards, or the logs are made into large raft booms and towed by tugs to a sawmill centre. The large sawmills are well equipped with machinery. They are able to cut the trunks into large square timbers several feet across, or into thin plywood a quarter-inch thick. It is a thrilling sight to visit a sawmill. The washed logs enter one end of the mill, and big hooks hold them in place, feeding them into buzzing circular saws. The logs are sliced into planks of different thicknesses. A planing machine smooths the surface and the planks or boards are piled outside the mill for seasoning.

Mining

The men in many settlements in British Columbia work almost entirely in the mining industry. Mines of the Cordillera are Canada's leading producers of lead and zinc, and are very important for copper, coal, gold and silver. As the mountains slowly rose, minerals which were formed far below the earth's surface also came up. Streams cutting into the mountain slopes now expose the ore. There it lies awaiting the prospector. Since the Cordillera is very rough and rugged, transportation is lacking in many sections. Only a small part of British Columbia has been prospected, but eager men roam the hills looking for the hidden wealth.

The Kimberley area of southeastern British Columbia produces about 10 per cent of the world's lead and zinc. The rich Sullivan Mine of that region has gold, silver, copper, antimony, cadmium, bismuth and tin as by-products. Similar lead-zinc ores are mined in the Slocan district, west of Kootenay Lake, but they are not as rich as the ores at Kimberley.

Ores from southeastern British Columbia are transported by rail to Trail, where one of the world's largest smelters is located. The smelter is run by water-power obtained from the Kootenay River near Nelson. The huge and complicated smelter extracts minerals from the rock and they are later refined to an almost pure state. At one time sulphur fumes from the plant destroyed all the vegetation in the area. Since 1930, however, these fumes have been mixed with nitrogen and hydrogen from the air, and phosphate rock from Montana, to make fertilizers. Thus, the fumes, instead of being wasted, are very useful to farmers all over Canada and in some foreign countries.

British Columbia was once the leading producer of copper in Canada, but new mines in Ontario and Quebec have surpassed the production of the west coast province. The largest copper mine is at Britannia Beach, a few miles north of Vancouver. The ores have a small amount of copper, but being located on the coast, can be transported cheaply by ship to a smelter at Tacoma, Washington. Miners also obtain copper at Copper Mountain, in the southern Interior Plateau.

Coal is found at several places throughout the Cordillera, but only certain locations have good quality and unbroken seams of commercial value. The cities of southwestern British Columbia obtain some of their coal from the central east side of Vancouver Island, near Nanaimo and Comox. High quality coal is found near the Alberta boundary in the Crowsnest Pass. Mining into the steep slopes is difficult there, but the hardy miners produce about half of British Columbia's coal. It is used by the railroads and shipped both south and west to industrial plants. Much of the coal used in British Columbia homes is imported from Alberta.

The gold rush of 1858 brought thousands of placer miners to the Fraser River and helped to give the new colony a start. Small settlements like Hope and Yale were prosperous mining towns at that time, and

161

the people at Barkerville had visions of making their town the capital of the colony. Most of the gold was soon panned out of the river sand bars, however, and the prospectors moved on to other mining fields. New prospectors who came into the Cariboo country of the interior looked for gold in the hard rock of the mountain sides. Several mines were found, and the province still produces some of Canada's gold. The largest gold mines are found along Bridge River, in the Interior Plateau west of the Fraser River. Gold is also mined at Hedley, west of Okanagan Valley, and at other smaller mines scattered over the province. Most of the miners live comfortably in well-equipped modern company towns.

Mercury was discovered in 1938 at Pinchi Lake, north of Prince George, by a geology graduate student from the University of British Columbia. This mine was one of the chief sources of mercury for the United Nations during World War II. The mine was closed after the war because mercury can be obtained more cheaply from ores in Spain.

There are many problems in developing the mineral resources of the Cordillera. Because of the mountains, transportation lines are hard to build and costly to keep in repair. In some places minerals have been found, but the cost of separating them from the containing rock was too high to permit mining. Although the mining of minerals ranks high in value, most of them are exported outside British Columbia for manufacturing.

Agriculture

Agriculture is the third most valuable industry in British Columbia, ranking next to forestry and mining. There are more people working on farms, however, than there are in the other two primary industries combined. Agriculture in the Cordillera is somewhat like that of the Maritimes in that it is scattered in small areas throughout the region. Each farming community is cut off from the others by mountains, and has transportation difficulties in shipping its products to market.

There are four main agricultural regions in British Columbia. Each of them grows different crops, and the farmers

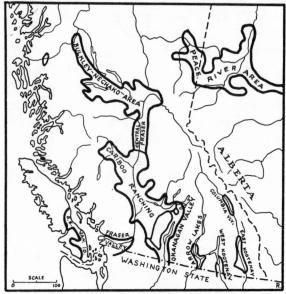

Agricultural Areas of British Columbia.

live differently from those in the other areas.

(1) The most important and best developed region is the dairying and mixed-farming area of the Lower Fraser River Valley and southeastern Vancouver Island.

(2) The fruit farms of the southern valleys of the interior have agriculture based on irrigation.

(3) The grasslands of the Interior Plateau are used chiefly for grazing cattle and some sheep.

(4) The pioneer farming belt along the Canadian National Railway crosses the central part of the province.

Farmers on the Fraser flood plain and on southern Vancouver Island carry on specialized agriculture. They raise dairy cows, and sell the fresh milk to the large city population nearby. Since the dairying region is so small and the population is so large, there is not enough extra milk to

162

be made into butter and cheese. These latter products are imported from the Prairies.

The Fraser Valley is the chief poultry region of Canada. Farmers raise chickens on large ranches, unlike most other farming regions of Canada where a few chickens are kept for eggs or meat. Eggs are sold to the cities of British Columbia, and some are shipped to eastern Canada.

tables for the city people and for canning.

On Vancouver Island agriculture is important on the Saanich Peninsula, north of Victoria, and along the southeastern coast. Gardeners raise early vegetables and berries and sell them to the mainland sections. The farmers of this section make use of the mild climate to produce flower bulbs such as narcissus, tulip and iris. Many of the bulbs planted by people

Courtesy B.C. Travel Bureau.

If water can be brought to the interior valleys of B.C., the level valley bottoms produce excellent orchards and vegetables. This seed-farm is located at Grand Forks, in south-central British Columbia.

Millions of eggs from the Fraser Valley are often sent to the British Isles in refrigerated ships.

With mild climate and fertile soils, the lower Fraser Valley also produces a large number of strawberries and raspberries. Many boxes of these berries are shipped east to stores in the Prairie Provinces. The Chinese gardeners on the delta also grow many kinds of fresh vege-

in other parts of Canada are first raised on Vancouver Island.

The narrow valleys of south-central British Columbia have a long growing season and bright summer days, but lack sufficient rainfall. The valleys were used for grazing of cattle in the 19th century before transportation lines were built from the coast. After railroads were laid across the province, farmers began to sell fruit to

163

the prairies where the climate was not suitable for fruit-growing. The farmers of the Okanagan Valley co-operated to build irrigation projects which brought water from the mountain slopes down to the valley bottoms. From Vernon in the north to Osoyoos on the United States border the Valley is now one of Canada's finest fruit regions.

The chief products of the Okanagan Valley are apples, peaches, pears, cherries,

to the pleasant green of the irrigated areas.

Other southern valleys of British Columbia are not as well developed as the Okanagan. They lack the expensive irrigation systems or have poor transportation to markets. At Creston, at the south end of Kootenay Lake, high-quality wheat is grown on the dyked lands of the Kootenay River delta. Ashcroft, on the Thompson River, produces excellent potatoes. Farm-

The orchards of the Okanagan Valley are Canada's chief source of quality apples. The orchards are raised by irrigation on the dry grassland slopes of the narrow valley. These orchards are located near Vernon, in the northern part of the Okanagan Valley.

apricots and canteloupes. In some years half of the Canadian apple crop is raised there, and nearly all of Canada's apricots. Vegetables of all kinds are grown, especially tomatoes and asparagus. This fruit region is unlike the Annapolis Valley of Nova Scotia where many other crops are raised. Okanagan farmers grow very few other products on their farms. At blossom time in spring the Okanagan Valley is a beautiful sight. The fragrant trees cover the terraces on both sides of the valley with a blanket of white blossoms, extending down to the blue water of the long lake. Higher on the slopes the dry brown grasslands and scrub forest are a contrast

ers irrigate the terraces above the river at Ashcroft with water caught in reservoirs on the slopes of the mountains.

Ranching is the chief occupation of farmers on the Interior Plateau, locally known as the Cariboo. Ranchers raise cattle and sheep on the grasslands and sell the meat to the cities in southwestern British Columbia. Cattle usually graze on ranges on the lower slopes in the spring and late fall but during the summer cowboys drive them into the higher pastures in the rolling plateau. A big roundup is held in the autumn and some of the cattle are slaughtered to save feeding them in barns all winter.

164

Although many of the ranches in the Cariboo are quite large, all of the grassland is not being used. Some areas lack transportation or have other difficulties in bringing cattle out to markets. The chief roundup centres for cattle in the Cariboo are at Williams Lake, in the centre of the region, and at Kamloops, in the south. These towns supply the surrounding ranches, and are of increasing importance as tourist and "dude ranch" centres.

Pioneer agriculture is found along the route of the Canadian National Railway across the northern part of the Interior Plateau. From Prince George to Prince Rupert several small agricultural settlements were established after the building of the railroad, but they have not grown much since then. The farmers raise clover and grass seed, flax, and small grains, but there is no large population nearby to buy their products. When the population of the Cordillera becomes larger many more farms can be cleared for settlement.

Fishing

British Columbia is the leading fishing province in Canada. The annual catch of her fishermen is exceeded in value only by that of the combined provinces on the east coast. Most of Canada's Pacific salmon are caught and canned at the mouths of west coast rivers.

Fishermen who know the habits and life-cycle of salmon know where they are going to be during the fishing season. In late summer or autumn salmon begin to collect in schools near the mouths of streams and swim upstream to hatching grounds in the quiet headwaters. The salmon swim hard against the current and sometimes jump obstacles. In the headwaters they lay their eggs and then die. The young salmon "fry" remain in fresh water for about a year and then swim downstream and out to sea. About four years later the grown salmon returns to the same stream

where it was born and tries to swim back to lay its eggs.

During the salmon season the waters at the mouths of the chief rivers are dotted with fishing boats. Fishermen stretch gill nets across the river mouths, and the salmon swim into them and are caught by

Courtesy Canadian Fishing Co. Ltd.

When the seine net is brought in to the boat, the threshing salmon are "brailed" into the hold of the vessel with large nets. The small crew share in the value of the catch.

their gills. The fisherman then hauls in the net and takes off the salmon. He allows enough fish to go by to lay eggs upstream for another year. When his boat is full the fisherman hurries to the nearest cannery to sell his fresh catch, or reloads it into special boats which visit the fishing grounds to collect the catch. Since fish will not stay fresh very long, most of the salmon are canned and later shipped to other regions.

Purse seine nets are also used off the mouths of streams. When a school of salmon is seen, a small fast boat puts its net down into the water. It then makes a wide circle around the school, putting out more net as it goes. Once the circle of net is complete it is then drawn together and the fish are forced to the centre. The water becomes so thick with fish within the circle that they can be bailed into a larger boat with hand nets.

Canneries are located along the coast or at river mouths near the fishing grounds. Although many people work in the canneries during the busy season, much of the canning is done by machinery. Tin cans are received at the cannery in flat form because they would be bulky to ship as empty cans. They are then made up into their round shape and are ready to receive the fish. As soon as salmon reach the cannery they are washed and their scales taken off by machine brushes. A machine called the "Iron Chink" cuts off their heads and tails. Other machines cut the salmon into various-sized pieces and pack them into cans. The tins are sealed, the salmon cooked, and then they are ready for shipment.

Tinned salmon is taken by coastal boats to a central port such as Vancouver or New Westminster for shipment to other parts of the world that do not have this tasty fish. About seven out of every ten cans are exported out of Canada, chiefly to Great Britain and Australia.

Halibut is the second most important fish in British Columbia. It is a big "deep water" fish, being caught off the coast rather than at river mouths. Halibut are hooked in the open sea west of Prince Rupert, and off the west coast of Vancouver Island. Both Canadian and American fishermen work in this area.

Halibut usually live near the bottom of the sea. They are caught with long lines having many hooks, baited with small herring. Boats cruise over the fishing grounds dragging several lines behind them, and also anchor some of the lines to buoys. Every so often fishermen haul the lines aboard and take off the big fish. No fishing is permitted during the winter months when the halibut are spawning.

Fishing boats rush the halibut to Prince Rupert for shipment to eastern Canada. Since the fish has a firm flesh it will keep fresh for some time, especially if properly refrigerated. Halibut are usually sold in the stores as fresh fish rather than in cans.

Fishermen also catch herring and pilchards off the west coast. Some of these small fish are canned, as sardines are on the east coast, but most are cooked and their oil pressed out. The waste left after the oil is obtained is ground into meal and sold for cattle or chicken feed to the farmers of the Fraser Valley.

There is some whaling carried on from Vancouver Island and the Queen Charlotte Islands. The industry has declined, however, owing to the gradual disappearance of the big whales. They are hunted in the North Pacific Ocean and the huge carcasses are towed to stations on the shore. After the valuable whale oil is pressed from the fat, most of the meat is shipped to the Orient.

Courtesy Canadian Fishing Company.

When salmon begin to migrate upstream in late summer, the fishing fleet waits off the mouths of the chief rivers. Seine nets are being put out around a school of fish. Since there are so many boats with efficient equipment, regulations are enforced to conserve the supply.

Manufacturing

British Columbia is the third most important manufacturing province in Canada, but it is far behind Ontario and Quebec. British Columbia's location on the coast is an advantage for manufacturing. Many of the factories change imports into products which are more easily shipped across Canada. Sugar refining, the blending of teas and coffees, the making of chocolate from cacao beans, and the

166

extracting of oil from coconut meat are all industries depending on imports.

Industries using wood usually rank first in value in British Columbia. The lumbermen in the woods support many more workers in the mills. Sawmill products are the most valuable to the province. Pulp and paper mills also help to swell the total of the wood-products industry.

The second industry of British Columbia is fish curing and packing. Men and women in the many small canneries along the coast can about half the fish caught in Canada. Forest resources of the land and fish resources in the sea are thus responsible for many of the jobs of workers in the cities.

Other valuable industries of the Cordillera are the making of fertilizers as a by-product of smelting at Trail, and the canning of fruits and vegetables grown locally. Ship-building was important during World War II and still remains one of the leading industries in the coast cities. Parts imported from eastern Canada are assembled into machinery at some factories. Slaughtering and meat packing of animals from the Interior Plateau or Prairies, and

Courtesy R. Steiner.

The University of British Columbia is the youngest university in Canada. The growing education centre gives cultural background and scientific training to young Canadians. The campus is located west of the city of Vancouver on a high bluff overlooking the city harbour entrance.

167

the manufacture of gasoline and petroleum products from California petroleum are other industries which depend on imports.

Cities

The Cordillera has only a few large cities, unlike the other regions of Canada. One-third of the people of British Columbia live in one city, Vancouver. There are only two other cities, Victoria and New Westminster, with populations above 15,-000. British Columbia is young and her cities are just beginning to grow. The small cities and towns in the mountains have small rural districts to support them. They have been less attractive than the one big city, Vancouver.

Vancouver is Canada's third city, and the leading port on the west coast. It is located near the head of an excellent deep inlet north of the mouth of the Fraser River. Miles of wharves for cargo vessels, grain elevators for prairie wheat, and piers for big ocean liners, all show its importance as a port. It is the terminal for transcontinental rail lines. Most goods leaving Canada from the west are sent to this port for shipment. (Map on page 158).

Vancouver is one of the centres of the lumber industry. Its numerous sawmills, planing mills, and shingle factories line one of the side-arms of the harbour. The city began as a sawmill in the last century, but developed other industries after it became a rail terminal in 1886. Many people in Vancouver still heat their homes with sawdust, since there is much lumber cut there and the climate is mild.

Vancouver is noted for its scenery. Snow-capped mountain peaks rise more than 4,000 feet above the water on the north side of the harbour. The mild climate encourages gardening, and residents have beautiful flower gardens most of the year. Stanley Park, where huge Douglas firs tower above scenic drives and shady walks, is a forested peninsula near the centre of the city. (Picture on page 6).

Victoria, the capital of British Columbia, is located on the southern tip of Vancouver Island. It is a beautiful residential city. Many people from all over Canada retire there because of its mild climate. The city has a sheltered harbour, where ocean liners call on their way to Vancouver or Seattle. *Esquimalt*, on the western side of Victoria harbour, is one of Canada's naval bases. It has one of the world's largest dry-docks.

New Westminster is located on the north side of the Fraser River delta. It is really part of "Greater Vancouver", along with the municipalities of Burnaby and North Vancouver. New Westminster is an important port in itself, being noted for the export of fertilizer from Trail and lumber and forest products. Many large sawmills are located along the river front. The city is a shopping centre for people from the small agricultural towns scattered over the lower Fraser Valley.

Trail is the largest city in the interior of British Columbia. Its importance is due chiefly to the huge smelter and refinery located there. Lead, zinc and other minerals are exported from the city, and fertilizers are manufactured from mineral impurities. In the fruit district of the interior the rapidly growing cities of *Penticton, Kelowna, Vernon* and *Kamloops* each had over 10,000 persons by 1948.

Parks

The Cordillera has more large parks than any other region. The National Parks are located in the Rocky Mountains, along the Alberta-British Columbia boundary. Provincial parks are scattered throughout the region. Both use the appeal of rugged mountains and thrilling scenery to attract tourists. Banff and Jasper National Parks are famous throughout the world. Located on the east slope of the Rockies in Alberta, they have the wonderful scenery of a towering mountainous region. Lake Louise near Banff and Maligne Lake near Jasper are like little blue gems amid the green of the forests. The white of the snowfields on the peaks above is reflected in their smooth waters. Both parks have hot springs, waterfalls, winding trails, deep canyons, and other attractive natural sights.

Waterton National Park is located in the southwestern corner of Alberta. Glacier Park adjoins it in the state of Montana, and the two parks are dedicated to the continual peace between Canada and the United States. The Canadian park is smaller than the American one, but is noted for the lovely colouring of its sculptured mountains.

Tourists may visit other mountain parks such as Yoho and Kootenay National Parks, on the British Columbia side of the Rockies. Yoho means "it is wonderful" in Indian language, and the scenery of this section, including the Kicking Horse Pass and Valley, justifies the name. Kootenay Park is a tiny park along both sides of the Banff-Windermere Highway preserving the natural beauty for the enjoyment of tourists.

Glacier and Mount Revelstoke National Parks are located in the northern part of the Selkirk Mountains. Glacier Park receives its name from the permanent icecap found on the high peaks. Five of the peaked mountains have crests more than 10,000 feet above sea level. Mount Revelstoke Park occupies only 100 acres on the plateau east of the Columbia River. It is a winter sports centre, noted for its good skiing.

British Columbia has such wonderful mountain scenery that all the provincial parks could not be described without repetition. There are 16 "Class A" parks, and more than 30 other parks, where tourists may enjoy the rugged grandeur of nature.

Tweedsmuir Park is one of the provincial parks in little-known wilderness country east of the Coast Range and north of Bella Coola River. It is visited by naturalists, mountaineers, and photographers who want beautiful scenery little touched by man. Hamber and Mount Robson Parks are in the Rockies on the British Columbia side of Jasper Park. They complete the large block of park reserves in the central Rockies. Wells Gray Park, north of the North Thompson River in the Interior Plateau, is a primitive forestland with big game. Garibaldi Park, known to many skiing visitors and summer mountain climbers from Vancouver, extends into the jagged peaks of the Coast Range north of that city. Strathcona Park, in central Vancouver Island, has forested mountain slopes and fine trout fishing for visitors to the Island.

Facts for Reference

Cities of British Columbia (1941)

Vancouver	275,353
Victoria	44,608
New Westminster	21,967
Trail	9,392
North Vancouver	8,914
Prince Rupert	6,714
Nanaimo	6,634
Kamloops	5,959
Nelson	5,912
Vernon	5,209
Kelowna	5,118

What People Do (1941)

Manufacturing	67,238
Agriculture	41,225
Forestry	18,296
Mining	14,214
Fishing	9,830
Service	63,105
Trade	41,157
Transport	26,781
Construction	19,561
Total	301,407

Things To Do

1. Make a pictorial map of the topographic features of British Columbia. First draw or trace an outline map of the province showing the political boundaries and chief rivers. Where there is a mountain range between rivers draw in a range of sharp-peaked mountains. Make the sizes of your mountain ranges proportionate to the elevations which are given in the chapter. Mountains of 5,000 feet should look half as high as mountains of 10,000 feet. Indicate the flat upland surface of plateaus with horizontal lines. When your pictorial map is finished read over the section on topography in this chapter and try to visualize your sketch map as you read.

2. (a) If you were going to spend a month's vacation in Vancouver what season of the year would you choose?

   (b) Read the section on climate and describe the weather that you would find during your vacation there.

   (c) What would the weather be like six months after your visit?

3. (a) List all the ways in which the logging methods in British Columbia differ from those in the Canadian Shield.

   (b) Explain why lumbermen have different ways of doing things in these two chief forest regions.

4. Compare the mineral resources of the Cordillera with those in the Canadian shield.

   (a) List minerals which are mined in both regions.

   (b) Make another list of minerals of the Cordillera that are not mined in the Shield.

5. (a) Where is irrigation practised in British Columbia?

   (b) Name the crops raised by this method of agriculture?

   (e) How does irrigation in the Cordillera differ from that in southern Alberta.

6. Pretend that you are a sockeye salmon and tell the story of your four-year life to your other fish friends. In your story tell them how your habits are different from theirs. Describe how you were able to elude the fishermen's nets and to swim strongly upstream to return to the place where you were born.

CHAPTER 24

YUKON TERRITORY

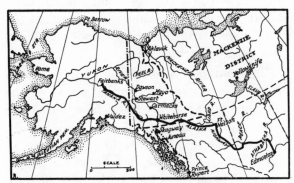

Yukon in the Northwest.

The Yukon is famous as "The Land of the Klondike". During the gold rush of 1898 the word "Yukon" became well known in many corners of the world. Many people still picture the Yukon as it was painted in those early days. The Territory has changed in recent years, and the famous Klondike is no longer typical of the whole region. Yukon Territory is large, having an area of more than 200,000 square miles, which is almost as large as Manitoba.

Yukon Territory was taken out of the vast Northwest Territories in 1898 and made a separate territory. The capital is at Dawson, where a Controller and Council are responsible for local administration. Government headquarters for the general administration of lands, mining, and revenue is in Ottawa under the Department of Resources and Development.

Topography

The Yukon is a region of hills, plateaus, and mountains. The Yukon Plateau, which occupies the central and western part of the Territory, is the central basin. The plateau has elevations of 2,000 to 2,500 feet. On all sides, except towards Alaska

on the west, high mountains tower above it. Within the plateau, numerous rivers have cut into the upland surfaces. They flow in broad, flat-bottomed valleys several hundred feet below the plateau level. Small towns and villages are located in the river valleys, rather than on the rocky uplands.

Yukon River is the main stream flowing through the plateau. Other streams from the surrounding mountains flow towards this central river. These streams, in turn, have numerous tributaries flowing into them from both sides. The drainage pat-

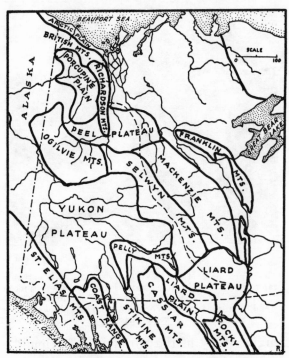

Landforms of the Northwest.

tern of the Yukon thus resembles the veins of a maple leaf, all leading to the central vein, the Yukon River, which flows westward through Alaska.

The southwestern part of the Yukon

171

plateau is cut off from the Pacific Ocean by the high St. Elias Mountains. These jagged, snow-and-ice-covered peaks are the highest mountains in Canada. Mount Logan towers to 19,850 feet, and several other peaks are much higher than Mount Robson in the Rockies. There is very little communication possible through these rugged mountains. The explorers who saw the high, icy range from the ocean never thought that there would be fertile valleys in the country to the north.

The southern rim of the Yukon Plateau is formed by the Coast and Cassiar Ranges. These mountains are rounded and lower than the spike-peaked St. Elias Mountains. The White Pass and Chilcoot Pass through the Coast Range were famous in the days of the Yukon Gold Rush. Although many tales are told of hardships in crossing these passes, they are only about 3,000 feet

Courtesy R.C.A.F.

The Mackenzie Mountains are an almost impenetrable range of bare, jagged peaks lying between Yukon Territory and Mackenzie District. The former Canol Road, built during World War II, followed this valley pass.

high. Many of the hardships of Klondike adventurers were due to lack of equipment and preparation rather than to the mountain barrier.

To the east several ranges of the rugged Mackenzie Mountains separate the Yukon Plateau and Mackenzie Valley. Row after

row of bare, jagged peaks form this mountain barrier which has altitudes of about 8,000 feet. Prior to the building of the Canol pipe line and road through this region in 1943, very few white men had ever been able to cross through this little-known part of Canada. Many of the mountain passes were explored by surveyors looking for a route for the road. Royal Canadian Air Force planes photographed the mountains from the air in order to make new and accurate maps.

The rounded hills of the Ogilvie Mountains rise above the northern rim of the Yukon Plateau. Only a few passes through these rolling mountains are well known. Some hunting and trapping are done in the southern sections, but otherwise people in the Yukon have had little reason to go into this region.

North of Ogilvie Mountains lies the Peel-Porcupine Basin. This plateau and valley are uninhabited except for the Indians living around the village of Old Crow on the Porcupine River. Part of the basin drains westward via the Porcupine River which empties into Yukon River at Fort Yukon, Alaska. People who wish to travel to Old Crow settlement from Dawson go by way of Yukon and Porcupine Rivers rather than through the Ogilvie Mountain. The Peel River drains east and northward to the delta of Mackenzie River. The Peel has cut down into the swampy surface of the eastern part of the basin.

The Peel-Porcupine Basin is separated from the Arctic Coast by another line of low mountains. The Richardson Mountains rise above the west side of Peel River near its junction with the Mackenzie River. They then curve to the northwest and merge into the British Range which runs along the Yukon Arctic coast. These ranges continue westward into Alaska. Sometimes Indians come into the valleys of these mountains for a few weeks to hunt caribou.

A narrow, swampy, tundra-covered

coastal plain lies between these northern mountains and the Arctic Ocean. Herschel Island, lying a short distance off the coast, was the headquarters for whaling fleets at the beginning of this century. From there American whaling vessels used to sail along the edge of the moving pack-ice in Beaufort Sea looking for large bowhead whales.

Climate

The Yukon has cold winters and cool summers. Weather observers at stations along the Alaska Highway and in the Yukon River Valley report the climate near their posts, but we have little record of temperatures and precipitation in the mountainous parts of the Yukon where no one lives. We can guess, however, that since the mountains are higher they will be colder, and since many are snow-covered most of the year, precipitation is greater than in the valleys.

Summer temperatures in the Yukon River valley may range from 65° F. to 75° F. in the afternoons. The record of 95° F. at Dawson is the hottest that it has ever been in the Yukon. Yukon summers are variable. Some summers are pleasant and mild. In such seasons warm air from the North Pacific crosses the coast mountains to the central plateau. Other summers are cool and uncomfortable. This is caused by cold air from the Arctic Ocean pushing southward over the plateau. Owing to the northern latitude of from 60° to 65°, the Yukon has long summer days. If the days are mild the residents are encouraged to garden.

Winter temperatures vary a great deal from place to place. Carcross, in southern Yukon, has a monthly average of zero degrees for January. This is milder than Winnipeg, in southern Manitoba. Mayo, in central Yukon, averages -13° F. in January, which is about the same average as that known in the northern Prairie Provinces. Dawson, in west central Yukon,

records a January average temperature of -21° F. This section is, therefore, one of the coldest parts of Canada.

The people of the Yukon experience winters that are very cold and others that are mild. The coldest winters occur when air from the Arctic Ocean settles down over the region for several weeks before moving eastward. Weather observers have noted temperatures of -50° F. at most stations sometime during the winter, and extreme minima of -67° F. have been recorded at three towns. The lowest temperature ever recorded in North America occurred at the meteorological station at Snag, near the Alaska border in February, 1947. The thermometer read -81° F. This temperature was lower than the thermometer was marked, and the men at the weather station had to scratch a place on the glass and determine the reading later.

Not much precipitation falls on the settlements in central Yukon because the surrounding mountains keep out most of the moisture. An average of 9 inches falls each year in southern Yukon, and 13 inches is measured at Dawson. Fortunately, almost half this amount falls as rain in the four summer months when it is needed for growing crops. Since summers are cool, the small amount of rainfall does not evaporate as rapidly as it would in more southerly places. Most of it soaks into the soil for the vegetation and crops.

There are only about two months without frosts in the Yukon valleys. In the southern part of the Territory there is an average of only 45 days between last spring frosts and first autumn frosts. Around Dawson a longer period of 75 days is about the same length as the period in the plateau of central British Columbia. The last spring frost is usually felt about the middle of June, and first autumn frosts occur in mid-August. The farmers who raise crops in the Yukon have to use varieties which ripen in a short time.

Mining

Gold was the lure which brought thousands of prospectors to the Yukon. In 1896 loose gold was discovered in the stream gravels near the mouth of the Klondike River. Prospectors had only to wash away the dirt and gravel, leaving the nuggets and flakes of gold. When news of the easy work was carried out by rich miners a gold rush started.

People from all over the world flocked towards the Yukon. Many were experienced prospectors, but others were untrained and not capable of looking after themselves in the rough country. Along with the honest and hardworking people who believed in the future of the Yukon, there were many adventurers and gamblers who came to the country to profit by other peoples' misfortunes. The early days of the Klondike rush were notorious for their rough lawlessness. For a time gangs of bad men completely controlled the port of Skagway, Alaska, and extracted tribute from everyone who came there. Soon the Royal North West Mounted Police (now the Royal Canadian Mounted Police) were sent to the Yukon to protect citizens and to bring law and order. These brave and

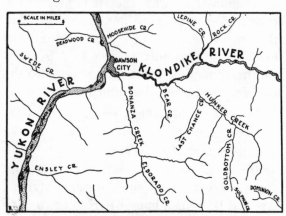

Goldfields of Dawson area.

strong red-coated officers brought fear and respect of the police force with them. Their fair but firm actions soon brought ordered development to the region.

By 1900 there was a busy population of about 30,000 people in Dawson and in the surrounding mining camps. They had come there by three main routes. Many came by boat to Skagway, in the Alaska Panhandle, and crossed the passes in the Coast Range to the headwaters of Yukon

Courtesy L. A. Milne.

Summer transportation on the Yukon River and main tributaries is by flat-bottomed, paddle-wheeled steamers. If their loads are large, sometimes they push barges ahead of them. This steamer is approaching Carmacks, Yukon.

River. All kinds of boats and rafts were built on the shores of Lake Bennett. Then, loaded with provisions, they were floated downstream. The only break in river transportation was at Miles Canyon and Whitehorse Rapids, south of the present town of Whitehorse. Supplies were portaged around these rapids, although many hurrying gold-seekers foolishly tried to run them. By 1900 a narrow-gauge railroad was built from Skagway to Whitehorse. North of Whitehorse, river steamers carried passengers the rest of the way down the broad Yukon.

A second, and longer, route to the Klondike was by way of Alaska. Coastal vessels from Seattle, U. S. A., took crowds around the southwest coast of Alaska to the mouth of Yukon River. From there river boats pushed upstream into Canada. It was usually late July before gold-seekers using this route reached the Yukon. Those who crossed by the route over the Chilcoot and White Passes in southern Yukon floated downstream as soon as the Yukon River ice broke up in mid-May.

A third route used by a few pioneers was via the "back door". This method of reaching the Yukon was to go north from Edmonton along the Athabaska and Mackenzie rivers. Near the mouth of Mackenzie River the prospectors had a choice of two routes. They could paddle upstream along Peel River, and portage through the unexplored Ogilvie Mountains. They then floated down tributaries of the Yukon River to the Klondike area. However, most men crossed a westward portage at Rat River to Porcupine River, and followed it downstream to Yukon River. Then they came back upstream to Dawson and the gold fields.

In the prosperous years around 1900 the Klondike River and tributaries produced over 20 million dollars' worth of gold each year. By 1906, however, most of the easily-worked gravels had been washed over and the value of gold production fell to about three million dollars per year. The population of Dawson also decreased steadily. From a booming, prosperous city of 30,000 in 1900, Dawson declined to a shell of its former self with less than 1,000 residents in 1941.

The Klondike is still producing gold after being worked over for more than 50 years. Lone prospectors with pans long ago gave way to groups of miners who shovelled the gravel into long wooden sluice boxes. These artificial channels had boards nailed across their bottoms to catch the gold as the gravel was washed downwards. The small placer miners were bought out by large companies which now operate hydraulic dredges in the river bottom. These huge dredges eat their way into ground which has previously been thawed with cold water. The gravel is carefully sorted inside the frame house on the dredge. Nearly every particle and fleck of gold is taken out and the useless gravel is dumped in ridges behind the dredge as it moves forward.

The Dawson area is the chief producer of gold in the Yukon, but streams in southern Yukon are also yielding golden riches. The Alaska Highway, across the southern part of the Territory, has opened up many areas which were formerly hard to reach. The Yukon appears to be "gold country", and as prospecting goes on each optimistic "sourdough" hopes that he will find another Klondike.

The Yukon has minerals in underground rock, in addition to its more famous gravels. Prospectors found silver-lead ores at Mayo, on Stewart River, as early as 1906, but no mining was done there for several years. Once mining started, however, the ore proved to be very rich. It paid the companies to mine it despite the high transportation costs of bringing supplies in by river boat.

Coal mines were opened near Carmacks, on Yukon River, in 1900. The mines never became important, however, because the coal was of low quality. Some residents used it to heat their homes during the long winter but most people used fuel wood from the surrounding forests. Even the river steamers used cord wood for fuel rather than the local coal. The mines finally closed in 1938, but re-opened in 1948 when timber was becoming scarce along the Yukon River.

Agriculture

Agriculture was begun in the Yukon around 1900 to raise food for the prospectors who crowded into the area. Settlers who were disappointed in their search for gold soon cleared several thousand acres of land on the terraces and lower slopes of Yukon River. Since transportation costs from southern areas were high they could sell their produce at a profit in Dawson and the mining camps. Newcomers pictured the Yukon as a cold, bleak area where only the hardiest person could survive. They were surprised to find that long days and warm summer temperatures encouraged the growth of most agricultural products.

As the Yukon population decreased, many farms were abandoned. There no longer were local markets, and in time, stores were able to import food cheaply from southern areas. Some farmers continued to raise grain and hay for work and pack horses. In recent years the increased use of trucks and tractors in place of horses caused the abandonment of still more farms.

Although general agriculture declined, gardening increased in importance in the chief towns. Most residents now have excellent gardens where they raise most of their vegetables and berries. Much of the garden crop is canned for winter use. The beautiful flower gardens and neat vegetable plots are among the colourful sights of Dawson.

There could be many more farms in the Yukon if people wanted to live there. Agricultural surveys show that the largest block of good land is located along the Alaska Highway west of Whitehorse. Several thousand acres are also located along the banks of the Yukon River, chiefly between Fort Selkirk and Dawson. Climate or topography do not prevent the raising of crops in the Yukon. There is land available, and crops will grow. The small population is not large enough for the sale of farm products. At the same time people who want to settle on farms have found land in more southerly parts of Canada.

Forestry

There is no lumbering carried on in the Yukon, similar to that which we know in other sections of Canada. The Territory has forests, however, which serve the residents and are a reserve for the future.

The best timber of commercial size is found in the Liard River Valley of southeastern Yukon and northeastern British Columbia. Some of it was cut by construc-

tion crews working along the Alaska Highway, but vast stands still remain. Some day when Canada's more accessible forests are cut down, the Yukon woodlands may be needed.

In south and central Yukon commercial timber grows in narrow strips along the river valleys. If we climb the slopes we see that the trees become smaller and fewer above 3,000 feet. Hills and mountains rising above this altitude have grassy tundra above the tree-line, and their peaks are barren rock. Along the Yukon River the forests supply fuelwood for the river steamers, and for residents to heat their houses.

In the Peel-Porcupine Basin to the north the trees are small and scrubby. They are useful only for fire-wood and as logs for cabins. The Arctic coast of the Yukon is treeless tundra on which herds of migratory caribou feed.

Trapping and Fishing

Trapping and fishing are the chief activities of the 2,000 Indians who live in the Yukon. A few white men also follow these occupations. They are usually more efficient than the Indians, who are content to live from day to day.

Trapping methods are like those used by Indians in other woodland regions of Canada. In summer the Indians usually stay near the settlements along the chief rivers. When the trapping season opens in the autumn, they go back into the interior.

There is no commercial fishing in the Yukon rivers, but there are enough fish for local use. Whitefish and salmon are eaten by both Indians and whites. The salmon swim all the way up the Yukon River from Bering Sea. They are caught around Dawson, but farther upstream near the spawning grounds their flesh is not as good.

Transportation

One of the problems of using the resources of the Canadian Northland is lack of transportation. Roads, railroads, airstrips and boats are costly to build, and in the North the costs are higher. For many years our northern resources were barely known. Many resources which were discovered were not used because they could not be sold as cheaply as those in southerly areas. It was not until the age of aeroplanes that the northern regions began to be opened up. Trips which used to take the old fur-traders months are covered in a few hours by air. Prospectors can now be flown directly to their chosen sites instead of losing most of the season travelling.

The first white men in the Yukon were fur-traders who travelled by canoe on the navigable waterways. Soon river boats from Alaska were steaming up the broad Yukon River. At the time of the gold rush several steamers were running from the river mouth to Dawson. The only railroad in the Yukon was built from Skagway to Whitehorse in 1898-1900.

For 40 years, until World War II, the Yukon was supplied by rail from Skagway to Whitehorse. Along the river north of Whitehorse, flat-bottomed boats brought food and equipment to the settlements. Except for some fast water at Five Fingers Rapids, near Carmacks, the Yukon River is navigable for almost 2,000 miles north of Whitehorse. The first boats going downstream leave Whitehorse the latter part of May, as soon as Lake Laberge is free of ice. All during the summer they run back and forth between Dawson and Whitehorse. The downstream trip takes about two days. Tourists enjoy the journey in the flat-bottomed steamers which pick their way carefully through the islands and sand-bars in the channel.

Aeroplanes began to carry mail and passengers into Yukon Territory in 1937. In 1939 the Canadian Government built a line of airfields from Edmonton to Whitehorse. When the United States entered World War II in 1941 these airfields were ready for planes carrying supplies to Alaska. In order to maintain them a road was built from airport to airport between March and November, 1942. This road became the Alaska Highway. It was taken over by the Canadian Army after the end of the war.

The Alaska Highway stretches 1,500 miles from Dawson Creek, in the Peace River country of British Columbia, to Fairbanks, Alaska. It passes through both rolling and mountainous country in northeastern British Columbia. The gravel highway crosses the hills and valleys of southern Yukon to Whitehorse. It then continues westward along the base of the mighty St. Elias Mountains, and into Alaska across the central plateau.

The Alaska Highway opened up new areas in southeastern and southwestern Yukon. These parts could not be reached by river transportation. The scenic beauties along the highway in the southwestern corner of the Yukon were set aside by the Canadian Government for consideration as a National Park. The highway also gave southern Yukon closer contact with the rest of the world. Overhead large cargo and passenger planes wing their way along the Northwest Staging Route from Edmonton to Alaska. On the ground, busses carry passengers back and forth between Edmonton and Fairbanks.

Population

The Yukon has a permanent white population of about 6,000 persons. Most of these people live in the two chief towns, Dawson and Whitehorse. The latter has about half of the white population of the Territory. Before the war, Dawson was a town of empty houses with less than 1,000 residents, and Whitehorse was a transportation terminal with even fewer people. Whitehorse became the centre of construction during the building of the Alaska Highway, since it was the only place with rail connections southward. Another "boom" hit the Yukon, and Whitehorse, like Dawson of 40 years before, grew rapidly to a city of 15,000. With the end of the war, army and civilians departed, and Whitehorse returned to something of its former life. It still remains the largest town in the Yukon, however, because of its importance as the cross-roads for north-south and east-west traffic.

Other settlements in the Territory are small. The mining town of Mayo has a few hundred people. Only a few dozen people live in the villages of Fort Selkirk and Stewart River. They are tiny trading-post settlements picturesquely located on the banks of the Yukon River. Other villages along the Alaska Highway are either stopping places, or outfitting centres for tourists or big game hunters.

Things To Do

1. (a) List the mountain ranges which almost surround the Yukon Plateau.
   (b) Which of these ranges have passes cutting through them?
   (c) How are the passes being used?

2. (a) Is the climate of the Yukon valley suitable for agriculture? Why do you think so?
   (b) How do the rainfall and the frost-free period of the Yukon compare with those in the agricultural areas of the Prairies?

3. If you were going to the Klondike during the Gold Rush days of 1897-98 which of the three chief routes would you choose? Explain why you would choose your route in preference to the other two.

4. Plan a tourist trip to the Yukon for next summer.
   (a) What will be your route if you leave by coastal steamer from Vancouver?
   (b) How many times will you have to change means of transportation before you reach Dawson?
   (c) Describe the scenery that you would see along your route and the settlements that you would visit.
   (d) Trace your route with a coloured pencil on a map.

Courtesy D. B. Marsh.

In September the first fall snows cover the grass at Aklavik, N.W.T. The Richardson Mountains, in the distance to the west are still snow-free. Aklavik is the most northerly settlement in the Mackenzie Valley.

CHAPTER 25

THE MACKENZIE VALLEY

The Mackenzie Valley is Canada's last large pioneer region. Settlements have existed there for more than 150 years, since the days of the early fur-traders. Within a few years after 1789, when Alexander Mackenzie explored the broad river to its mouth in the Arctic Ocean, adventurous fur-traders had opened posts among the curious Indians.

For many decades this hard-to-reach region lay isolated in the northwest. Brigades of York boats crossed the portages from the Churchill or Saskatchewan rivers to the Athabaska River, and floated downstream to the lonely posts. The trip back was much more difficult. The French-Canadian or Indian boatmen had to paddle very hard against the current. Sometimes it took three or four years before furs from this region were delivered to England.

Throughout the 19th century, when the St. Lawrence Lowlands and the Prairies were being settled, the Mackenzie Valley remained the far-away home of a few white traders and missionaries. It was not until the coming of aeroplanes that people could reach the Valley without weeks and weeks of tiresome travelling. The first

aeroplane flew to the oil field at Norman Wells in 1921. In the following years other planes entered the region, and before long they became the chief method of travel. Many Indians who had never seen a train or an automobile became quite familiar with aeroplanes. The Mackenzie Valley is no longer isolated. Gradually we are learning more and more about its resources and possibilities.

Topography

The Mackenzie Valley is the northern part of the Great Plains region. Although the Peace River belongs to the Mackenzie River drainage system, it has been described with the prairies. North of the Peace River country the rivers of northern Alberta flow northward towards the Mackenzie. Northern Alberta is almost uninhabited except for tiny settlements along the rivers. Between the rivers there are vast areas of poor scrubby trees, with many open grassy sections, and innumerable swampy muskegs.

Let us pretend that we are accompanying one of the northern "bush pilots" on a flight down the Mackenzie Valley. After leaving Fort Smith, on the southern border of Mackenzie District, we would fly

179

over a flat, swampy plain south of Great Slave Lake. The Caribou Hills, located along the Alberta-Northwest Territories border to the southward, rise about 1,000 feet above the forested plain. These hills have an escarpment along their northern edge, over which tumble several beautiful waterfalls. North of the Mackenzie River and west of Great Slave Lake, the plateau of the Horn Mountains also stands out above the valley lowland. Only a few Indians hunt in these hilly sections.

If we follow the Mackenzie River northward we find that the Franklin Mountains

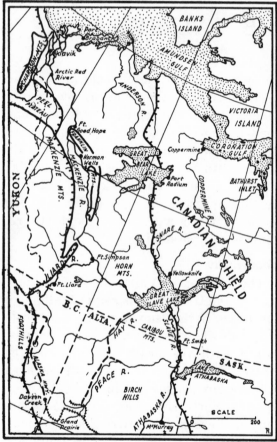

The Mackenzie Valley.

divide the Valley into two sections. These mountains, on the east side of the river, are the foothills of the rugged Mackenzie Mountains to the westward. Between the Franklin and Mackenzie Mountains the plain narrows to about 40 miles in width. East of the Franklin Range the plain

stretches across muskeg, lake-dotted country to the edge of the Canadian Shield.

The Franklin Mountains end near Fort Good Hope, and the plain widens to the north. Below us we see ribbons of trees along the rivers, and broad areas of tundra lie between the tributaries. Trees grow over 20 feet high in the delta of the Mackenzie River, and are found within a few miles of the Arctic coast. East of the delta the trees disappear, and the Arctic tundra begins.

The mouth of the mighty Mackenzie River has the largest delta in Canada. Its channels begin to branch and divide about 100 miles from the ocean. They spread out to the east and west, becoming more and more numerous, until the delta is over 50 miles wide.

As the river nears the ocean its speed decreases. Much of the silt and sand which it has been carrying is dropped in the river bed. The silt accumulates, forming sand bars, and finally islands. The river then has to branch around the islands. This process has been going on for hundreds of years as the V-shaped delta has gradually grown out into the ocean. The delta is now a maze of criss-crossing channels, winding back and forth over the lowland. Between the channels are numerous small lakes which have been cut off from the main stream, and which flood each spring. From the air the whole area appears to be more water than land. Because of the abundance of shallow lakes and ample vegetation the delta is the home of thousands of muskrats. Many Indians, Eskimos, and some white men make their living trapping in this area.

Climate

The Mackenzie Valley is somewhat colder in winter and a little warmer in summer than Yukon Territory. Winters are generally very cold. Cold air from the Arctic Ocean often moves straight south into the valley because there are no moun-

180

tain barriers to keep it out. Although winters have occasional mild spells, they do not occur as frequently as in the Yukon. January monthly temperatures average 15°F. or 20°F. below zero at all settlements. The thermometer seldom registers above zero during December and January. Residents at most places have shivered with minimum temperatures of –60°F. Until 1947 the lowest temperature ever known in North America was the –79°F. recorded at Fort Good Hope, on Mackenzie River.

Towards the end of April days are bright and clear and temperatures begin to rise above freezing. In May the ice melts in the rivers and lakes, and residents in the southern parts seed their gardens. From June to August summer comes to the Valley. Temperatures rise above 70°F. during the daytime and drop to about 50°F. at night. At some time during the month a maximum of 80°F. or 85°F. will be recorded. At all stations except Aklavik, temperatures of 90°F. or more have been known. Although the northern part of the valley is north of the Arctic Circle, the whole valley can become quite warm in summer. Residents of the Mackenzie Valley smile when they see tourists visiting the region in summer with their fur coats and winter clothing.

As in other northern regions, there is not much precipitation in the Mackenzie Valley. About 10 to 13 inches fall during the year. Sometimes we think of the north as a land of deep snows, but the Valley receives about the same amount of snow as Winnipeg and only half as much as Toronto or Montreal. About half the precipitation falls as rain during the four summer months, but in some years there is scarcely enough for crops. Much of the soil along the rivers is sandy, and the rainwater sinks down too deeply for growing plants.

The frost-free period varies a great deal from year to year and from place to place.

Fort Norman, in the central part of the Valley, has an average period of only 44 days without frosts. This growing season is about the same as that of some places in the plateau of southern Yukon. Crops at Fort Resolution, on the south side of Great Slave Lake, have an average of about 90 frost-free days in which to grow. Settlers there have a growing season as long as that of the farmers in the Peace River, much farther south.

The gardens and crops are helped by long periods of daylight during the summer. There are 24 hours of light for a few days around the end of June at places north of the Arctic Circle. At Fort Norman at this time, the sun just dips down below the horizon in the north and then starts another circle in the sky. Even in the middle of August, Aklavik, in the Mac-Kenzie River delta, has 18 hours of sunlight. In the southern part of the region the days are also long but there is always some darkness. People in the Mackenzie Valley often find it difficult to sleep in the summer when the days are so long. In winter, however, the days are very short and men must do their outside work in a few hours.

Mining

Mining replaced the fur trade as the most valuable industry of the Mackenzie Valley in 1938. The mineral wealth comes from three chief products—petroleum, pitchblende, and gold. The last two are mined in the edge of the Canadian Shield, but are taken out through the Valley.

Pioneer drillers sank the first oil well at Norman Wells, on the Mackenzie River, in 1920. They found oil, but since there was no one living nearby to use it the wells were capped. After pitchblende was discovered on the east side of Great Bear Lake in 1930, oil was needed to run the mining equipment. The wells on the Mackenzie River were opened again and oil was sent to the new radium mine.

Shipping oil from Norman Wells to Port Radium is not easy. The boats have to go upstream against the strong current of the Mackenzie River. Even good boats can make only three or four miles per hour. At Bear River, which drains the cold, clear waters of Great Bear Lake,

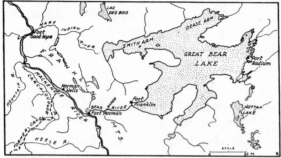
Norman Wells—Port Radium Area.

the boats turn eastward and fight against its current. After about 40 miles they can go no farther because of the rapids where the Bear River cuts through the Franklin Mountains. The oil and other supplies are taken off the boats and transferred by trucks over an 8-mile portage road. A short pipeline has been built to carry the oil around the rapids, but other supplies are still moved by trucks.

At the east end of the rapids everything is again loaded on a flat-bottomed river boat. This boat continues eastward to Great Bear Lake. There supplies are again unloaded and this time placed on a larger lake boat, which carries them across huge Great Bear Lake to the mine.

Many new wells were drilled at Norman Wells during World War II, and oil was shipped to Alaska by pipeline. The oil field proved to be a valuable one, which produced one-tenth of Canada's oil in 1944. With the abandonment of the pipeline, however, production decreased. The wells now supply only the small population of the Mackenzie Valley. We know, however, that oil is there and when needed it can be used.

The story of the discovery of pitchblende is an historic chapter in the development of the Northland. In 1900 a geologist hurrying along the eastern shores of Great Bear Lake reported stains of "purple, red, and brown" on the rocks. Thirty years later a prospector reading the report decided that the description resembled that of silver ore which he knew around Cobalt, Ontario. He flew into Great Bear Lake and brought back samples of a very heavy, black rock. The ore was pitchblende, which contained the rare mineral, radium. Scientists in the Canadian Government tested the ore and finally found a way of extracting the radium from it.

The next problem was how to start a mine in this far-away country. Some of the equipment was sent by train from Edmonton to the end of the railway at Waterways. From there it went some 1,500 miles by river boat to Great Bear

Courtesy J. L. Robinson.

The famous pitchblende mine at Port Radium, on Great Bear Lake, N.W.T., is noted for its radium and uranium products. The home and dormitories of the miners are perched on the steep rocky hills near the small mine (left).

Lake. Everything had to be transferred from boat to boat several times on the way, just as the oil was from Norman Wells. Other machinery and supplies were flown in directly by large freight planes. These were the days when planes in northern Canada carried a greater tonnage of air freight than those of any other country.

By 1933 miners were digging out pitchblende ore which was taken over 3,000 miles to Port Hope, on Lake Ontario, for refining. Within a few years the production from Great Bear Lake was large enough to reduce the price of radium by one-half. The price of $25,000 per gram before World War II showed how scarce radium was in the world.

In 1944 the pitchblende mine at Port Radium was taken over by the Canadian Government. Its production was kept secret. After the atomic bombs were dropped on Japan, it became known that the source of uranium used in the bomb was the same pitchblende ore which came from Great Bear Lake. The mine is there-

Courtesy R.C.A.F.

The Canadian Shield forms the eastern boundary of the Mackenzie Valley. This view, taken near Yellowknife, N.W.T., shows the stunted forest, low rock hills, and many small lakes which are characteristic of the Canadian Shield.

fore producing two valuable products— radium and uranium.

The third known mineral resource of the Mackenzie Valley is gold. It was discovered at Yellowknife Bay in 1934. The next year a small gold rush resulted in the building of the town of Yellowknife, where there had been only a bare rocky

hill the year before. By 1942 there were six producing gold mines in the Yellowknife area. A shortage of labour during the war, however, forced them to close down. Once the war was over the prospecting boom started again, and thousands of people flocked to this new "Eldorado of the North".

Yellowknife had an orderly growth, however, unlike that of Dawson 50 years before. When it grew too large for its original rocky hill, the Canadian Government surveyed a new townsite on level land nearby. The government also built a permanent airport there so that people of Yellowknife could have daily air service to Edmonton.

Trapping and Fishing

The fur trade was the attraction which led to the exploration of the Mackenzie Valley. For 150 years furs were the chief resource carried out of the region by the long York boats. The fur catch gradually declined. Certain fur-bearers were killed off by too much trapping. In order to conserve them for use of the natives, most fur-bearers are now protected during certain months by government regulations prohibiting trapping. Since the number of fur-bearers is limited, no more white trappers were allowed in the Northwest Territories after 1938. Indians now do most of the trapping in the region.

Indians in the Mackenzie Valley live in much the same way as they do in other woodlands of Canada, except that they are not on reservations. Most of them have built log cabins at the settlements and live there for two or three months of the summer. Since Indians eat fish most of the summer, the sites of many of the settlements were originally chosen because of their good fishing grounds.

In the fall the Indians go back into the woods or along a tributary stream where they may camp with several other families. At these main camps they live in rough log cabins, or in tents covered with spruce branches. The man of the family visits his trapline every week or so. During the winter he traps red and cross foxes, mink and lynx. In the spring his chief catches are beaver and muskrat. In the Mackenzie River Delta there are so many

An Indian boy at Fort Good Hope on the Mackenzie River, N.W.T., eats a slice of bread and butter. His overalls and cap were obtained from the trading store in return for furs.

muskrats that the Indians rarely trap any other animal.

Indians usually stay out in their winter camps during all the snow season. Sometimes the men make trips by dog-team and sled to the nearest store for supplies. On the two religious holidays of Christmas and Easter, however, as many as possible come in to the mission churches at the

settlements. After trapping season closes in the spring, they once more return to the settlements to start fishing.

The fur catch of the Mackenzie Valley is important to Canada. The chief fur-bearer caught is the muskrat. This little animal is found all over Canada wherever there are lakes, rivers and lowlands. The Mackenzie River Delta has all of these desirable features within a small area. So numerous are the muskrats that for ten years after 1935 the natives and a few white trappers were able to trap or shoot about 200,000 of them each spring without decreasing their numbers. Muskrats are caught by two methods. Before the ice breaks up in the delta in May the Indians and Eskimo catch the muskrats by placing traps near their burrows in the low banks of the channels. After the river ice breaks up in June, hunters travel from lake to lake and from channel to channel in small canoes and shoot the muskrats in the water with a .22 calibre rifle. A good hunter may get as many as 200 skins in an evening's work. In late June and early

Two Hare Indians at Fort Good Hope, N.W.T., repair their net in preparation for the fall fishing in the Mackenzie River.

July the trappers come to Aklavik, in the centre of the delta, to trade their spring catch for goods from the stores.

Commercial fishing began in Great Slave Lake in 1945. Fisheries surveys had first been made of it, Great Bear Lake, and the Mackenzie River. The fish scientists found that the number of whitefish and trout was sufficient for commercial companies to take a large catch from Great Slave Lake, and still leave enough for the Indians. In Great Bear Lake, however, the waters are so cold that fish grow too slowly to permit commercial fishing.

Most of the streams and other lakes of the Mackenzie Valley have a good supply of fish for the residents. The chief use of fish is for dog feed. Much of the fishing is done in the autumn, when the fish can be dried and frozen. They are then kept to feed the dogs on the trail in the winter. Indians eat fish most of the year, and the well-flavoured Mackenzie River whitefish is a frequent and tasty item on the table of most white residents.

Agriculture

Gardens have been raised successfully throughout the Mackenzie Valley since the time of the first fur-traders. When transportation was difficult and expensive in the early days residents were forced to raise some of their own food. There was a larger acreage under cultivation in the Valley at the beginning of this century than there is at present.

At all the settlements residents raise gardens with most of the common vegetables and flowers. A few commercial gardeners at Yellowknife raise a surplus and sell their products at good prices in the town.

There are a few farms in the Valley. They are usually operated by the Roman Catholic missions. They keep 20 or 30 cows for milk for the residential schools, and usually have a few hundred chickens for meat and eggs. Through the years farmers have found that barley ripens nearly every year, oats in three out of five years, and wheat only about once in five years in the southern part of the Valley. Wheat has been raised as far north as the Arctic Circle, but in most years it fails to ripen. At one time a small dairy farm was operated at Aklavik, only 50 miles from the Arctic Ocean. The farmer in charge often had trouble selling his milk, however, because people were used to drinking powdered or canned milk.

There is little doubt that there are thousands of acres in the Mackenzie Valley which could be used for agriculture at some time in the future. Much of the region is swamp and muskeg, however and probably will never be useful At present the local residents are usually employed at some activity other than farming. Food is therefore shipped in from other agricultural areas farther south. As population increases in the Mackenzie Valley the land cleared for agriculture also expands. After better lands farther south in Canada are occupied, the Mackenzie Valley will support its share of settlers.

Forestry

Away from the rivers most of the Mackenzie Valley is poorly forested. The trees are too small and scrubby to be considered as commercial timber. The best timber is found along the terraces of Liard River, and along Slave River south of Great Slave Lake.

Small crews of lumbermen cut timber in the delta of Slave River. Portable mills saw the logs into lumber, and barges take it across the lake to Yellowknife. Yellowknife, located on the bare rocky hills of the Canadian Shield, lacks lumber for use in the mines and for buildings.

Other small portable sawmills operate near settlements along the Mackenzie River. Since the forests are also valuable for protection of game and fur-bearers, forest fire protection service was started by the Canadian Government in 1946

Transportation

We have already read how transportation by air helped to speed the development of the Mackenzie Valley. We have also noted some of the problems of water transportation in moving goods into and

185

out of the region for mining. These difficulties should not make us think, however, that there is a poor water transportation system. Each year the squat river boats carry a large tonnage of freight cheaply to settlements all along the river, and they do it in spite of difficulties which Nature has created.

As soon as the ice in Athabaska River breaks up in May, paddle-wheeled steamers begin pushing flat-bottomed barges down the river. From the end of the railroad at Waterways, to the Northwest Territories border, valuable freight and next winter's supplies are carried about 250 miles. Near Fort Smith, on the Alberta-Northwest Territories boundary, 16 miles of rapids stop river traffic. All freight is taken by trucks over two portage roads and reloaded into different boats at Fort Smith.

From Fort Smith to the Arctic Ocean there are 1,400 miles of uninterrupted waterway. Boats have been plying these waters since the days of Alexander Mackenzie and the fur-traders. Paddle-wheeled steamers began to operate as early as 1886. They took supplies to the trading settlements and brought out the cargoes of furs. Modern diesel tugs and steel barges now run on the river in large numbers. In a season, they can make two, and sometimes three, return trips from the southern end of the Territory to the Mackenzie Delta.

Winter roads have been used in the Mackenzie Valley for many years. They are not the same kind of roads that people in southern Canada know. Winter roads are trails over frozen lakes and muskegs and through the woods where trees have been knocked down by bulldozers. In winter, they are hard, frozen highways over which tractors pull long lines of boxcars on sledges. Some of the roads have been used even by sturdy trucks.

The main winter road extended from the Peace River region to Hay River, on the southern side of Great Slave Lake, and across the lake ice to Yellowknife. Because of the growth of Yellowknife, the Canadian and Alberta Governments decided to make this winter road permanent. In 1946 they began gravelling it for summer use. Other permanent roads in the Mackenzie Valley are short and usually connect the airports and settlements. There are no all-season roads between settlements.

Air transportation has brought the Mackenzie Valley to within a few hours' distance from Edmonton. Flying started in the region in 1921 and by 1928 there was a great deal of prospecting done by air. In 1929 daring pilots were flying air mail to Aklavik. They brought letters in days, where formerly people had to wait almost a year until the river broke up.

All of the flying before 1940 was done with float planes in summer, and ski-equipped planes in winter. There is a period of about six weeks in the spring, when the ice is cracking and breaking, when planes cannot land. There is another six weeks' period of no flying in the fall after lakes have frozen over, and before the lake ice is thick enough for landing.

During World War II airfields for wheeled planes were cleared at every settlement as far north as Norman Wells. The use of these fields declined after the war when there was less rush freight to carry. The float-equipped planes increased in number, however, because they may land anywhere on the lake-dotted plain of the Mackenzie Lowland. Float planes are also used to carry prospectors and supplies into the Canadian Shield north and east of Yellowknife.

Population

In 1948 there were about 7,000 white residents in the Mackenzie Valley. About 5,000 were in the town of Yellowknife and vicinity, on the northeastern side of Great Slave Lake. Unlike visions of what we might expect in a frontier "boom town", Yellowknife is quite similar to mining towns in southern parts of Canada. It has grocery stores, hotels, drug stores, barber and beauty shops—in fact, everything that is necessary to supply a busy population of a few thousand people.

Courtesy J. L. Robinson.

The town of Yellowknife grew up around a rocky hill jutting into Yellowknife Bay. The town later expanded into a new residential area to the south. Several rich gold mines operate nearby.

The chief difference that we would notice about Yellowknife is its distance from other places. Whereas southern mining towns often have other towns nearby, and roads and railroads leading to them, Yellowknife stands all by itself on a rocky knoll jutting into Great Slave Lake. The nearest settlements are tiny fur-trading posts miles away on other shores of the large lake.

The other settlements of the Mackenzie Valley are small. Port Radium, where pitchblende is mined, has about 250 persons living on the rocky shores of Great Bear Lake. All buildings and recreational facilities of the settlement are supplied by the mining company. A doctor and a hospital are there for the men's protection. Fresh vegetables and fruits are flown in. Norman Wells is also a company town, operated by the Imperial Oil Company. From 100 to 200 persons work there, depending upon the rate of production of the oil wells.

The remaining settlements first started as fur-trading posts or missionary centres, and have grown very little. In addition to the old resident fur-traders, missionaries, or policemen, at most places there are radio operators, weather observers, government officials, doctors, nurses, and teachers. They have their own community social life. In summer many of these settlements look little different from small rural villages in southern Canada.

Things To Do

1. Pretend that you live with one of the fur-traders at Fort Simpson in the Mackenzie Valley and that you are going to write a letter to a friend in Ontario describing your climate. How would you describe the winters? How would they differ from those in Ontario? Tell your friend about the coming of spring and how the ice breaks up in the wide Mackenzie River. Your friend may think that it is cold all the time in the North so tell him about the mild summer, and how flowers and vegetables grow in the gardens.

2. (a) List the three chief minerals mined in the Mackenzie Valley.

   (b) Where are they found?

   (c) Which of the minerals is the most important to the world? Why do you think so?

3. Describe the life of an Indian trapper and his family. What does he do in the summer time. Describe how he moves his family into the forest, and traps during the winter months. Name the fur-bearing animals that he catches in his traps.

4. Draw a map of the Mackenzie Valley showing the main transportation routes. Make lines of one colour to show the routes followed by the steamers and barges on the rivers. Use another colour to show the usual routes of aeroplanes. With a third colour mark in the permanent road from the Peace River to Hay River settlement.

CHAPTER 26

ARCTIC ISLANDS

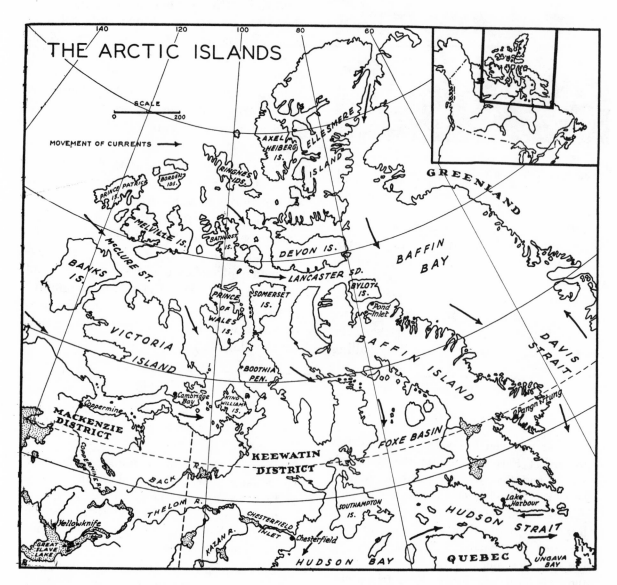

Canada's Arctic Islands cover a vast area north of the Canadian mainland. From east to west they stretch for 1,500 miles, and extend about the same distance from south to north. Cape Columbia, the northern tip of Ellesmere Island, and the most northerly known land in Canada, is about 450 miles from the North Pole.

Many of the Arctic Islands are large. Nine of them are larger than Vancouver Island, the largest island in southern Canada. Baffin Island is about the same size as the Province of Manitoba. No one knows exactly how many islands there are in the Archipelago. At least 40 islands are larger than 100 square miles in area, and there are hundreds of smaller islands.

Topography

There are three types of land forms in the Arctic Islands. The eastern sections facing towards Greenland are high and mountainous. The western islands, facing out into the Arctic Ocean, are generally low or rolling. Between these two areas the central islands are plateaus or are hilly.

Baffin Island is Canada's largest island. Its east coast is a high mountain range which rises abruptly out of the sea. The range averages 5,000 to 7,000 feet high, but peaks of almost 10,000 feet were found by aeroplane pilots during World War II. Many of the mountains have permanent ice-caps, and from them long, twisting glaciers discharge into the sea. The high sharp peaks, and ribbons of white ice going down to a blue sea, make some of the most thrilling scenery in Canada.

The southern coast of Baffin Island is not as high nor as scenic. Its bare rocky hills rise gradually from Hudson Strait

Courtesy J. L. Robinson.

The barren, rocky hills of southern Baffin Island are typical of the general topography and lack of vegetation over most of the Eastern Arctic. A few patches of snow still remain in mid-July.

to a plateau of about 2,500 feet elevation. For miles and miles in the interior there is nothing but bare brown rock. The valleys are filled with boulders and pieces of broken rock; the hillsides and ridges are solid rock. In some places moss clings

to the rocky slopes, and bits of grass grow in sheltered nooks.

The west coast of Baffin Island is flat, swampy tundra. In summer the area is covered with vegetation, flowers bloom in many colours, and mosquitoes buzz over the wet parts. This lowland is quite similar in appearance to the tundra stretching west of Hudson Bay.

Devon and Ellesmere Islands are part of the eastern mountain chain. The eastern half of Devon Island is a huge ice-cap which spills over the steep coasts like white frosting on a chocolate cake. Similar ice-caps are located at three places on Ellesmere Island, Canada's most northern island. Its area is one and a half times that of the Maritime Provinces. Northern Ellesmere Island, facing the endless ice floes of the Arctic Ocean, is formed by a high, sharp-peaked mountain range. Its peaks look much like those of the Rockies and Selkirks, but are covered with more ice and snow. Ridge after ridge of red peaks rises in the interior. From the air they look like ploughed furrows but really have elevations of about 10,000 feet.

Axel Heiberg Island, to the west of Ellesmere Island, is also mountainous. The interior of the island has never been explored, and only a few white men have ever travelled along its western coast. Men who have flown over it, however, report that it is rugged, and has small ice-caps and glaciers.

Several of the central Arctic Islands are plateaus into which steep ravines have cut their way back from the coasts. Included within this plateau or hilly region are Melville and Boothia Peninsulas of the mainland, Somerset Island, northwestern Baffin Island, northern Prince of Wales Island, western Devon Island, Cornwallis Island, Bathurst Island, and Melville Island. The interiors of many of these islands have never been explored on foot. Many of the coasts are walls of sedimentary rock which rise directly from the sea. Elevations are

Devon Island is a flat-topped plateau of sedimentary rock. Steep-sided ravines have cut back into the interior. A permanent ice-cap lies in the distance to the right.

from 700 to 1,000 feet. The flat-topped surface of the interiors is covered with broken slabs of loose rock, cracked by centuries of frost action.

Some of the western Arctic Islands are low, but others have hilly areas. King William Island, eastern Victoria Island and southern Prince of Wales Island are flat grassy lowlands covered with innumerable lakes. The low coasts rise gradually from the sea in gravel ridges. The western parts of Victoria Island and Banks Island are rugged and hilly. In some places the hills are rocky, and in other places the rolling slopes are covered with waving grass in summer. The name "Arctic Prairies" has been given to some of these grassy regions.

In the northern Arctic Islands, Prince Patrick, the Borden Islands, and the Ringnes group are low but rough. The lowland coasts slope up to low, steep-sided hills. Some of the ridges form circles around a rough core of hills. Streams are

small and short because they flow for only a short time in the summer. They are wearing away the rock, however, because there is no vegetation cover to protect it. Some of the tundra-covered lowlands support roaming herds of musk-ox, in one of their last sanctuaries in the world.

Climate

The Arctic Islands are cold in winter, and cool in summer. Everywhere in this treeless region average monthly temperatures are under 50°F. The Eskimos dress in warm furs to protect themselves in winter, but in summer sturdy clothes which we would use for camping or hiking are quite suitable for the north.

Because of the great extent of the Arctic Islands there are differences in climate from place to place. We know little about the climate of the most northern group of islands because weather records have been kept for only a few years. Explorers report that it is very cold in winter, some-

190

times reaching 50°F. or 60°F. below zero. In summer, the snow melts from the land since the temperature rises above 32°F.

Winters are coldest in the area between Victoria Island and Melville Peninsula. Although thermometer readings are not as low as they are in the Mackenzie Valley or

This Eskimo boy at Cambridge Bay, southern Victoria Island, speaks good English and is an expert engine mechanic. He goes to school at Aklavik, N.W.T., in the winter and is brought home to his parents in summer.

Yukon, it stays continuously cold for a long time. Southeastern Baffin Island is not as cold as other parts of the Arctic because of open water off the coast of Labrador and Greenland. Winter temperatures there average about the same as Winnipeg, but there are not as many thaws or day-to-day changes.

Summers in the Arctic are cool. The sun begins to shine for a long time each day in April and May. The snow gradually melts from the ground, but stays on northern slopes until July. The ice in the bays and inlets is loosened when streams start to flow into them. In late June or early July the ice between the southern Arctic Islands breaks up and drifts out of the harbours with the currents or winds. Afternoon temperatures rise into the 70's during July and August, and at some places have even reached 80°F.

About the middle of September ice begins to form across the lakes and bays in the northern part of the Arctic Islands. By the end of October or early November coasts are again frozen over. The Arctic is cut off from ship transportation for another nine months.

The Arctic is often incorrectly called a land of six months' darkness and six months' light. The North Pole, where there is no land and where no one lives, is the only place having six months of darkness or daylight. Farther south with each degree of latitude the length of full day or darkness (depending on the season) decreases to five, four, three months, and so on to one day of complete darkness or daylight at the Arctic Circle.

For example, at latitude 76 degrees North, on Ellesmere Island, nights of 24 hours would begin about the end of October, when the sun no longer rose above the horizon. For several weeks afterwards, however, a light glow on the southern horizon would appear around noon. Soon this light would disappear and for about two months there would be darkness, lighted only by the stars and moon and the white snowfields. After the middle of January a soft pink light would appear on the southern horizon. Each day it would become brighter. Finally the red ball of the sun would peek above the horizon. The long night would be over.

Thereafter the sun would rise a little

higher in the southern sky than it did the day before. The days would become longer and the nights shorter. By the end of April there would be no sunset. The sun would simply dip down into the horizon in the north, and then rise to circle again in the sky. In the middle of June the sun would circle directly above, lighting the whole top of the world north of the Arctic Circle. Towards the end of August the sun would once more dip below the northern horizon. Each night it would stay down a few minutes longer, until on September 21 there would be 12 hours of day and 12 hours of night. After that the days would continue to be shorter until the sun disappeared once more about the end of October.

Ocean Currents and Ice Conditions

Because of their island character, the physical geography of the Arctic Islands is somewhat different from the mainland of Canada. One of the differences is the movement of ocean currents. The direction of this movement affects ice conditions and water transportation.

The huge Arctic Ocean north and west of the Arctic Islands is covered with a mass of moving ice floes. These floes are carried by currents and winds from east to west in a clockwise direction. The pack-ice pushes southward wherever possible, and much of it enters the North Atlantic east of Greenland. The water and ice which flow into the channels between the Canadian Arctic Islands is also carried southward. Because of the shape of the Canadian mainland and **Alaska**, however, the currents have a back-eddy and are pushed to the east and finally find an opening into the Atlantic through Davis and Hudson Straits. Thus, currents are drifting through the Arctic Islands from the north and west towards the south and east.

During the winter most of the channels between the Arctic Islands freeze over.

The most northern group of Arctic Islands becomes a solid "land mass" at this time. The land is joined together by flat bridges of solid ice from 5 to 10 feet thick.

In July this land-fast ice begins to break away from the shore. Winds, currents, and tides gradually break it up, and the loose floes move with the general drift of currents towards the North Atlantic. The large masses finally melt off the coast of Newfoundland. The icebergs are last to melt and sometimes cause shipwrecks. It was this movement of ice that caused the early Arctic explorers so much trouble when they were searching for the Northwest Passage. In Hudson Strait the ice has drifted eastward by the end of July and ships can sail into Hudson Bay. Farther north loose drift ice does not clear out of the channels until late August. In the narrow channel between Greenland and Ellesmere Island and in M'Clure Strait, north of Banks and Victoria Islands, the floes do not disappear before it begins to freeze again in September.

The open season for ships is short in the Arctic Islands. In Hudson Strait there are about 2½ months without ice, but with frequent fog. Farther north, the period of open water lasts only a few weeks. In some places the ice stays throughout the year.

When we read the stories of the first explorers such as Frobisher, Davis, Hudson, and Parry, who sailed into the unknown seas in tiny wooden sailing ships, we should marvel at what they accomplished. Since most of the explorers entered the Arctic from the east, they had to head right into the ice floes. Their stories are full of accounts of troubles and disappointments in trying to force their way through the endless floes to the unknown beyond.

Natural Resources

The resources of the Arctic are few. The region has very little which could be of use to people in more southern parts of Canada. It has no trees and therefore no lumbering. There is very little soil and almost no summer, and therefore no agriculture. The area is so hard to reach and transportation costs are so high that very little prospecting has been carried on.

Courtesy J. L. Robinson.

The tiny trading post settlements of the Canadian Arctic may have only a few white residents. The area lacks trees for lumber and gardens are grown under glass. This Hudson's Bay Company post at Cape Dorset, Baffin Island, is in a good fur-trapping area.

The one resource which is exported out of the Arctic is the white fox. This beautiful fur-bearer lives north of the tree-line on the Arctic tundra. Since its fur is desired for warmth and ornament by people in more southerly regions, Eskimos have been taught how to trap white foxes. At one time Eskimos had to worry about getting enough food to live. Now they buy much of their food from the trading store. Although Eskimos seldom starve as they used to, their prosperity varies from year to year. In years when foxes are numerous they can buy guns and ammunition for hunting, utensils for their homes, boats, and extra clothing. In other years when foxes are scarce they may catch only one or two. Then the Eskimos have to hunt for their food in the sea and on the land. Some of the younger Eskimos are becoming trappers and are not as good hunters as their fathers.

White foxes are found over all of the Arctic Islands, but are trapped only in the southern group of islands. There are many foxes about every four years, especially if their prey, the little Arctic mouse called the lemming, is also plentiful. Eskimos trap white foxes in steel traps which are cleverly covered with a thin slab of hard snow. During the trapping season from November to March the Eskimo father and sons visit the trap-lines while mother and daughters look after the clothes and cooking in the snow-block igloo.

The mineral resources of the Arctic Islands are not fully known. Many of the islands are of sedimentary rock where coal, oil, or natural gas might be found. Little prospecting has been done, however, because the islands are so far away. Coal has been reported by many explorers, and sometimes used by them during the cold winters. Most of the coal is of poor grade, however, and cannot be moved to other areas without crumbling. A small coal seam has been mined for several years at Pond Inlet on northern Baffin Island and used by the residents for winter fuel.

On southeastern Baffin Island traces of mineralization have been reported. At different times a little graphite, mica, and garnet have been mined. On the Arctic mainland, south of Victoria Island, copper has been known since the days of Samuel Hearne's expedition from Churchill to Coppermine River in 1771. Both Indians and Eskimos used it for implements. Modern mining companies say that it is not rich enough, however, to compete with copper ores farther south.

There is no agriculture in the Arctic Islands, but small gardens are raised under glass at most settlements. The soil is usually imported on annual supply ships. Quite often storm windows which are taken off the house in spring are the glass covering. Gardening is only a hobby under such conditions. A few vegetables are raised to add variety to the canned food which all residents must eat.

Although exportable resources are few

in the Arctic, there is wildlife on the land and in the sea which is sufficient to feed the native Eskimo population. Eskimos of the Arctic Islands are coastal dwellers, unlike those who live in the interior of the continent. Their chief food is seal meat. Seals are plentiful along the coasts in summer, and in winter are shot or harpooned through their breathing-holes in the ice. Other sea animals are white whales and walrus, which are used chiefly for dog feed. The large Greenland, or bowhead, whales are seldom seen now. Most of them were killed off by the whalers of the last century. Fish are netted or speared as they swim up the streams in the autumn. The Arctic Islands Eskimos do not eat as much fish as their Eskimo cousins on the mainland.

Land animals are not so plentiful on the Arctic Islands as on the Arctic mainland. The largest herds of caribou on western Baffin Island would be considered small among the thousands in Keewatin District. Polar bears are more numerous on the islands than farther south, and their heavy fur makes good sleeping robes or pants. Musk oxen have almost disappeared since they were so easy to kill with guns. When danger approached the musk oxen would form a motionless circle, with the young ones protected inside, and dare the enemy to charge them. The remaining few on the far northern Arctic Islands are carefully protected by Canadian laws, and no one may kill them.

Transportation

The navigation season in the Arctic Islands is short because of ice conditions. Since there are only a few white residents living in the region, only a few ships enter it. For many years the annual supply ship for the settlements on Baffin Island was the sturdy old icebreaker "R. M. S. Nascopie" owned by the Hudson's Bay Company. Each year she came into the Arctic in July, bringing the annual mail, food,

and equipment to the posts. She brought in new people to the settlements and took others out for a rest. On board were visiting government officials and doctors. On the return voyage to Montreal her holds were filled with bales of foxes. The old "Nascopie" was famous throughout the Eastern Arctic for more than 35 years. She was wrecked on a submerged reef off southern Baffin Island in 1947 and ended her days in the icy waters which she had ploughed for so long.

The shipping route through Hudson Strait and across Hudson Bay to Churchill has been used since 1930, when the huge grain elevators were built there. During August and September the boats are loaded with grain and take their golden cargo overseas to Europe.

In the western part of the Arctic small schooners carry supplies to the few settlements. Freight is shipped on flat-bottomed steamers down the Mackenzie River, and transferred near the delta. Since river boats cannot travel along the open Arctic coast, schooners carry on. During August and September they travel through Amundsen Gulf and into Coronation Gulf. If supplies are needed farther east in Queen Maud Gulf, Eskimo boats usually carry the cargo.

The difficulties of travelling through the Arctic Islands are well illustrated by the search for the Northwest Passage. For over 300 years vessels tried to find a route through the many Arctic channels, but grinding ice floes always blocked the way. Many ships were caught in the ice and crushed, but other navigators kept trying. It was not until the present century that the Norwegian explorer, Roäld Amundsen, navigated from east to west along a southern route from 1903 to 1906.

The vessel which finally conquered the passage from both directions was the Royal Canadian Mounted Police schooner "St. Roch". This small, sturdy ship had been travelling amid the ice floes of the

Western Arctic every year since 1928. The quiet captain, Henry Larsen, and hard-working crew had just as many adventures in the ice as the early explorers. It was simply their duty to bring supplies to the police detachments, however, and they never boasted of their deeds. During the three summers of 1940 to 1942, the police schooner worked eastward through the ice and shallow seas off the mainland coast, and completed the Northwest Passage for the first time from west to east. In 1944 the "St. Roch" returned to the Western Arctic by way of a more northern route, becoming the first and only vessel to navigate the Passage in a single year.

Population

Eskimos are the chief inhabitants of the Arctic Islands. They live north of the tree-line on the Canadian mainland, and in the southern group of Arctic Islands. No one lives on the far northern Arctic Islands, except for a few Eskimo helpers at the police posts, and weather observers at several points.

There are about 8,000 Eskimos in Canada. They may be divided into four main groups of about 2,000 each. They are found in the Western Arctic, Keewatin District, Arctic Quebec and Baffin Island. In the Western Arctic—which is the mainland coast of Mackenzie District, and Banks, Victoria, and King William Islands —there is a great contrast in kinds of Eskimos. Those in the western sections, especially around the delta of Mackenzie River, are quite modern in appearance. Most of them speak English, wear white man's clothes part of the year, and carry on trading. The Eskimos in the central interior of the Arctic are the most primitive in Canada. Some of them still live like their ancestors of hundreds of years ago. Many of them saw their first white man sometime after 1920.

The Eskimos of Keewatin District and Arctic Quebec were described in the sec-

tion on the Canadian Shield. Many of those in the interior of Keewatin District are caribou-eaters who hunt and fish on the tundra most of the year. The Eskimos of northeastern Keewatin District and Arctic Quebec are coastal dwellers, who get their food and some clothing from the

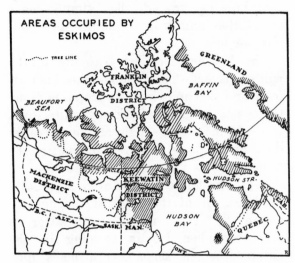

animals in the sea. They are similar to the fourth large group on Baffin Island.

The coastal-dwelling Eskimo of Baffin Island has a seasonal round of activities which gives him food and clothing in a land which has few resources. In autumn he pitches his tent of seal-skin or canvas near the mouth of a good fishing stream. Most Eskimos now use fish nets obtained from the trader, but some northern families still spear the fish as they swim upstream. If there are any caribou in the area the Eskimo hunter will make occasional trips inland to try to kill them for food and winter clothing. In his small boat he will also hunt among the offshore islands for walrus which will be used for winter dog feed.

As soon as the ice forms along the coast and snow begins to fall, the Eskimo family makes a snow igloo. This winter home is made of circles of snow blocks piled on one another and leaning inward to form a dome. A low opening, tunneled underneath the snow and closed with snow blocks, serves as a door, and keeps the

195

cold air out. This snug home needs very little heat since none escapes outside through doors or windows. The igloo is heated with a small coal-oil stove or with a shallow stone lamp in which seal fat is burned. Eskimos have no housing problem because when they want to move to a new hunting ground, they simply leave their igloo, and in a few hours have built another one.

The Eskimo does his trapping in the winter. Every week or so he takes his dog-team and sled and visits his trap-line along the coast. He brings back any white foxes which he may have caught and later trades them at the posts. The rest of the time he is hunting his ''bread of life''—seals.

Seals are hunted either at their breathing-holes, or at the edge of the floe ice where they come up in open water to breathe. When ice is forming in the autumn the seal keeps several holes open so that it can come up to breathe. Eskimos find these holes, and wait there motionless for many long, weary hours. When the seal pokes his head up, the Eskimo's harpoon flashes down, and the family has something to eat for a few more days.

Sometimes in spring the seal climbs out of his hole and rests in the sun on the sea-ice. In order to get close to the seal without frightening it, the Eskimo approaches from behind a square white cloth. He peeks through a hole in this screen and when close enough shoots the seal with his rifle.

The Eskimo has to be a good hunter to be successful at the edge of the floe ice which surrounds his coasts in winter. He stands armed with his rifle; nearby his light kayak, or canoe, is ready. Sometimes he paddles around quietly in his kayak, but the movement may frighten the seals away. When the seal puts up his nose to breathe the Eskimo has only the small head as a target. If he kills the seal, the fat body will float for a short time. The hunter jumps into his kayak and races for

the seal. When close enough he throws his harpoon. To the end of the harpoon is attached a seal-skin float, which acts as a buoy and holds up the seal until he is ready to bring it in.

In summer, the Eskimos of Hudson Strait and the east coast of Hudson Bay travel in low, smooth-gliding kayaks. These one-man boats are made of sealskin stretched tightly over a wood framework. The Eskimo hunter uses a two-bladed paddle. Many Eskimos no longer use the kayak.

When the shore ice breaks up in summer, families begin to work towards the nearest trading post, hunting as they travel. They all try to arrive about "ship-time". This is the time when the annual supply vessel comes with new trading goods. The ship also carries doctors, nurses and a dentist who will look after their health troubles at that time.

An Eskimo summer camp consists of tents on the rocky beach at Cape Dorset, Baffin Island. The canvas tents are obtained from the trader, and each holds one family.

For the Eskimos ship-time is a grand reunion. Several hundred of them get together and tell of their hunting experiences of the past winter. They visit one another,

196

holding native dances and sing-songs. The long winter is over, and their troubles are forgotten. In a few days the vessel is unloaded, the Eskimos get their new trade goods, and the ship leaves the harbour for another year. Gradually the Eskimos depart to their hunting grounds, and another hunting season starts again.

There are only a few white residents in the Arctic Islands. There are only about 200 in the whole Canadian Arctic, including the Arctic mainland. Their tiny settlements are clusters of buildings containing four or five people. Nearly every settlement has a trading store, usually operated by the historic Hudson's Bay Company. Missionaries of the Church of England and the Roman Catholic Church are also scattered throughout the North. Government representatives include the dependable Royal Canadian Mounted Police who patrol from camp to camp; weather observers and radio operators, who warn us what kind of weather is moving southward; and government doctors who try to care for the widely-scattered migratory Eskimo people.

Things To Do

1. Draw a map of the Canadian Arctic Islands. Use your crayons or coloured pencils to shade in all mountain areas. Make the mountains dark brown and the plateaus or hilly sections light brown. Colour the lowlands green. Which colour covers the largest area on the islands?

2. Draw a map of the Arctic Islands and draw in the parallels of latitude every five degrees apart. Using the table at the end of this question, shade in the areas having one to two weeks of total darkness for 24 hours during the winter. Use another colour to show the areas that have two to four weeks of winter darkness. Similarly use other colours to show the areas that have two, three, four and five months of total darkness. Remember that the period of darkness is the same along each parallel, and in winter the length of the period increases to the northward. Notice how many of the Arctic Islands have some daylight every day.

1-2 weeks' darkness - 66 degrees to 67 degrees
2-4 weeks' darkness - 67 degrees to 68 degrees
1-2 months' darkness - 68 degrees to 70 degrees
2-3 months' darkness - 70 degrees to 75 degrees
3-4 months' darkness - 75 degrees to 80 degrees
4-5 months' darkness - 80 degrees to 85 degrees
5-6 months' darkness - 85 degrees to 90 degrees

3. If you were working at the meteorology station at Nottingham Island, at the western end of Hudson Strait, describe the ice conditions you would find there from June 1st to November 1st. Tell how the ice breaks up from the coast and starts to drift away with the currents. When does this usually happen? When is all the ice finally gone? When do the small lakes and rivers begin to freeze over in the autumn? Describe how the land-fast ice gradually builds out from the shore and becomes thicker and thicker.

4. (a) Draw a map of the usual water transportation routes in the Arctic Islands. How many islands have no ships calling at their shores? List the reasons.

   (b) Draw the route followed by the R.C.M.P. schooner "St. Roch" in 1944. How does this route compare with those of the early explorers of the Arctic?

5. Pretend that you are an Eskimo boy learning to do the things that your father does so that you will be a good hunter and trapper when you grow up. Describe what you would do from season to season as you worked with your father throughout the year.

Courtesy Ontario Department of Travel and Publicity.

Much of Canada's economy centres around wheat. It is a product for which Canada is famous abroad. The growing, marketing and transporting of wheat employs many Canadians, and the exported product feeds many of the world's people.

CHAPTER 27

CANADA AND THE WORLD

Canadians live in the world. We are not only residents of cities, villages or farms within the political boundaries of Canada, we are members of a world society. As Canadians we should try to learn more about our own neighbourhood, then about our whole country, and finally try to understand something about the big world.

As citizens of Canada we must first know about our own country. We must appreciate the feelings and desires of other Canadians who have different resources than we do. The Maritime fisherman, the Quebec lumberman, the Prairie farmer, and the British Columbia miner all have different viewpoints because of their occupations. In addition, as world citizens we must also know about other parts of the world, their resources and peoples.

As a member of world society, Canada must understand other nations. Part of that understanding will come from know-

ing the history and politics of other countries, part from knowing about their economic systems, and part from a knowledge of their geography. We must understand why people in the tropics have to live differently from us. People in deserts or mountains will not have the same outlook on life as people in industrial cities. Part of the understanding of other peoples comes from being familiar with their environment and the problems which they have in adjusting themselves to it.

Our lives and activities in Canada are closely connected with those of people in other lands, although we do not often realize it. The price which a prairie farmer receives for his wheat depends partly on how much rain there has been in Argentina, and how good the crop is in Australia. Lumbermen in Quebec might be forced out of work if a big newspaper closed down in the United States, or if the Soviet Union began exporting the products of her vast forests. Factories might have to stop

198

production in Ontario if valuable vegetable oils were not received from the tropics, or if miners in Malaya or Rhodesia were too weak to work. No one works by himself. Everything we do must have the co-operation of others. It usually comes from someone near us, but many times help is obtained from resources and people in far-away places.

Canada is a large, rich country, but we lack many resources which make our lives more comfortable. We import oranges, lemons and pineapples which we cannot grow in our cool climate. Our machinery could not be made without imported manganese, tin, and chromium. Our textile mills run on cotton from the United States and wool from New Zealand.

Similarly, Canada has many things which other parts of the world lack. Our nickel and copper supply raw materials for many industries in the United States and Great Britain. Half the American newspapers are printed on Canadian newsprint. Many European families eat Canadian wheat and flour.

The world is now too small for any part of it to remain separate and alone. Our excess resources help other nations and their workers to turn out products which we can use in our lives. This interchange of goods is known as Foreign Trade, and much of Canada's prosperity depends on it.

During World War II Canadians were reminded how much they depended on other parts of the world. With submarines off our coasts and ships being used to carry men and munitions, many products which we had taken for granted were missing. There was a great shortage of sugar, coffee and chocolate. Ships running the blockade from South America carried such little-known, but important, items as chinchona, iodine, castor oil, and hemp. Without these products, and many others, our war industries would have been unable to produce.

Our troubles during war-time only emphasized the dependence of the countries of the world on each other's resources. Men in business and industry have to know about the resources of Canada, but they also must know about the resources of other countries. They have to know where they can buy raw materials for their factories. If the products are not found in Canada, they want to know the closest source, or the source with the best transportation. In the same way they want to know about the geography and peoples of other countries so they can sell their goods at the proper season and in the best places.

The world has always been round, but air travel which expanded during World War II emphasized the fact. The geography of the world changes very slowly, but its bearing on our lives is continually changing. The continents and world resources are so arranged that most of the world's population lives in the Northern Hemisphere. If planes fly between the centres of population and production their direct "Great Circle" routes go northward. A plane flying from Chicago to London, England, would pass over central Quebec and the southern tip of Greenland. If a plane flies directly from New Orleans to Tokyo it crosses over northern British Columbia and central Alaska. Canada now finds herself on the route of important air lanes.

Canada's position on new world air routes give her many responsibilities and some advantages. Since the safety of aeroplanes is largely due to knowledge of weather conditions, Canada has opened new weather stations to report on the movements of air masses. Long-range planes flying over Canadian territory want emergency air bases below them, and therefore fields have been cleared in many far-away places. Canada has co-operated with other nations to help world air transportation. This is but one example of how we are a part of the whole world, and must play our part in it.

We should be proud of Canada. We should be proud of our mines and forests, farms and factories. We should be able to see in our minds the towering Rockies, the broad Prairies, the forested Shield, the busy towns of the Lowlands, and the scenic

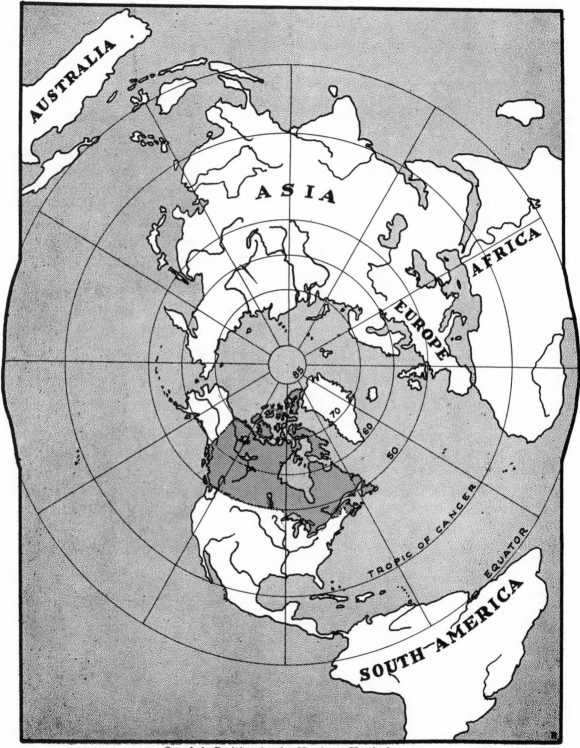

Canada's Position in the Northern Hemisphere.

hills of the Maritimes. We should understand how the fishermen in Nova Scotia and Newfoundland live, and how the lumbermen of New Brunswick work in the woods. We should appreciate the faith and friendliness of the Quebec farmer, and the industrial organization of the Ontario business man. We should know the problems of the Prairie farmer, and understand the transportation difficulties of people in British Columbia. We should glory in the tales of the Yukon Gold Rush, and feel the enthusiasm of the new pioneers in the Mackenzie Valley. We should admire the friendly honesty of the hardy Eskimos, and the patient loneliness of men who occupy the northern outposts. This is our Canada—from Atlantic to Pacific, from Great Lakes to Arctic Ocean. It is a big country, and it is a rich country. It is rich in resources, and it is rich in the people who live there to develop them.

SOURCES OF INFORMATION

There have been many books written on Canada or parts of Canada for both teachers and pupils. Lists of these books may be obtained from the libraries in large towns or cities. The more that can be added to your school library to be used for assigned reading, the more valuable will be the study of the land, resources and peoples of Canada.

Periodicals are the best source for recent and detailed information. Two of the most useful in Canada are "The Canadian Geographical Journal" and "The Beaver". The Journal is published monthly and contains authoritative articles on the resources and peoples of different parts of Canada. A bibliography of articles arranged by provinces and subject has been published by the Journal. The Geographical Aspects series, published by the Canadian Geographical Society, Ottawa, describes each of the provinces of Canada for school children. "The Beaver" specializes in articles on Northern Canada, and is noted for its excellent pictures.

Each of the provinces and the two Territories issue factual information about their resources, cities, transportation, etc.

This free material may be obtained either from the Tourist and Publicity departments or from various provincial Resource departments. The various Canadian government departments in Ottawa also publish information about their activities, and present the over-all picture of resources in Canada. Much of this information is assembled in the Geographical Branch, Department of Mines and Technical Surveys, Ottawa. The standard reference book on most subjects in Canada is "The Canada Year Book", prepared by the Bureau of Statistics, Ottawa. This book has detailed factual information and excellent charts and graphs.

Maps of Canada, and of parts of Canada, may be obtained from the Surveys and Mapping Branch, Department of Mines and Technical Surveys, Ottawa. A catalogue showing the cost and scales of the maps may be obtained from the Branch. Maps vary in scale and size from 100 and 200 miles to one inch for the whole of Canada—to one, two, four and eight miles to one inch for small sections of the country.

Maps of the area around your school will be supplied by either your provincial or dominion governments.

INDEX

The index does not include topics which are listed in the table of contents, material covered in the exercises at the end of each chapter, nor names on maps.